VOCAL FOLD PHYSIOLOGY

VOCAL FOLD PHYSIOLOGY

Edited by Kenneth N. Stevens and Minoru Hirano

UNIVERSITY OF TOKYO PRESS

Proceedings of the Vocal Fold Physiology Conference held in Kurume in January 15-19, 1980 as a project of the Voice Foundation, New York.

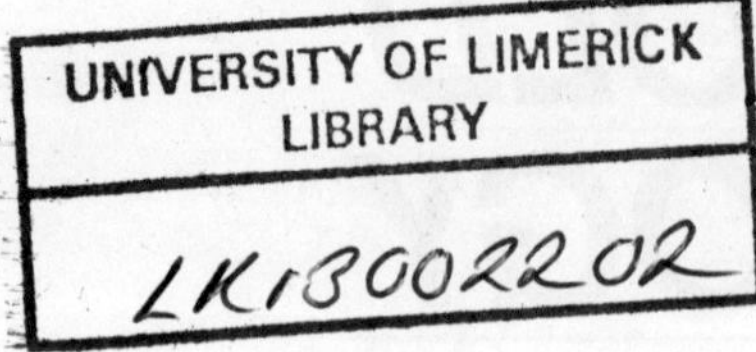

UTP 3047-67620-5149
ISBN 0-86008-281-4
Printed in Japan

CONTENTS

FOREWORD

The material in this monograph was delivered at a Conference on Vocal Fold Physiology on 15-19 January of 1980 at Kurume University in Japan. The planning of this conference represents the first step in a joint 5-year project which was conceived by several people who acted as members of the Scientific Board of the Voice Foundation. They were Drs. Hirano, Fujimura, Titze, and Gould originally, and now Dr. Stevens is playing a pivotal role in the project as editor of the monograph. It was felt that a subject so involved as that relating to a better understanding of vocal fold vibration would require the joint work of representative researchers in the world who have different disciplines and working environments. It is in that sense of a cooperative venture that we started and proceeded.

Our problem concerns the physiology of the minute motion that constitutes the basis of the complexity of voice. Research must involve consideration of the physics and physiology of the intricate biological structures using advanced techniques, such as computational simulation of the tissue vibration. The goal of this initial conference was to achieve a common base line upon which subsequent projects could evolve in a balanced, well-planned way.

The next meeting will be more than just a report, and will, hopefully, reflect a greater degree of collaborative effort. The project goals call for intimate cooperation of all the leading laboratories involved in this project. Only in that manner can a more complete understanding be obtainable in the four future years.

The Voice Foundation will help as possible and as needed.

The desirability is to have the meetings in different geographical areas so that more complete involvement of the different research groups can be achieved.

Wilbur J. Gould
Chairman
The Voice Foundation

PREFACE

During the past decade, there have been several experimental and theoretical developments in vocal fold physiology that have potential of advancing significantly our understanding of the mechanism of vibration and control of the vocal folds during speech and singing. These advances have been in three areas:

1) observation of the state of the vocal folds and their pattern of vibration, using a variety of experimental techniques;
2) studies of the structural properties of the vocal folds; and
3) theoretical studies and models of the mechanisms of vibration and laryngeal control, often based on computer simulations.

This experimental and theoretical work has been motivated in part by the need of laryngologists, singing teachers, and speech pathologists to improve their techniques for the remediation of laryngeal disorders.

The new studies in these several areas have, however, often proceeded rather independently, and the relationships between the results from the different areas have not been fully exploited. The experimental observations of vibration patterns and electromyographic signals, the forces due to aerodynamic processes, and the properties of the vocal fold surfaces and of the tissue internal to the surfaces are all aspects of a common mechanism that can only be understood completely if data from all of these sources can be brought together and explained in terms of a comprehensive model.

The Conference on Vocal Fold Physiology, held in Kurume, Japan on January 15-19, 1980, was organized in response to the need for exchange of information between researchers from different disciplines who are involved in these various facets of vocal fold physiology. A goal of the Conference, apart from exchanging information in the form of prepared papers by the participants, was to stimulate discussion that would help indicate areas where new research is needed within the forthcoming years in order to fill in crucial gaps in our knowledge of vocal fold behavior. The Conference was conceived by Dr. Minoru Hirano, Dr. Osamu Fujimura, and Dr. Wilbur J. Gould, who prepared a list of participants from the United States and Japan. Detailed organization of the Conference was carried out by Dr. Hirano and his staff at Kurume University.

This volume contains edited versions of the papers presented at the Conference. In addition, an edited version of the discussion of each presentation at the Conference is included, and in most cases this discussion is inserted after the text of the paper. In some cases, however, authors of papers chose to incorporate into their manuscripts some of the points raised in the discussion, with credit to the discussant where appropriate.

Some historical perspective to the Conference is given in an opening paper by Dr. I. Hiroto (Chapter 1) and in closing remarks by Dr. I. Kirikae (Chapter 27). These two senior investigators, who have contributed significantly to advancing our understanding of vocal fold physiology, pointed out that some of the ideas discussed at the Conference are outgrowths of concepts that have developed over the past century. The remaining papers in the volume are divided into six Sections according to topic. The papers in each of these Sections were edited by a section editor, as indicated in the Table of Contents and in the text.

Section I on Basic Morphology and Physiology provides a background on the morphology of the laryngeal system and the pulmonary system that underlies phonation, including recent findings concerning the layered structure of the vocal fold and its vascular network. Also included in this initial section is a paper on the properties of muscular tissue that may be relevant to an understanding of the control of the larynx (Chapter 6).

Section II contains four papers that report observations of vocal fold vibration using four different techniques: high-speed motion pictures (Chapter 7), X-ray stroboscopy (Chapter 8), ultrasonic observation (Chapter 9), and quantitative observation of excised larynges (Chapter 10). Each of these techniques is shown to give different kinds of insights into movements of points on the vocal fold surfaces and internal to these surfaces, and on the waves that propagate along the surfaces.

A series of papers that report on electromyographic observations of laryngeal muscles (Chapters 11-13) and some aerodynamic-acoustic observations of larynx behavior (Chapters 14-15) are given in Section III. Section III ends with a theoretical paper (Chapter 16) concerned with physiological mechanisms for vocal control.

Three different models of vocal fold vibration are described in Section IV. The models differ in the way in which they account for the physical properties of the vocal fold and the manner in which these properties are controlled. In one model (Chapter 17) each vocal fold is represented by two coupled masses, and the system is driven by forces arising from aerodynamic effects. In a second model (Chapter 18), attention is focused on a detailed representation of the distributed viscoelastic properties of the vocal folds. The third model (Chapter 19) incorporates mechanisms for independent control of the body and the cover of the vocal folds.

Section V contains a series of four papers on modes of vibration of the vocal folds. These papers examine the factors influencing the waveform and frequency of glottal vibration during speech (Chapter 20), the acoustic interaction between the glottal source and the vocal tract (Chapter 21), mechanisms for control of abduction-adduction of the glottis (Chapter 22) and the control of pitch in singing (Chapter 23).

The first two papers of Section VI (Chapters 24 and 25) describe some recent work on measurement of the physical properties of vocal fold tissue, both *in vivo* and in excised larynges. The final paper of Section VI (Chapter 26) discusses how computer simulation can be used in conjunction with observations of vocal fold properties to lead to an integrated model of vocal fold behavior. This chapter, together with the discussion that follows it, provides a summary of the areas where future research is needed in order to understand more completely the many aspects of vocal fold physiology reported in the chapters of this book.

The editors acknowledge with gratitude the contributions of many individuals who made the Conference possible and who played a part in editing and organizing the manuscripts. We acknowledge especially the efforts of Dr. Wilbur J. Gould and of Dr. Osamu Fujimura, who provided contributions in all phases of the Conference and its editorial aftermath. The section editors--Dr. Stuart Strong, Dr. Thomas Baer, Dr. James Abbs, Dr. Ingo Titze, Dr. Martin Rothenberg, and Dr. Fujimura--were most effective in editing and coordinating the manuscripts in the various sections of the book.

The Conference and the preparation of the book were made possible by grants from the Voice Foundation and from the Department of Otolaryngology, Kurume University, and that support is gratefully acknowledged.

Kenneth N. Stevens
Cambridge, Massachusetts

Minoru Hirano
Kurume, Japan

VOCAL FOLD PHYSIOLOGY

CHAPTER 1
INTRODUCTORY REMARKS

Ikuichiro Hiroto

Department of Oto-Rhino-Laryngology,
Faculty of Medicine, Kyushu University,
Japan

The progress of science depends mainly on the development of new techniques for research work, founded in the improvement of laboratory apparatus and of knowledge in other scientific fields. In the field of laryngeal physiology, we have employed ultra-high-speed cinematography, electromyography, radiography and various measurement methods as such new techniques. These research techniques have brought great progress to laryngeal physiology. Especially, the scientific achievement of ultra-high-speed cinematography corresponds to that of microscopy in the field of morphology. It is not possible to discuss the vibration of the vocal folds without observation by ultra-high-speed cinematography, just as histology cannot be considered without microscopic findings.

Personally speaking, it gives me great pleasure that this Vocal Fold Physiology Conference is held in Kurume University, where I worked on laryngeal physiology for 11 years to 1970, and my successor Professor Hirano is now actively involved in the same field. Here, ultra-high-speed cinematographic studies of the vibration of the vocal folds were first done in Japan.

As an introduction to this conference I wish to describe some of my research which was carried out at this university.

I. OBSERVATION OF THE VIBRATION OF THE VOCAL FOLD IN SLOW MOTION PICTURES

As you know, at the onset of the vibration of the vocal

folds during phonation, the mucous membrane of the vocal fold which is set at the paramedian position begins to move as a rippling wave. This wavelike movement becomes larger and the glottis becomes completely closed after several vibrations.

An example of this vibratory pattern of the margin of the vocal folds is shown in Fig. 1. Dr. Svend Smith performed a similar analysis of the slow motion picture from the Bell Telephone Laboratories, and reported that the vibration of the vocal folds begins with an inward movement. He pointed out the importance of the Bernoulli effect in the mechanism of the vibration of the vocal fold. However, it is very difficult to decide whether the first movement of the vocal fold is an inward movement or an outward movement in my figure as well as in Dr. Smith's figure.

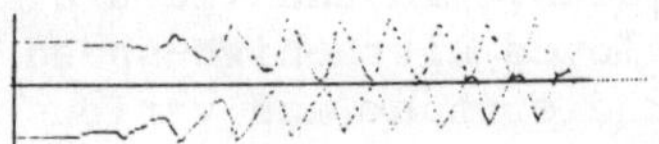

Fig.1. Vibratory pattern of the two margins of the vocal folds at the beginning of phonation.

In an experiment with an excised human larynx, in which humid air is blown up from the trachea, the glottis is gradually widened by the increase of the subglottic pressure and then the vibration begins, as shown in Fig.2a.

Fig.2. Vibratory pattern of the two margins of the vocal folds for excised larynges as observed from above (a) and from below (b).

A window was opened at the anterior inferior portion of another excised larynx and covered with a plate glass in order to observe the lower surface of the vocal fold during vibration. In this experiment, the membranous portion of the vocal fold is forced upward and outward at the beginning of the increase of the subglottic pressure, and a ridge is noticed at the border between the vocal fold and the subglottic region. After the vocal fold moves outward and the glottis is opened, the undulating movement of the mucous membrane begins. Figure 2b is a vibratory pattern of the vocal fold observed from below.

Both a and b of Fig.2 show a similar pattern. The vocal folds are gradually moved outward first and then periodic regular movement begins. The outward movement of the vocal fold precedes the onset of vibration in the excised larynx where no muscle activity exists. In the living subject, such an outward movement is scarecely noticed, probably due to the existence of the muscle activity. I have doubt about the theory of the Bernoulli effect from these experiments.

In another experiment, one half side of the excised human larynx was replaced with a plate glass, and the vibration of a vocal fold was observed from the side. The mucous membrane of the subglottic region is gradually forced upward by the increasing subglottic pressure and a ridge is created on the level of the lower lip of the vocal fold between the anterior commissure and the vocal process of the arytenoid cartilage. After this ridge becomes well defined, a rippling wave occurs from this ridge to the upper surface of the vocal fold. The rippling wave changes to a regular large undulating movement of the mucous membrane after several periods.

When humid air is forced upward through the excised larynx, undulating movement is always found on the mucous membrane. However, when the air is not humid, the mucous membrane becomes dry and the undulating movement of the mucous membrane diminishes. Finally the glottis remains open with a spindle shape, and the vocal fold does not vibrate at all.

These results indicate that the vibration of the vocal fold is the undulating movement of the mucous membrane itself. At the beginning of phonation, the vocal fold adducts and becomes tense by the contraction of the intrinsic laryngeal muscles. The mucous membrane of the lower surface of the vocal fold is displaced upwards on the firm underlying tissue by the air flow, and forms the vibratory portion of the vocal fold. When the sliding of the mucous membrane is disturbed or the viscoelasticity of the mucous membrane is lost, vibration of the vocal fold is not maintained.

The tension of the underlying tissue is also important in normal vibration. In unilateral laryngeal nerve paralysis, the undulating movement of the mucous membrane is usually noticed earlier on the healthy side than on the diseased side at the initiation of phonation, as Dr. von Leden has reported. This observation means that it is more difficult for the mucous membrane of the vocal fold to perform a sliding motion in response to the air flow when the underlying tissue is not so tense due to the muscle atrophy. When the muscle atrophy is advanced, an irregular flapping movement of the mucous membrane is noticed instead of the periodic regular undulating movement.

II. ANALYSIS OF THE UNDULATING MOVEMENT OF THE MUCOUS MEMBRANE OF THE VOCAL FOLD

One cycle of vocal fold vibration is divided into three phases. In the opening phase, the vocal fold is blown upward on the whole, and the undulating wave moves on the mucous membrane from the lower part to the upper part. After the width of the glottis reaches a maximum, the glottis begins to be closed by the protruding lower lip in the closing phase. Then the upper lip moves inward and the closure of the glottis becomes firm in the closed phase.

The lateral excursion of one vocal fold in one vibratory cycle is illustrated in Fig.3. The solid line in the figure gives an indication of the glottal width. The rising section of the solid curve in the opening phase is determined by the movement of the upper lip, and the declining section in the closing phase is defined by the motion of the lower lip. This very popular figure shows the movement of the margin of the vocal fold in the lateral direction, that is, the movement in only one dimension.

In order to observe the two-dimensional movement of the upper lip, the junction of blood vessels of the mucous membrane near the margin of the vocal fold was chosen as the point to be traced. Figure 4 shows its movement in the vertical plane during one vibratory cycle of the vocal fold. This point moves forward and slightly inward at the very beginning of the opening phase and then changes its

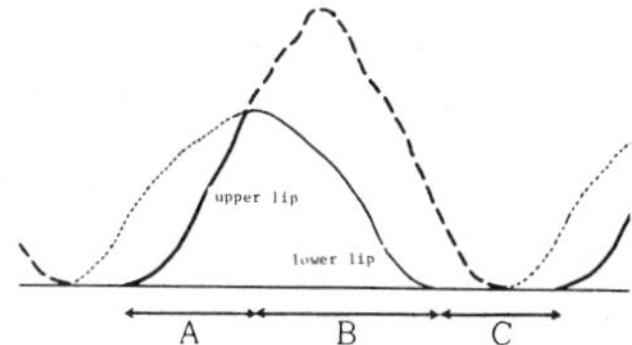

Fig.3. The vertical axis represents the glottal width during the vibratory cycle of one vocal fold, plotted as a function of time. The solid lines and the thick dotted line are drawn from actual observation. The thin dotted line is drawn from conjecture. The thick line shows the movement of the upper lip and the thin line that of the lower lip. A: opening phase; B: closing phase; C: closed phase.

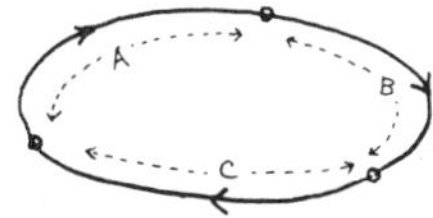

Fig.4. Trajectory of a point on the upper lip of the vocal fold, in a vertical plane, during a vibratory cycle. A: opening phase; B: closing phase; C: closed phase.

direction outward and upward. In the closing phase, it moves still outward at the early stage and turns downward and inward at the terminal stage. In the closed phase, it moves inward and returns back to the starting point. The locus of the movement of the upper lip is found to be always oval for any point on the vocal fold and in all conditions. The long axis of this ellipse is at a right angle to the margin of the vocal fold.

If the lateral excursion of the point on the upper lip is plotted as a function of time, the symmetrical thick solid and dotted curve is obtained, as shown in Fig.3. The movement of the lower lip cannot be observed from above in the opening phase as well as in the closed phase. However, since the undulating movement of the mucous membrane or the vibration of the vocal fold is a regular periodic movement, the locus of the movement of the lower lip should be also symmetrical and its cycle should be the same to that of the upper lip. Based on this thought, a thin dotted curve is drawn as the movement of the lower lip while it is covered by the upper lip. The cycle of both curves is the same duration and the amplitude is larger in the upper lip than in the lower lip. Therefore, it is supposed that the movement of any point between the upper lip and the lower lip is also symmetrical and its cycle has the same duration as that of both lips, but its amplitude is larger than that of the lower lip and smaller than the upper lip.

In summary, then, the vibration of the vocal fold is an undulating movement of the mucous membrane which is larger in the higher portion of the margin of the vocal fold.

III. VIBRATORY VARIATION OF THE SUBGLOTTAL PRESSURE DURING PHONATION

The subglottal pressure rises prior to the phonation. When it reaches a value of 20 or 30 mm H_2O, the vocal fold begins to vibrate. Subglottal pressure continues to rise after the onset of vocal fold vibration and reaches a value of about 40 mm H_2O, and this pressure is maintained during phonation. This is the mean subglottal pressure which was measured with a U-tube of water. Although the subglottal pressure has been thought to remain unchanged during phonation, it really fluctuates in synchrony with the opening and closing of the glottis when observed by modern measurement techniques.

Figure 5 shows the subglottal vibratory pressure variation which was recorded from the tracheostoma of a patient with maxillary sinus carcinoma. The upper curve shows the pressure and the lower curve the speech wave. The subglottal pressure rises to a maximum value of 60 mm H_2O when the

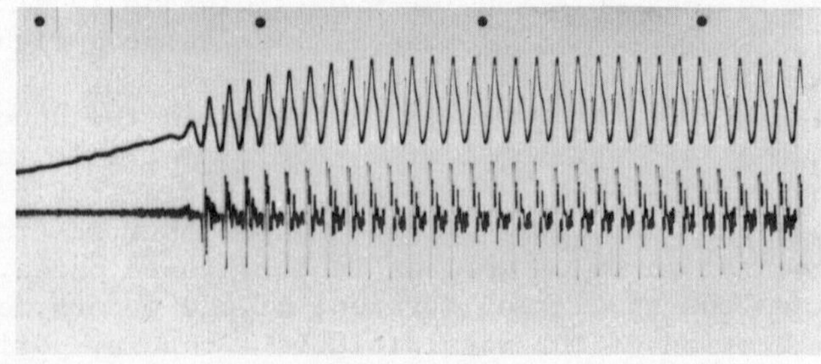

Fig.5. Recordings of subglottic pressure (upper curve) and acoustic speech wave (lower curve).

glottis is closed during phonation and it descends to a minimum value of 30 mm H_2O when the glottis is opened during phonation. This minimum value in the pressure variation is approximately the same as the pressure at the onset of vocal fold vibration. Therefore, it is reasonable to suppose that the vocal fold closes the glottis by the viscoelasticity of its mucous membrane with the descent of the subglottal pressure at the closing phase of the vibratory cycle. The idea of the Bernoulli effect may be not necessary in explaining the mechanism of vocal fold vibration, because this concept of the Bernoulli effect was accepted at a time when the subglottal pressure was thought to remain unchanged during phonation.

The results I have reported are of course not conclusions, but problems which should be discussed in this Conference. Several of these findings and their elucidation may be amended or modified. New results or concepts will be presented from a more modern viewpoint. I expect that profitable discussions and new results will emerge from this Conference.

REFERENCES

Hiroto, Ikuichiro (1966) The mechanism of phonation: Its pathophysiological aspect. (In Japanese) Pract. Oto-laryngol. (Kyoto) 39, 229-291.

Matsushita, Hideaki (1969) Vocal cord vibration of excised larynges: A study with ultra-high speed cinematography. (In Japanese) Otologia (Fukuoka) 15, 127-142.

Yoshida, Yoshikazu (1969) A study of the vibration of the vocal cord with ultra-high-speed motion pictures. (In Japanese) Jap. Jour. Otol. (Tokyo) 72, 118-136.

I. BASIC MORPHOLOGY AND PHYSIOLOGY

Section Editor: M. Stuart Strong

Departments of Otolaryngology,
University Hospital and Boston
University School of Medicine,
Boston, Massachusetts

CHAPTER 2
THE MORPHOLOGY OF THE PHONATORY ORGANS AND THEIR NEURAL CONTROL

M. Stuart Strong and Charles W. Vaughan

Departments of Otolaryngology, University Hospital and Boston University School of Medicine, Boston, Massachusetts, U.S.A.

INTRODUCTION

The embryology and the phylogenetic development of the larynx have been extensively reviewed in the past; the evidence is convincing that the larynx was primarily developed as a sphincter to protect the lower airway from being inundated by ingested material. While the primitive larynx seen in lower forms of life bears little resemblance to the complex organ seen in higher animals, they both have in common the ability to separate the airway from the foregut during the ingestion of food. *The larynx functions primarily as a protective sphincter*.

The demands of a complex organism lead to the development of *additional functions*; these functions depend in part on whether the larynx is open, closed lightly, or closed tightly. They include the following:

Open larynx	Respiratory Circulatory
Effort closure of the larynx	Protective Deglutitive Tussive Expectorative Fixative
Open larynx with approximated folds	Emotional Phonatory

The *respiratory* and the *circulatory* functions are closely related; while the open larynx provides a conduit for the passage of air to and from the lungs, it also provides a point of constriction in the air passage which results in resistance to airflow. This resistance to airflow is necessary for gaseous exchange in the lungs and also has a profound effect on the flow of blood returning to the right side of the heart. During inspiration, the resistance at the larynx creates a negative pressure in the chest which enhances venous blood flow towards the heart.

The protective and deglutitive functions are inseparable and represent the most primitive function of the larynx. During deglutition the larynx must close tightly so that none of the bolus, either liquid or solid, enters the lower airway. When this function is compromised, the larynx becomes a liability and the larynx must be either removed or closed surgically.

The tussive and expectorative functions are brought into play whenever foreign material gains access to the tracheobronchial tree. The larynx is forcibly closed against rising intrathoracic pressure until sudden opening of the larynx allows an explosive escape of air from the lower airway which carries the foreign material with it. Irritation in the trachea produces the illusion of a foreign body in the airway, and the same mechanism is brought into play.

Closure of the larynx with effort has a fixative function which operates whenever the muscles of the trunk and limbs need to perform with maximum efficiency. The chest wall must be fixed when the arms are called upon for maximum exertion or even when the abdominal muscles must perform efficiently. Individuals who do not have the capacity to close the larynx do have a disability in performing heavy work.

Emotional and phonatory functions are similar because they are both associated with the passage of air through lightly approximated folds; the energy of the air column forces the folds into oscillation and produces sound. These functions of course have achieved their maximum development in man. An immensely wide variety of sounds can be produced by the human larynx to express emotions such as pleasure, grief, fear, and anger; and equally wide varieties of sounds are used in speaking and in song. It is these functions of the vocal folds that are understood so poorly and are in need of study.

FUNCTIONAL ANATOMY OF THE LARYNX

Supporting Skeleton

The supporting skeleton of the larynx varies with age; in the newborn the cartilagenous framework is type III collagen and is weak and flexible. After maturing, the cartilage becomes type I hyaline cartilage except for the epiglottis and parts of the vocal processes of the arytenoids which remain elastic.

At about 20 years of age, centers of ossification appear and may eventually replace all of the cartilage with bone. These changes in the skeleton of the larynx are not known to have any effect on the phonatory function of the vocal folds.

The cricoid cartilage is shaped like a signet ring and rests on top of the first tracheal ring; it articulates with the two wings of the thyroid cartilage at the two cricothyroid joints. Movement at the cricothyroid joints is largely rotatory with only minor sliding action. The two arytenoid cartilages are shaped like traingular pyramids and rest on the upper surface of the posterior rim of the cricoid cartilage on either side of the midline. The cricoarytenoid joints provide for two motions: one is a gliding motion in an anterolateral direction and the other a rotatory motion in which the arytenoid rotates backward and outwards on the rim of the cricoid plate. The lateral movement appears to be the more important of the two, but there is still much to be learned about the motion of the arytenoid cartilages on the cricoid. The epiglottis has a ligamentous attachment at the junction of the two wings of the thyroid cartilage. It appears to play little or no part in phonation. In man, the epiglottis probably has lost the function it performs in animals in which it articulates with the soft palate during nasal respiration.

The articulating joints between the cartilages are synovial in character and as such may develop arthritis in response to rheumatoid disease, infection or trauma.

Intrinsic Muscles

The intrinsic muscles of the larynx play a key role in phonation and voice regulation.

The thyroarytenoid muscle (vocalis) makes up the bulk of the vocal folds. Unopposed contraction of the thyroarytenoid muscle produces posterior rotation of the thyroid cartilage on the cricoid cartilage, an increase in the vibrating mass of the vocal fold, and decreased tension, with corresponding increased thickness of the covering of the vocal fold.

The cricothyroid muscle opposes the action of the thyroarytenoid muscle by producing anterior rotation of the thyroid cartilage on the cricoid cartilage. At the same time unopposed contraction of the cricothyroid produces a decrease in the vibrating mass of the vocal fold with an increase in the vocal fold tension and thinning of the covering membrane.

The lateral cricoarytenoid muscle along with the interarytenoid muscle are responsible for adduction of the arytenoids and the attached vocal folds. Although the attachments of the lateral cricoarytenoid muscle and the shape and direction of the articular facet on the cricoid make understanding of the adductive role of the lateral cricoarytenoid muscle difficult, this function has been repeatedly confirmed by EMG studies.

The posterior cricoarytenoid muscles are solely responsible for abduction of the vocal folds. It is probable that this abduction is achieved by rolling the arytenoid cartilage backwards and outwards rather than by rotation of the arytenoid around a vertical axis through the cricoarytenoid joint.

Vocal Folds, Ligaments, and Membranes

The epithelial lining of the larynx is mostly ciliated pseudo-stratified columnar epithelium except for stratified squamous epithelium over the opposing edges of the vocal folds and the laryngeal surface of the epiglottis. The squamous epithelium over the vocal folds along with the underlying lamina propria provides the "cover" of the vocal fold which plays such an important role in sound production.

The submucosa contains numerous tubulo-alveolar glands and large amounts of collagenous and elastic fibers. Over the vocal folds this layer is very loose (Reinke's space) and allows motion between the "cover" and the underlying muscle or "body" of the vocal fold.

The remaining structure of the larynx is composed of several elastic ligaments and membranes:

The conus elasticus forms an elastic membrane that extends from the upper border of the cricoid cartilage to near the free edge of the vocal fold on each side. This attachment has much to do with the way the vocal fold oscillates when activated by glottic air flow. In addition to the conus elasticus, a thin separate sheet of elastic fibers (the cricothyroid membrane) arises from the upper border of the cricoid cartilage and is inserted into the lower border of the thyroid cartilage. This membrane is most conspicuous anteriorly near the midline.

The thyrohyoid membrane extends from the upper border of the hyoid bone; it is perforated by the superior laryngeal neurovascular bundle near its lateral border.

The thyroepiglottic membrane extends from the upper border of the thyroid cartilage to the anterior surface of the epiglottis along the line of mucosal reflection from the base of the tongue.

All of these membranes are elastic and, after being stressed, return to their original positions. This is a major factor in laryngeal function during respiration when the larynx folds and unfolds in an accordion-like fashion.

Blood Supply

The superior laryngeal artery is a branch of the superior thyroid artery, and supplies the supraglottic and glottic area of the larynx. The inferior laryngeal artery is derived from the thyro-cervical artery and supplies the subglottic area. Usually the veins follow the arteries.

Lymphatics

The tissues of the vocal folds are sparsely supplied with lymphatics. However, lymphatics arising from all other tissues cephalic to the conus elasticus pass through the thyrohyoid membrane into the mid deep jugular chain of lymph nodes. Vessels arising caudal to the conus elasticus drain inferiorly into the paratracheal nodes.

Extrinsic Laryngeal Musculature

The strap muscles (sternohyoid, sternothyroid, thyrohyoid and omohyoid muscles) position the larynx in the neck and help "fold" and "unfold" the larynx during respiration. They also have the capacity to draw the thyroid cartilage anteriorly relative to the cricoarytenoid complex, thereby increasing tension in the vocal folds.

The constrictor muscles have the capacity to modify the angle of the thyroid cartilage. This may have functional significance in voice control.

The diaphragm and abdominal muscles pull the trachea caudally during inspiration and tend to "unfold" the larynx.

INNERVATION OF THE LARYNX

Motor Nerves of the Laryngeal Muscles

Direct control is centered primarily in the inferior paracentral and postero-inferior frontal regions of the cerebral cortex, especially of the dominant hemisphere. Indirect control is maintained by cerebellar relays from the anterior cerebellar cortex through the reticular formation and the basal-ganglia. Disturbances of indirect control produce dyskinetic disease with spasticity.

The intrinsic laryngeal muscles are supplied by nerves arising in the nucleus ambiguus in the medulla oblongata. These fibers are myelinated and vary in size from 6 to 20 microns; they have slow conduction velocities of 50 to 60 meters per second. The fibers reach the larynx by the vagus nerve on each side and are not segregated into distinct abductor and adductor bundles as originally described by Semon.

The motor fibers reach the cricothyroid muscle via the ipsilateral superior laryngeal nerve. All other intrinsic muscles are innervated by the ipsilateral recurrent laryngeal nerve. In the case of the interarytenoid muscle, the innervation is from both recurrent laryngeal nerves.

Motor Nerves of the Strap and Pharyngeal Muscles

Motor fibers arising in the nucleus ambiguus travel via the vagus nerve to the pharyngeal plexus. Branches from the pharyngeal plexus supply the thyropharyngeal and cricopharyngeal muscles. Motor fibers arising in the anterior horn cells of cervical segments one, two and three run with the hypoglossal and ansa-hypoglossal nerves to the strap muscles.

Laryngeal Afferent Nerves

The fibers which supply touch and pain sensation to the laryngeal mucosa are both myelinated and unmyelinated. They travel in the superior laryngeal nerve from the supraglottic area and in the recurrent laryngeal nerve from the subglottic area. The somatic reflex activity of the larynx can be abolished by topical or general anesthesia.

The fibers from articular mechanoreceptors, myotaxic mechanoreceptors, and deep pain receptors are similarly both myelinated and unmyelinated. They travel with the pain and touch fibers. These fibers adapt slowly to sustained stretch and are not affected by topical anesthesia.

Autonomic Nerve Supply

Sympathetic nerve fibers from the superior middle cervical ganglia travel with the superior and recurrent laryngeal nerves and expedite vasoconstriction, secreto-motor activity, and increased tone of the cricopharyngeus muscle.

Parasympathetic nerves from the dorsal nuclei of the vagus travel via the recurrent nerves to produce vasodilatation and secretory activity.

Extralaryngeal Afferents

Aortic arch baroreceptors, chemoreceptors, and pulmonary mechanoreceptors travel with the recurrent laryngeal nerves to the deep musculature of the larynx. The fibers transfer via the ramus communicans to the superior laryngeal nerve and thence to the nodose ganglion of the vagus nerve. These fibers, deep in the paraglottic musculature, are sensitive to stretch and pressure during laryngoscopy and may drastically affect cardiac rhythm. The reaction cannot be abolished by topical or general anesthesia. Nerve block of both superior laryngeal nerves with local anesthetic will abolish the cardiodepressant reflex.

BASIC PHYSIOLOGY OF THE LARYNX

The various movements of which the larynx is capable are largely based on the physical qualities of the system. Both the elastic and dynamic capabilities of the tissue have a profound effect on the laryngeal function.

Effort closure is brought about by an accordion-like folding action of the larynx when it is raised towards the base of the tongue as well as by the adduction of the intrinsic muscles of the larynx.

The normal inspiratory air flow during respiration is accomplished by an unfolding of the larynx best noted in deep inspiration. This mechanism is dependent on a negative pressure being supplied by the lungs and diaphragm. During expiration, the larynx undergoes a relative degree of folding.

Sound production occurs most ideally when a stream of air is provided by the lungs and the stream passes through a relatively unfolded and open larynx. The stream is perturbed by the gentle (weak) approximation of the vocal folds. The stream is further modified by the resonating and articulating systems of the pharynx, mouth, nose, etc.

REFERENCES

Fink, B.R. (1975) The Human Larynx: A Functional Study. New York: Raven Press.

Wyke, B.D. and Kirchner, J.A. (1976) Neurology of the larynx. In Scientific Foundations of Otolaryngology, Hinchcliffe, R. and Harrison, D.(Eds.). Chicago: Year Book Medical Publishers, Inc., pp. 546-574.

Hirano, M. (1975) Phonosurgery: Basic and clinical investigations. Otologia (Fukuoka) 21, 239-440.

DISCUSSION

Strong: Since there is no visible rotation of the arytenoid around a vertical axis during abduction-adduction movements, the role of the posterior cricoarytenoid and lateral cricoarytenoid muscles needs to be re-evaluated. The most important component of abduction is probably the sliding of the arytenoid laterally on the sloping facet of the cricoid. This motion could be accomplished by the obliquely inserted fibers of the posterior cricoarytenoid and also by the lateral cricoarytenoid. After completion of the lateral slide of the arytenoid, forceful abduction is accomplished by a backward rocking of the arytenoid on the cricoid, resulting in rotation of the vocal process upwards and outwards. The lateral cricoarytenoid appears to be poorly placed if it is supposed to function as an adductor.

Isshiki: I am very much interested in your idea that contraction of the lateral cricoarytenoid muscle is not ideal for adduction of the vocal cord. Recently, I developed an operation for arytenoid adduction to correct vocal cord paralysis. Before performing this surgery on patients, we used cadaver larynges and searched for the most effective direction of traction on the muscular process of the arytenoid to obtain adduction of the vocal cord. It apparently was not along the direction of the lateral cricoarytenoid muscle but along a more anterior direction. We think that combined contraction of the lateral cricoarytenoid muscle and the lateral thyroarytenoid muscle adducts the vocal cord most effectively. I support your idea.

Hirose: I agree that the action of the posterior cricoarytenoid muscle contraction can be divided into two rectangular directions in terms of vectors, one of which is the long axis of the facet of the cricoarytenoid joint. However, we must take into consideration the fact that the posterior cricoarytenoid attaches not to the facet but to the muscular process of the arytenoid, which stays more or less perpendicular to the long axis of the facet. Thus the action of the posterior cricoarytenoid must be interpreted as producing a rotation of the arytenoid backwards along the axis of the facet, which results in

elevation as well as abduction of the vocal process.

Hirano: In our stimulus studies, we stimulated the lateral cricoarytenoid muscle electrically under visual observation in excised canine and human larynges. It was evident that the lateral cricoarytenoid adducted the tip of the vocal process of the arytenoid cartilage; as a result, the entire vocal fold adducted.

Abbs: Several years ago we did some analysis of the contribution of various masticatory muscles on jaw opening and closing during speech. In the course of our investigation we came upon some work in orthopedic biomechanics* on analyses of the knee joint which revealed multiple centers of rotation (i.e., joint rotation and translation). This essentially creates a situation where an individual muscle's moment arm changes considerably with variation of the center of joint rotation.

Inasmuch as the cricoarytenoid joint has a considerable degree of freedom both for translation and rotation, the simple view of lateral and posterior cricoarytenoid muscles contributing to adduction and abduction respectively, at least in a linear or one-to-one manner, may have to be analyzed in more detail with knowledge of cartilage kinematics.

---

* Frankel, V.H., Burnstein, A.H., and Brooks, D.B. (1971) Biomechanics of internal derangement of the knee. Journal of Bone and Joint Surgery 53A, 945-962.

CHAPTER 3
THE PULMONARY-LARYNGEAL SYSTEM

W. J. Gould

Lenox Hill Hospital, New York

INTRODUCTION

In a general consideration of the relationship between pulmonary function and laryngeal vocal production, it should be emphasized that the primary function of the larynx is that of a spincter-like valve of the pulmonary tract. The muscular folds control the potency of this protective mechanism. In man the larynx has become an organ of voice production with its function dependent upon the manner in which air flows from the pulmonary system. The larynx as a unit houses the muscular spincter in a relatively rigid multi-hinged tubular structure consisting of three cartilage and bone units which are linked by ligaments, hinged at connecting joints and moved by muscles. The cricoid cartilage supports the arytenoid and its auxiliary cartilages which control the motion of the vocal folds.

Although we know that there are certain relationships and facts that we can refer to, analysis of the relationship of subglottic pressure to the phonatory effort is still unsatisfactory. Wyke's studies (1967, 1968) addressed the phonatory reflex mechanisms of the larynx. Kirchner and Suzuki (1968) and Tanabe, Kitajima, and Gould (1975) have studied the laryngeal phonatory reflex and analyzed the effect of anesthetization of the internal branch on the superior laryngeal nerve. These investigators were able to evaluate the reflex function of the intrinsic monitoring receptor which is capable of signaling the relative position, movement, and tension of the vocal cords and related laryngeal structures independent of the auditory feedback mechanism.

The role of the subglottic air pressure control sensors has been recently discussed at the Symposium on the Care of the Professional Voice, at the Julliard School, New York, in 1979. It is hoped that it will be possible to provide a method of monitoring the mechanism by which improvement in pulmonary function can result in improved laryngeal function.

PULMONARY ASPECTS OF VOICE

To produce either the spoken word or singing, controlled exhalation of air from the lungs is necessary. This control is provided by the respiratory "bellows", consisting of the lungs and the muscles of expiration in the thorax and the abdominal wall, as well as the muscles of the back, neck and shoulder girdle. For both types of vocalization, it is important that the bellows fill rapidly and empty at a relatively steady average rate.

Exhalation is part of a complex of voluntary motor skills that an individual can develop to a greater or lesser degree throughout his or her life. Unless the person has experienced voice training (or has had voice problems), however, this breath control is usually an unconscious act that utilizes basic reflex patterns of both the voluntary and non-voluntary nervous systems. These systems coordinate the respiration required for life support, and that necessary for vocalization and such efforts as running, lifting and other tasks. They are a combination of respiratory and posture mechanisms (Gould, 1971).

The expiratory force must be sufficient to "drive" the laryngeal apparatus, although it may vary depending on the amount of phonatory effort expended, i.e., low for a whisper and high for a shout. This force is measured in terms of subglottic (intratracheal) pressure and must be at least 2 cm H_2O to produce a whisper, between 2 and 12 cm H_2O for normal conversation and about 95 cm for loud shouting (Draper, Ladefoged, and Whitteridge, 1960; Rubin, 1963, 1967; Bouhuys, Proctor and Mead, 1966; Sears and Newsom Davis, 1968; Hixon, 1973). The effort involved will in part depend on the lung volume, being greatest when the residual volume is low and least when the vital capacity is high.

LARYNGEAL ASPECTS OF VOICE

A subglottic pressure of at least 2 cm H_2O measured at tracheal or alveolar level is required to force apart the adducted vocal folds. The vocal folds will remain forced apart by the air pressure created by the pulmonary exhalation force until overcome by the closing effects of both the tension of the folds themselves and the suction created by the Bernoulli effect at the surface of the vocal folds. These forces adduct the folds. As long as there is a sufficient subglottic pressure, this process will repeat itself and by regularly interrupting the expired air flow through the glottis, periodic variations in sound pressure are created.

The initiating force is voluntary and follows an inspiration that provides the air supply. The vibration, or valving effect, of the vocal folds is created by the adduction and exhalation process described previously. Variations in the frequency of this vibration are heard as changes in pitch. Pitch changes according to the mass, length, and tension of the vocal folds, but these factors are modified by a neural control mediated by sensation, which activates the intrinsic muscles of the larynx either directly or reflexively (Wyke, 1974, 1979).

The vertical position of the larynx is another variable in voice production. The extent of its tilt affects the tension of the vocal folds and, consequently, their frequency of vibration. Other variables that determine the properties of the radiated sound during voice production include pharyngeal and upper airway resonating characteristics.

DISCUSSION

Modifications of the pulmonary-laryngeal relationship produce profound changes in the intensity, fundamental frequency and quality of the voice. During any one exhalation, the phonetic segments of speech or sung phrases are continuously altered. Great variation is possible within a single phonetic segment and the meaning of an utterancee can be strongly influenced by rhythm, duration, stress, and intonation. The manner in which phonetic segments are grouped into words and phrases, or the suprasegmental organization, creates the prosodic qualities of speech and singing.

To alter intensity and fundamental frequency of a segment, as well as stress and intonation, a multitude of adjustments of the laryngeal musculature and pulmonary system is required. Intensity is determined by the magnitude of the subglottic pressure, which is a result of voluntary effort. Although producing greater intensity would seem to require a greater effort, this increased effort is largely subjective, and the consciousness of the effort decreases, with training, until it almost appears that less effort is necessary (Sears, 1974). With training, a speaker or singer can improve the coordination of the subglottic, laryngeal, and supraglottal movements, leading to increased control of pitch and intensity regardless of environmental variations of acoustic interference.

Sequences of speech segments are produced by establishing a baseline pressure in the lungs. This baseline pressure may be subjected to a momentary increase if emphasis is to be placed on a particular segment. Baseline pressure is achieved through a balance between the forces of the muscles that expand and compress the rib cage and diaphragm and the passive forces created by elastic recoil of the lung. These different components that contribute to the baseline pressure change as the lung volume decreases, so that constant adjustment of the muscle forces is necessary to maintain this baseline pressure. These forces vary from person to person and are affected by the individual's physical condition, e.g., the content and shape of his or her thoracic and abdominal cavities as well as posture. It is also critical to know the lung volume at the start of an utterance, because as lung volume decreases, more expiratory muscle pressure is required to overcome the increasing recoil pressure. A dual control is thus established. Depending on the percent of vital capacity with which the individual starts, the amount of pressure necessary for the compensating action will vary. More muscular effort is required, for instance, if the vital capacity is low initially (Anderson and Sears, 1964).

Vital capacity is a measure of the usable air available for a particular individual. In the trained singer, for example, there is often an increase in available air following reduction of the residual volume, a trend that appears to be currently in favor (Gould and Okamura, 1973). Additional benefits are an increase in both the intensity and duration of the utterance. In speaking, subglottic pressure may vary from 2 to 12 cm H_2O depending on individual circumstance, while in singing, the variation is from

2 to 50 cm H_2O with a flow rate of 100-200 mℓ/second. The trained adult will utilize 5,000 cc of air for 40 seconds of tonal production (Proctor, 1968).

The knowledge of lung volumes is essential to better evaluate the potential energy reservoir available. Our efforts are currently being directed to the study of the volume of expiratory air expelled, and the effort involved in the various phases of normal expiration; this research may aid us in determining the efficiency of the apparatus.

Clearly, a series of problems must be solved before a more complete understanding of the pulmonary-laryngeal function can be achieved. We plan, for example, to examine airflow during a relatively unimpeded utterance by using such techniques as the hot-wire anemometer while simultaneously determining the respiratory volume.

SUMMARY

The relationship of the pulmonary system to laryngeal function is complex.

Defects in or misuse of the pulmonary apparatus lead to laryngeal dysfunction.

A clear understanding of the pulmonary laryngeal system is needed so that preventive or corrective measures may be taken during voice training more intelligently.

REFERENCES

Anderson, P. and Sears, T.A. (1964) The mechanical properties and innervation of fast and slow motor units in the intercostal muscles of the cat. J. Physiol., 173; 114-129.

Bouhuys, A., Proctor, D. and Mead, J. (1966) Kinetic aspects of singing. J. Applied Physiol. 21; 483-496.

Draper, M.H., Ladefoged, P. and Whitteridge, D. (1960) Expiratory pressure and airflow during speech. Brit. Med. J., 18 June; 1837-1843.

Gould, W.J. (1971) Effect of respiratory and postural mechanisms upon action of the vocal cords. Folia Phoniat., 23; 211-224.

Gould, W.J. and Okamura, H. (1973) Static lung volumes in singers. Ann. Otol. Rhinol. Laryngol. 82; 89.

Hixon, T.J. (1973) Respiratory function in speech. In Normal Aspects of Speech, Hearing and Language, F.D. Minifie, T.J. Hixon and F. Williams (eds.), Englewood Cliffs, N.J.: Prentice-Hall.

Kirchner, J.A. and Suzuki, M. (1968) Laryngeal reflex and voice production. Ann. N.Y. Acad. Sci., 155; 98-109.

Proctor, D.F. (1968) The physiologic basis of voice training. Ann. N.Y. Acad. Sci., 155; 208-228.

Rubin, H. (1963) Experimental studies on vocal pitch and intensity in phonation. Laryngoscope, 73; 973.

Rubin, H. (1967) Vocal intensity, subglottic pressure and airflow in relationship to singers. Folia Phoniat., 19; 393.

Sears, T.A. (1974) The afferent regulation of learned movements. Brain Research, 71; 465-473.

Sears, T.A. and Newsom Davis, J. (1968) The control of respiratory muscles during voluntary breathing. Ann. N.Y. Acad. Sci. 155; 183-190.

Symposium for the Care of the Professional Voice (1979) The Julliard School, under the auspices of the Voice Foundation.

Tanabe, M., Kitajima, K. and Gould, W.J. (1975) Laryngeal phonatory reflex. Ann. Otol. Rhinol. Laryngol. 84; 206.

Wyke, B.D. (1967) Recent advances in the neurology of phonation: phonatory reflex mechanisms in the larynx. Brit. J. Disor. Commun., 2; 2-14.

Wyke, B.D. (1968) Effects of anaesthesia upon intrinsic laryngeal reflexes. J. Laryng., 82; 603-612.

Wyke, B.D. (1974) Laryngeal neuromuscular control system in singing. Folia Phoniat. 26; 295-306.

Wyke, B.D., in preparation, Julliard Symposium Lecture, June 1979.

DISCUSSION

Kirikae: Dr. Gould's paper has discussed interesting observations on the respiratory or pulmonary function in phonation, particularly on coordinate action between the respiratory muscles of the chest and abdomen in reference to the training of singers.

It is quite important to maintain the breath stream as constant as possible in singing in order to avoid abnormal fluctuations in pitch and intensity, as seen in the case of vocal tremolo. For this adjustment of the so-called "support of respiration", referred to in German as "Atemstütze", the importance of the role of the tension of the diaphragm has particularly been pointed out, as well as the contributions of other respiratory muscles. This holds true in both Western and Japanese styles of singing as well as in speech, I believe. I also think that similar respiratory control is necessary for performance on wind instruments.

It may be interesting to mention here a technique used by some singers of Japanese traditional music like "Gidayu" or "Joruri", which is one of the important accompaniments of the Japanese "Kabuki". These singers are known to use a roll of cloth tightly bound around the belly in order to enhance the tension of the abdominal wall and to support the diaphragmatic action during the performance.

Strong: The practical significance of pulmonary function testing is not always readily apparent. If you have fully trained singers, it is unlikely that they would be found to have any pulmonary deficiency, certainly not if they are currently successful as fully trained singers. If they get into pulmonary difficulty, they cannot be successful. I think it is most important not to forget the pulmonary strategies used by the semi-trained singer, or amateur singer who perhaps has had no training and is singing by instinct. That group of individuals, of which there is a fairly large number, are likely to get themselves into organic difficulty. Without an adequate respiratory reserve, they undergo all kinds of stresses and strains, producing visible organic changes on the vocal folds. For a while, when I got interested in this topic, we were doing pulmonary function studies on everybody who had a vocal problem, and by and large it was not very rewarding. Then, when we became more selective, we were able to pick out the ones who had the higher probability of having a pulmonary dysfunction. Some of the dysfunction could be corrected occasionally, and other times it could not, depending on the age of the individual, the length of their smoking habits, and things of that kind that interfere with the pulmonary reserve. But I think that pulmonary function is something that we cannot ignore. It is obviously an inherent component of phonation. It doesn't really get very much attention, and it is important for us not to forget about the bellows. It's a friendly instrument.

Stevens: Anyone who has worked with the speech of the deaf is well aware that they very often have phonation problems, and many teachers of the deaf recognize that the source of those problems quite often is in the pulmonary system, rather than the way in which the vocal folds themselves are controlled.

Abbs: The control of the respiratory system from a neural point of view is a very interesting problem, and one that has been alluded to by various people in the past. Of particular interest is the fact that if one changes lung volume to sustain a tone one has to apply different levels of muscle force to create the same subglottal pressure. The question that I'd like to hear addressed would be: How do we think the nervous system does this? How do we learn to do it? Is it centrally programmed entirely? It seems to me that we learn this adjustment rather unconsciously. We speak fairly freely of conscious control of vocal intensity level. How trained singers do it I don't know. Do they in fact sense subglottal pressure, vocal intensity, or some combination of those things? How good is that sense? Can they use it under conscious control? How do they go about learning it?

Hirano: Empirically, I feel that the perception of subglottal pressure is very important for singers in adjusting or readjusting vocal fold tension. I don't have any experimental evidence for that, but that's my impression. Dr. Titze might have some comments on this question, because he's a good singer.

Titze: The only evidence that I have is anecdotal. Voice

teachers spend maybe 50 percent or more of their effort in straightening out the breathing apparatus in order to get the singer to produce properly. Maybe that is just convention, but on the other hand, there may be a lot to it. It seems to be where much of the pedagogical emphasis is put.

Abbs: I've been struck by Dr. Hixon's reports over the last few years, showing that there are varying degrees of abdominal and rib cage adjustment. I don't know if he has done anything with trained singers, but he has worked with untrained singers in the past. Singers might sing a passage one time, primarily making the change in this two-dimensional space via an abdominal adjustment and the second time primarily via a rib cage adjustment.

There is almost a phenomenon of motor equivalence operating there, inasmuch as the same end is achieved with two different sets of muscles operating in a compensatory manner. These observations imply, at least to my way of thinking, that some sort of lower-level neural control mechanism is making these adjustments possible. I don't know if trained singers do the same thing.

Hirano: In terms of the choice of the abdominal or rib cage muscles in controlling breathing rate, I think that there could be an essential difference between the two sets of muscles with respect to the reflex adjustments of the laryngeal muscles. If you keep your rib cage high with your intercostal muscles in a kind of inspiratory posture, it is rather difficult to have very tense muscle activity in the throat, because there is some reflex mechanism between the inspiratory muscles and the abductor muscles. When inspiratory muscles are activated, there is a tendency for abductor muscles to be activated and adductor muscles to be inhibited. On the other hand, were you to put the primary force in the abdomen, your larynx would tend to close. So I think the difference in usage of different respiratory muscles can be reflected in laryngeal adjustment. Even though one uses the same subglottal pressure, the quality of one's voice may be different.

CHAPTER 4
THE STRUCTURE OF THE VOCAL FOLDS

M. Hirano, S. Kurita, and T. Nakashima

Department of Otolaryngology, Kurume University, and Department of Pathology, Kurume University, Japan

We have previously presented a structural model of the human vocal fold in which significance of the layer structure was pointed out (Hirano, 1975, 1977). Figure 1 shows a frontal section of a human vocal fold at the middle of the membranous portion and its schematic representation. This paper describes two additional aspects of the vocal fold structure: variations of the layer structure along the length of the vocal fold and the development of the layer structure in man.

I. VARIATIONS OF THE LAYER STRUCTURE ALONG THE LENGTH OF THE VOCAL FOLD

The layer structure schematized in Fig.1 varies along the length of the vocal fold. Figure 2 presents a horizontal section of an adult male vocal fold and shows the thickness of each layer of the mucosa. The measurements were made at five frontal sections: A, at the anterior macula flava; C, at the middle of the membranous portion; B, at the midpoint between A and C; D, at the midpoint between C and E; and E, at the posterior macula flava. The values for five males in their twenties were averaged to obtain the data in the upper part of Fig.2.

The cover is the thickest at the midportion, and it becomes thinner towards the anterior and posterior ends. The intermediate layer is the thinnest at the midportion and it becomes very thick near the ends, forming two masses of elastic fibers; these are called the anterior and the posterior macula flava. The deep layer is the thickest in the posterior part. The structure near both ends appears to act as a cushion whose purpose is to protect the ends from mechanical damage which may be caused by vibration. The results shown here indicate that the vocal fold is the most pliable near the midpoint of its membranous portion, because of its location and also because of its structure.

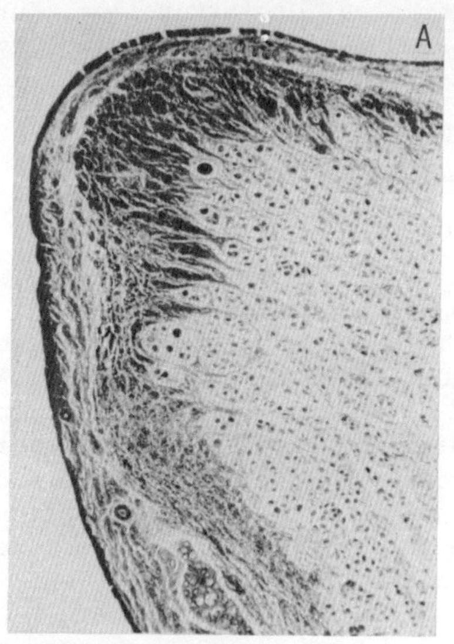

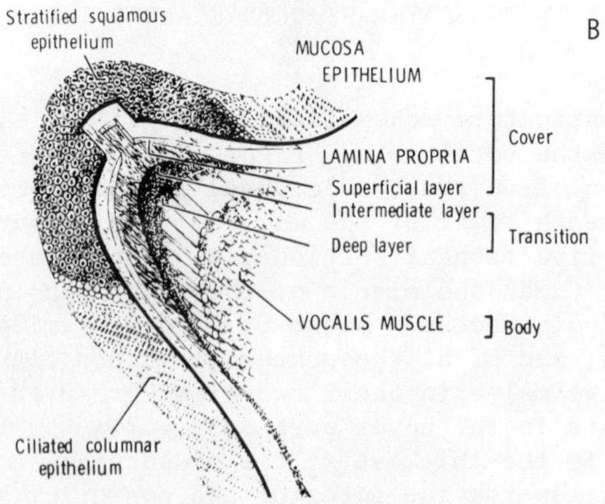

Fig.1. A frontal section of a human vocal fold at the midpoint of the membranous portion (A) and its schematic representation (B).

Figure 3 shows examples of frontal sections at the five locations identified in Fig.2.

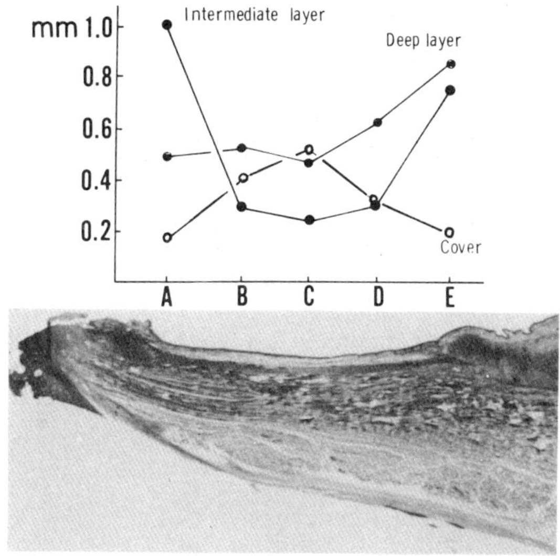

Fig.2. The relative thickness of each layer of the mucosa is represented graphically at the top; the locations for the measurements are indicated on the horizontal section of a vocal fold.

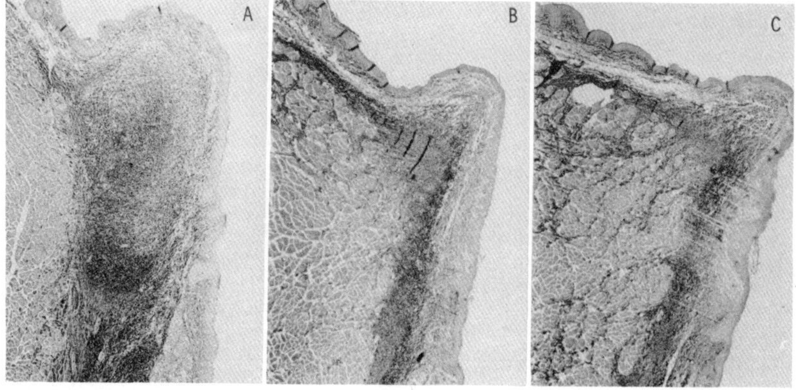

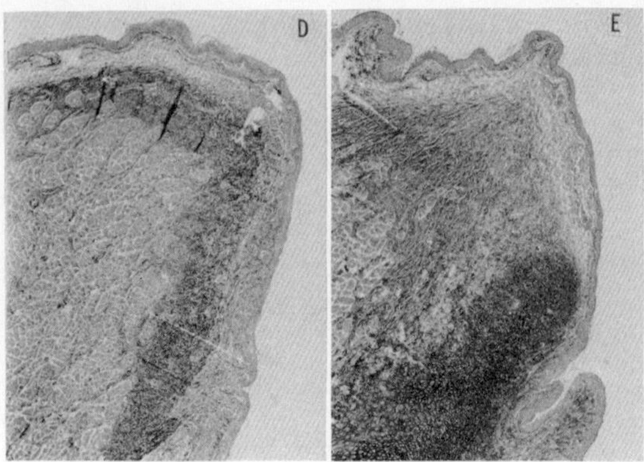

Fig.3. Frontal sections of a vocal fold at the five locations shown in Fig.2.

II. DEVELOPMENT OF THE VOCAL FOLDS

1. Development of Gross Structure

Measurements of the vocal fold length were made with 48 male larynges of various ages. Figures 4, 5, 6 and 7 present the results. There is no doubt about the location of the anterior end of the vocal fold at the anterior commisure. However, the position of the posterior end does not seem to be clearly defined. In this study we defined it to be located at the posterior end of the laryngeal ventricle.

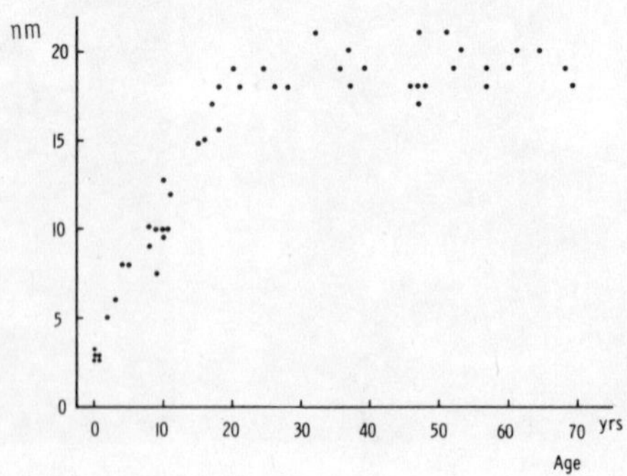

Fig.4. The length of 48 male vocal folds as a function of age.

The length of the entire vocal fold is approximately 3 mm in newborns. It increases with age to reach the adult length at or near the age of 20. In adults, the length of the vocal fold is approximately 20 mm (Fig.4). The length of the membranous portion is approximately 2 mm in newborns and 15 to 18 mm in adults (Fig.5). The growth of the cartilaginous portion is not so marked as that of the membranous portion (Fig.6). Its length is approximately 1 mm in newborns and 3 mm in adults. Thus, the ratio of the length of the membranous portion to that of the cartilaginous portion is much greater in adults than in infants (Fig.7).

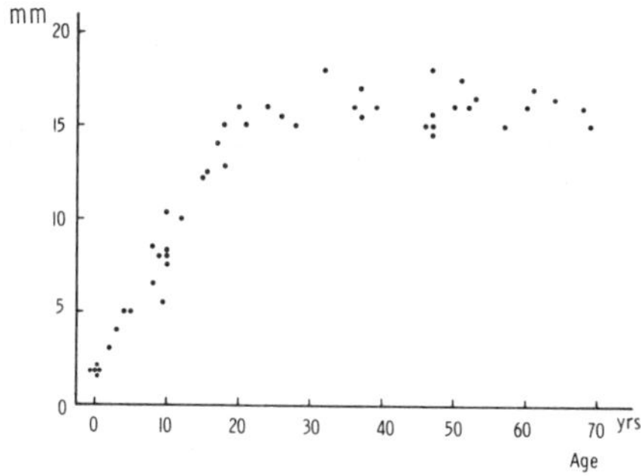

Fig.5. The length of the membranous portion of 48 male vocal folds as a function of age.

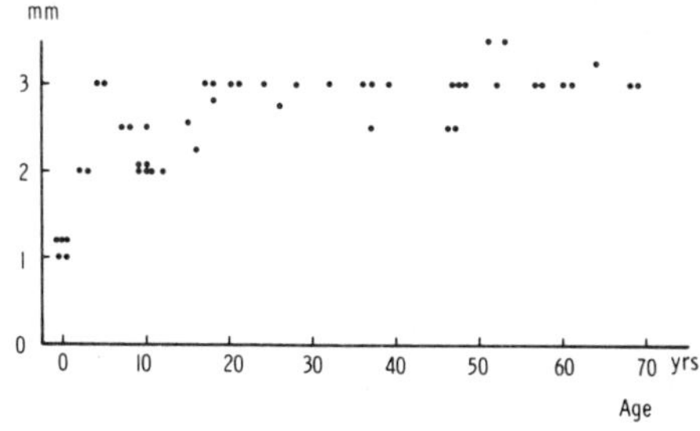

Fig.6. The length of the cartilaginous portion of 48 male vocal folds as a function of age.

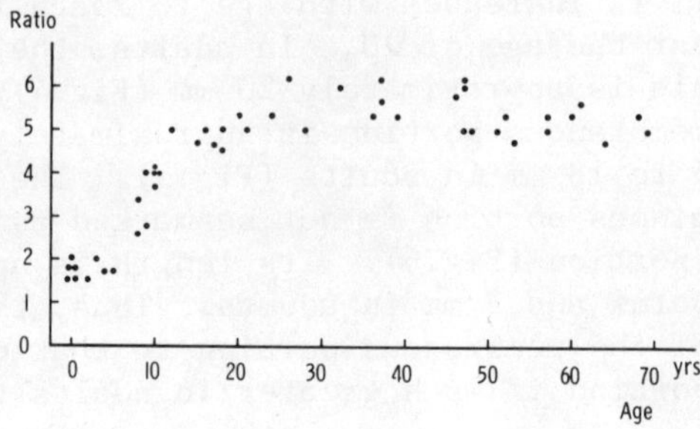

Fig.7. The ratio of the length of the membranous portion to that of the cartilaginous portion in 48 male vocal folds, as a function of age.

Vibratory movements of the vocal fold take place chiefly at the membranous portion. The results shown here suggest that adults have a greater capability for regulating vocal parameters, such as pitch, intensity and quality of voice, than do children.

2. Development of the Layer Structure

Figure 8 shows the thickness of the mucosa measured at the middle of the membranous portion of the vocal fold of the 48 larynges. There is a tendency for the thickness to increase with age. The increment, however, is much smaller than the increment in length. Figure 9 gives the

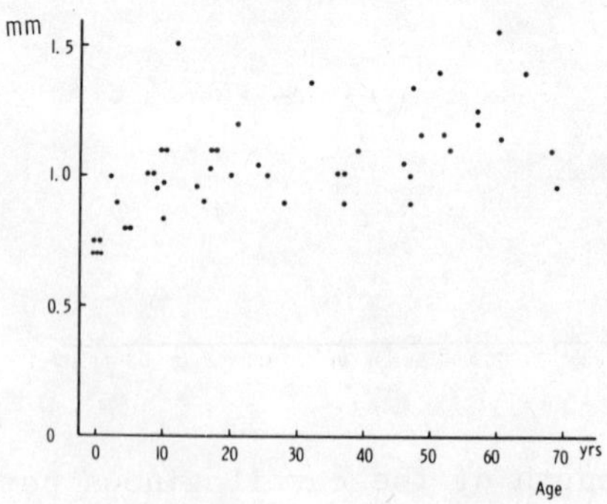

Fig.8. The thickness of the mucosa at the midportion of the membranous portion in 48 male vocal folds, as a function of age.

ratio of the thickness of the mucosa to the length of the membranous portion, and shows that the ratio is much greater in young children than in adults.

Figure 10 illustrates the histology of the vocal fold at various ages. In a newborn, no vocal ligament is observed. The entire lamina propria looks rather uniform and pliable in structure. The fibrous components are slightly dense only at the ends of the vocal fold. In a four-year-old child, a thin and immature vocal ligament is observed. The vocal ligament is still immature at the ages of 12 and 16. It is only after puberty that a mature layer structure forms.

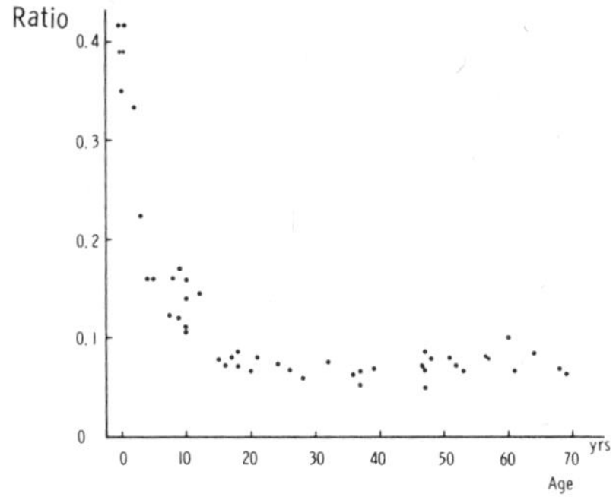

Fig.9. Ratio of the thickness of the mucosa to the length of the membranous portion in 48 male vocal folds, as a function of age.

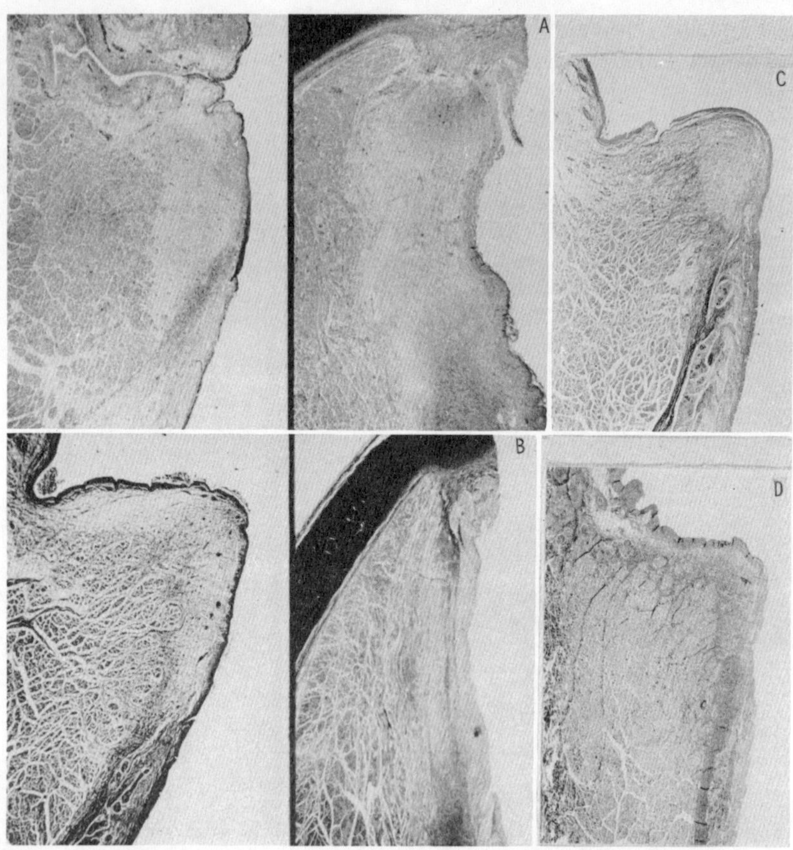

Fig.10. Histological pictures demonstrating the layer structure of vocal folds at various ages. A: a male newborn; B: a four-year-old male; C: a twelve-year-old male; D: a sixteen-year-old male. In parts A and B, both frontal sections (left) and longitudinal sections (right) are shown, whereas only frontal sections are given in parts C and D.

ACKNOWLEDGMENTS

This investigation was supported in part by a Grant-in Aid for Scientific Research (No. 337040, 557402), from the Japanese Ministry of Education, Science and Culture.

REFERENCES

Hirano, M. (1975) Phonosurgery: Basic and clinical investigations. Otologia (Fukuoka) 21, 239-440.

Hirano, M. (1977) Structure and vibratory behavior of the vocal folds. In Dynamic Aspects of Speech Production, M. Sawashima and F.S. Cooper (Eds.) Tokyo: University of Tokyo Press, 13-27.

DISCUSSION

Fujimura: How does the extent of body-cover separation vary between males and females and also between adults and children?

Hirano: It is difficult to quantify the extent of body-cover separation simply on the basis of morphological findings. However, the border between the cover (including the vocal ligament) and the body is clearer in children than in adults. There is no marked difference in the clarity of the border between the two layers in males and females.

Fujimura: One wonders if the nonuniform longitudinal distribution of the cover thickness tends to make the cover behave differently from a model that assumes that the cover and body have been integrated into a continuous medium.

Sawashima: We often use the term "membranous part of the vocal fold", but I do not think that this is an authentic anatomical term. The usual anatomical terms are the "membranous part of the glottis" and the "cartilaginous part of the glottis".

Hirano: Anatomically there are no membranous or cartilaginous parts of the vocal fold; they are applied only to the glottis. However, from a clinical point of view we often need to differentiate the two parts, so that the use of the terms is of some value.

Titze: The longitudinal variation in structure seems to be ideally suited to support mechanical stress. Longitudinal stress is greatest at the points of constraint (stress doubles at the end points, as does pressure at a fixed boundary in a duct). On the other hand, collision stress is greatest at the midpoint of the fold; this stress can be most easily absorbed by changing lateral tissue momentum to vertical momentum of the mucosal layer during collision.

Kirikae: I was impressed by your presentation of the developmental changes that take place in the child's larynx.

I think these findings should give us insight into the mechanism of instability of the voice during adolescence, i.e., mutation of the voice. Would you comment on this matter and on the cause of the triangular glottal chink (i.e., "Mutationsdreiecke") often observed at the posterior commissure in a subject having mutational problems?

Hirano: We have not been able to relate directly the instability of the voice during mutation to the histological findings. The instability seems to be related to muscular dysfunction. We have not investigated "mutationsdreiecke". Generally speaking, a triangular chink at the posterior glottis can be observed in the following conditions: (1) in normal subjects, (2) if the PCA is activated during phonation along with the adductor muscles, and (3) in falsetto.

Isshiki: Do you have any histological data regarding the lowering of the vocal pitch in the aged?

Hirano: There is a tendency for the development of edema in the superficial layer of the lamina propria in aging people. In general, muscular activity becomes reduced in old people.

Baer: Have you performed any experiments with excised larynges from children? Such experiments might define the functional significance of the structural differences noted between adults and children.

Hirano: It is probably that such studies would be informative, but freshly excised larynges from children are very difficult to obtain.

CHAPTER 5
VASCULAR NETWORK OF THE VOCAL FOLD

S. Mihashi, M. Okada, S. Kurita, K. Nagata, M. Oda, M. Hirano, and T. Nakashima*

Department of Otolaryngology, School of Medicine, Kurume University, Japan

* The Second Department of Pathology, School of Medicine, Kurume University

I. DISTRIBUTION OF THE BLOOD VESSELS IN THE HUMAN LARYNX

1. Blood Supply of the Larynx

The arteries that supply the larynx are 1) the superior laryngeal artery, 2) the cricothyroid branch, and 3) the inferior laryngeal artery. The former two arteries are usually arborized from the superior thyroid artery. The superior laryngeal artery enters the larynx through the lateral portion of the thyrohyoid membrane and the cricothyroid branch enters through the cricothyroid membrane. The inferior laryngeal artery is a branch of the inferior thyroid artery and enters the larynx posteriorly. These three arteries make a direct anastomosis with each other.

Figure 1 shows the left selective superior thyroid angiogram, and clearly demonstrates these direct anastomoses.

The selective thyroid angiography was performed in the following way. An incision was made in the preauricular region to expose the superficial temporal artery. A thin catheter was then inserted and passed through the external carotid artery into the superior thyroid artery. The contrast medium was then injected in one bolus and a series of X-ray photographs was taken.

2. Vascular Network of the Vocal Fold

2a. Material and method

Fresh cadaver larynges and/or total laryngectomy specimens were employed as the material. The distribution and the course of the fine blood vessels of the vocal fold were observed by following two different techniques.

Softext contact microangiography. After the bilateral

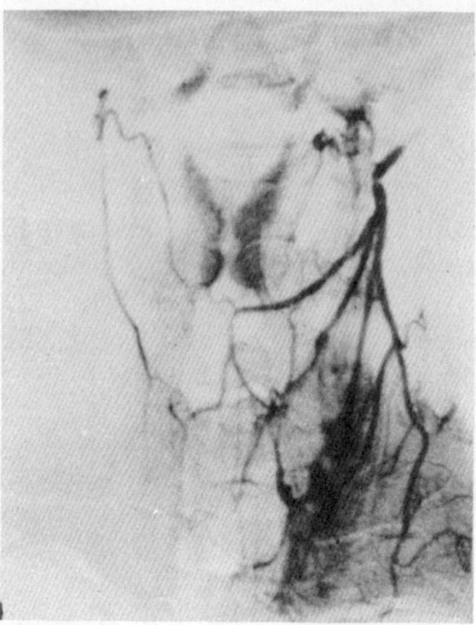

Fig.1. The selective superior thyroid artery angiogram.

superior thyroid arteries had been cannulated with polyethylene tubing, the clotted blood was washed out with saline solution. The contrast medium was injected until the radiopaque medium began to run out of the drainage vein. The larynx was then fixed in 10% formalin and the vocal fold was sectioned in horizontal, sagittal and frontal planes. Each specimen was X-rayed with an ultra soft X-ray generator.

Silicone rubber compound injection and clearing technique. The silicone rubber compound was injected in a similar way. After the injection, the specimen was kept overnight at room temperature. Thereafter, the specimen was immersed in graded alcohol for 5 days and then in methyl-salicylate solution. At this stage, the specimens became completely transparent with the exception of the injected materials in the vascular bed. The precise three-dimensional vascular architecture could be visualized under the stereomicroscope. Ordinary light microscopic investigation was performed, and demonstrated the relationship of the vessels filled with injected material and the surrounding tissues.

2b. Observations of the horizontal section specimens

Figures 2 and 3 show the softex contact microangiogram of two horizontal sections of the vocal fold as schematized in Fig.4. In the mucosal layer (Fig.2), the blood vessels show a strong tendency to run parallel to the longitudinal axis of the vocal fold, especially at the free edge.

Fig.2. Softex contact microangiogram (right vocal fold) corresponding to sectional plane A indicated in Fig.4.

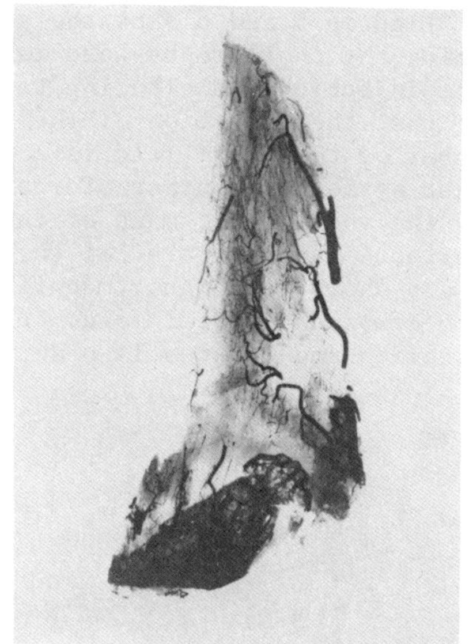

Fig.3. Softex contact microangiogram corresponding to sectional plane B indicated in Fig.4.

Further away from the free edge, the vessels run perpendicularly to the longitudinal axis of the vocal fold in increasing numbers. In the muscular layer (Fig.3), the blood vessels enter from the deep margin of the vocal fold, traverse the longitudinal axis and show a tree-like distribution.

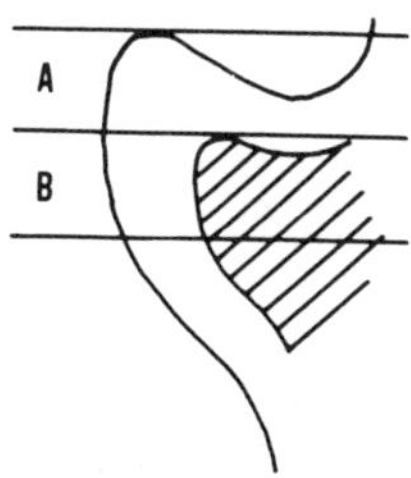

Fig.4. Schematic representation of vocal fold showing locations of sections A and B for Figs.2 and 3.

Figures 5 and 6 show the superior plane of the vocal fold; the photographs were taken of specimens prepared by the injection and clearing technique. In these photographs, the direction of the vessels on the superficial layer of the vocal fold is more clearly demonstrated than that by softex contact microangiography. On the free edge of the vocal fold, most of the vessels run in a slightly tortuous fashion parallel to the longitudinal axis. Figure 6 shows the higher magnification of the midportion of the membranous vocal fold. Direct anastomosis between the arteries and venules is observed sporadically.

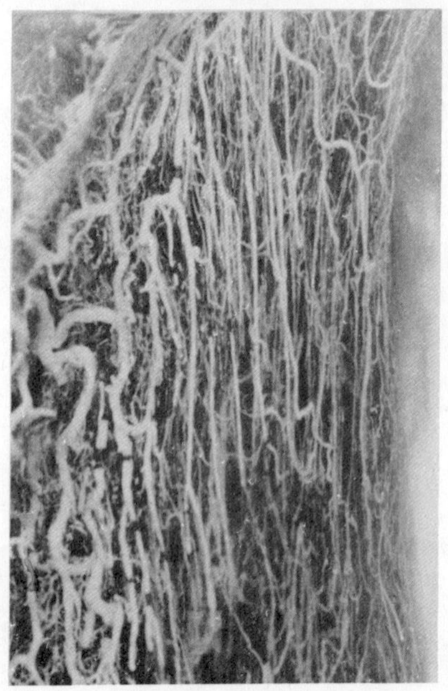

Fig.5. Superior surface of a vocal fold specimen prepared by injection and clearing technique.

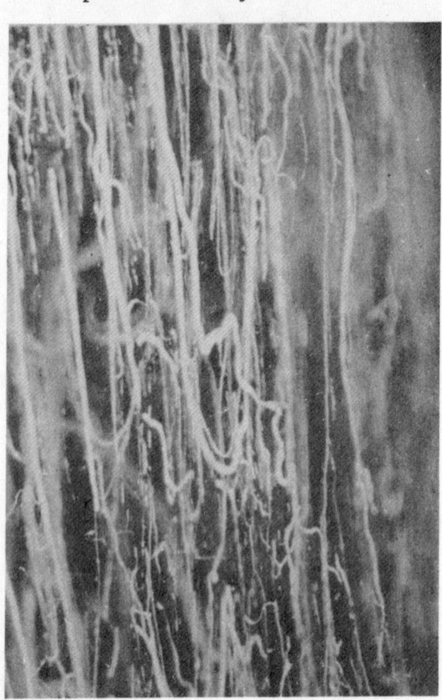

Fig.6. Higher magnification of the specimen shown in Fig.5.

In summary, observation of horizontal section specimens reveals the course of the blood vessels to be parallel to the free edge and demonstrates that direct anastomosis between the arterioles and venules characteristically takes place.

2c. Observation of the sagittal section specimens

Figures 7 and 8 show the medial aspect of the vocal

fold after clearing. Several coarse vessels in the subglottic area run upward towards the anterior and the posterior ends of the vocal fold; they then loop around each end and proceed along the longitudinal axis of the vocal fold. These vessels seem to be larger in diameter near both ends of the vocal fold and become gradually smaller near the midportion of the vocal fold. There are few vessels which pass directly to the membranous portion of the subglottic area. The subglottic area is abundant in vessels presenting a reticular pattern. Figure 9 shows a higher magnification of the middle of the membranous portion. In this area, the vessels are rather sparsely distributed in a reticular pattern. Direct anastomosis between arterioles and venules is observed once again.

Fig.7. Medial aspect of a vocal fold after injection and clearing.

2d. Observation of the frontal section specimens

Figure 10 shows the softex contact microangiogram taken from the frontal section specimen at the midpoint of the membranous portion, and Fig.11 shows the photomicrogram after clearing on the same plane as in Fig.10. The most significant finding is that the blood vessels in the mucosa near the edge of the vocal fold are clearly separate from those in the mucosa on the upper and lower surfaces of the vocal fold as well as from those in the vocalis muscle.

As mentioned above, the vessels of the free edge of the vocal fold enter almost exclusively from either the anterior or the posterior end. It would be very interesting to know the direction of blood flow in these parallel vessels.

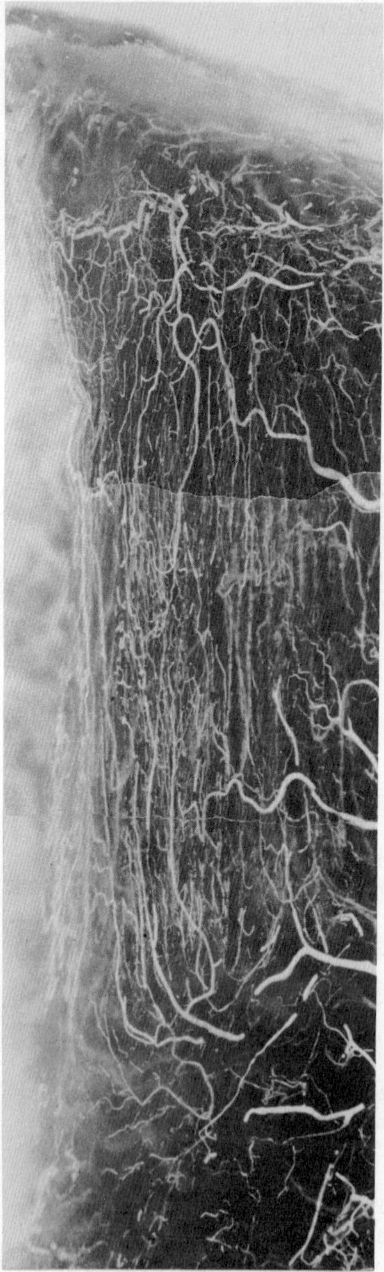

Fig.8. Higher magnification of the specimen shown in Fig.7.

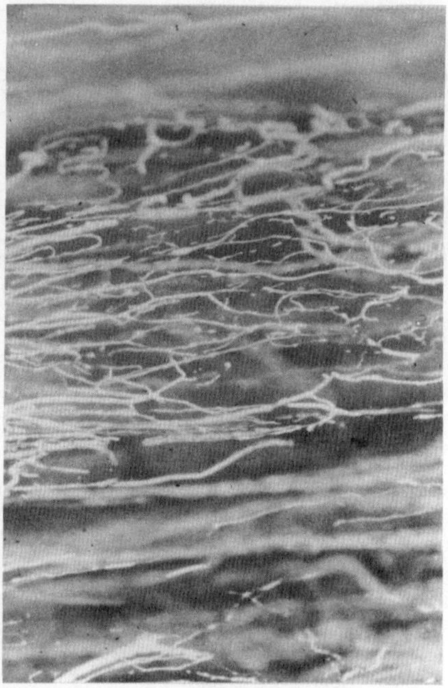

Fig.9. Higher magnification of the inferior portion of the vocal fold.

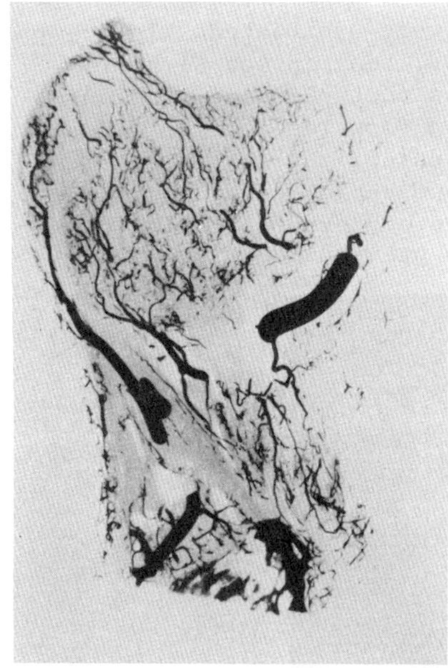

Fig.10. Softex contact microangiogram of a frontal section of the midportion of the vocal fold.

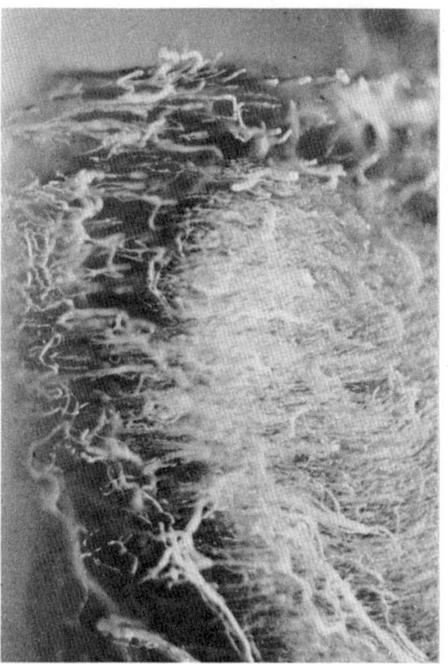

Fig.11. Photomicrogram of the specimen in Fig. 10 after injection and clearing.

II. DISTRIBUTION OF THE BLOOD VESSELS IN THE CANINE LARYNX

1. Blood Supply of the Larynx

Blood is supplied to the canine larynx by the superior laryngeal, cricothyroid and inferior laryngeal arteries similar to the human larynx. But the ramification of each vessel is somewhat different from those of human. Figure 12 shows an anterior view of the larynx taken by the softex contact microangiography. The superior laryngeal artery originates directly from the carotid bifurcation. The cricothyroid and inferior laryngeal arteries are branches of the superior thyroid artery, which arises from the common carotid artery at the level of the first tracheal ring.

2. Vascular Network of the Vocal Fold

2a. Material and method

Mongrel dogs were employed as the experimental material. Under an intravenous anesthesia both common carotid arteries and the external jugular veins were cannulated. In order to prevent clotting of the blood, heparin was first injected. The vascular system was then perfused with warm Ringer's solution (37-40°C) at a flow rate of 120 mℓ/minute. After commencing the perfusion, the softex contact microangiography and the silicone rubber compound injection and clearing technique were employed following the same procedure described in the previous section.

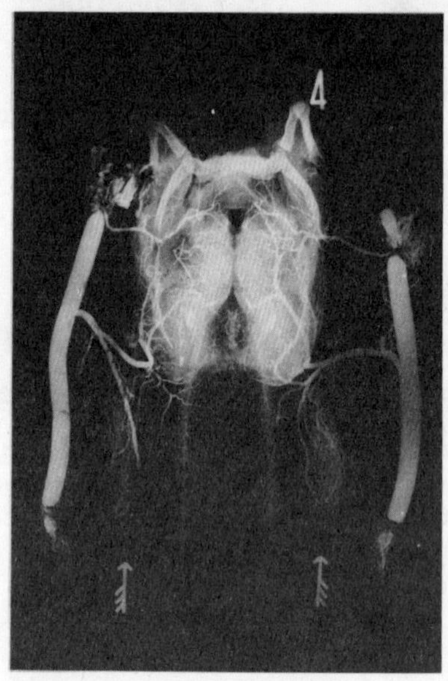

Fig.12. Softex contact microangiogram of the larynx in the coronal plane.

2b. Results

Figures 13 and 14 show the softex contact microangiogram of two horizontal sections of the canine vocal fold at the same levels as in Fig.4. In the mucosal layer (Fig.13), the parallel course of the vessels on the free edge is clearly demonstrated. In the muscle layer (Fig. 14), the blood vessels enter from the deep aspect of the vocal fold and run transversely across the longitudinal axis and arborize beneath the epithelium.

Figure 15 shows the medial aspect of the larynx after softex microangiography. The direction of the vessels and the vascular pattern are almost identical with those of the human which were demonstrated in section I-2c.

Figures 16 and 17 show a photomicrograph of a specimen

taken from the frontal section specimen at the midpoint of the membranous portion after the clearing technique. The vascular distribution is substantially the same as that of the human which is demonstrated in section I-2d. There is a distinct boundary between the mucosa and the muscular layer near the free edge of the vocal fold.

On the basis of these observations, it is evident that the vascular network of the canine vocal fold is substantially the same as that of the human.

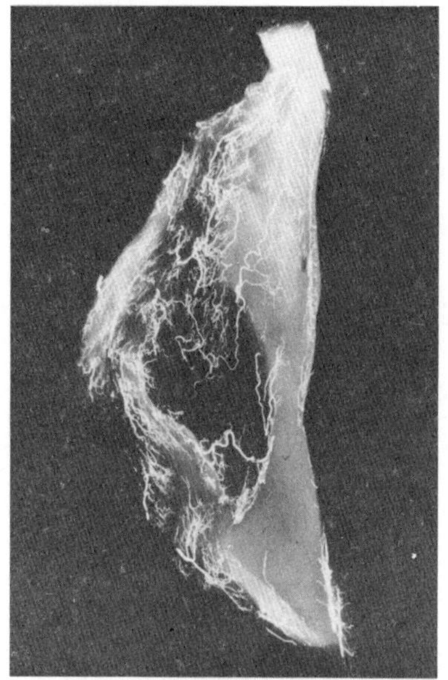

Fig.13. Softex contact microangiogram of a canine vocal fold corresponding to sectional plane A in Fig.4.

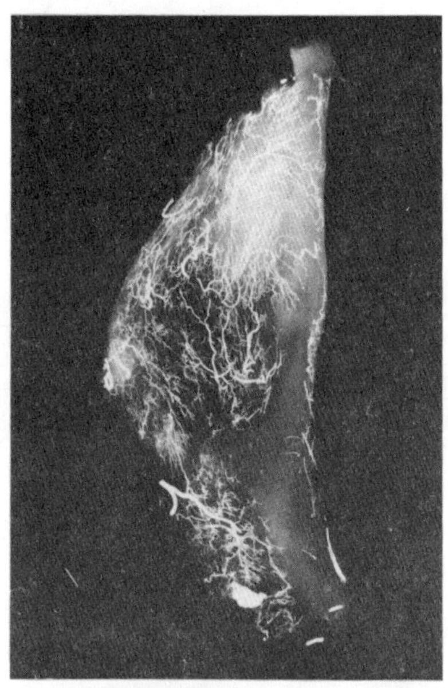

Fig.14. Similar microangiogram to that in Fig. 13 corresponding to sectional plane B in Fig.4.

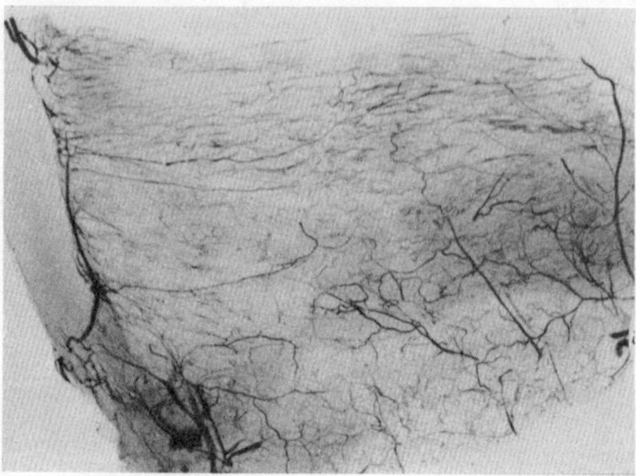

Fig.15. Medial aspect of the canine larynx after softex contact microangiography.

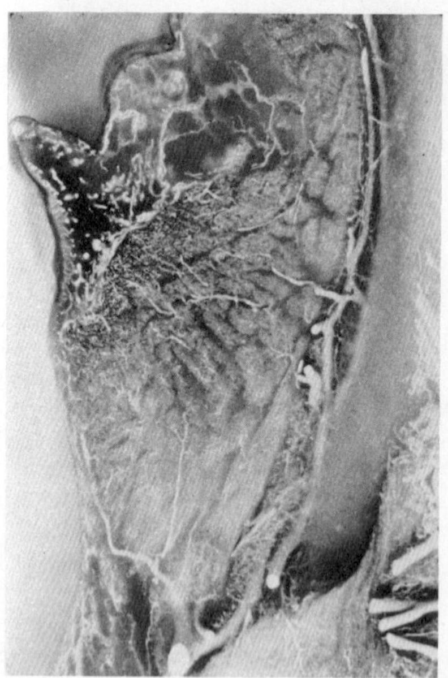

Fig.16. Frontal section of the midportion of the canine vocal fold after injection and clearing.

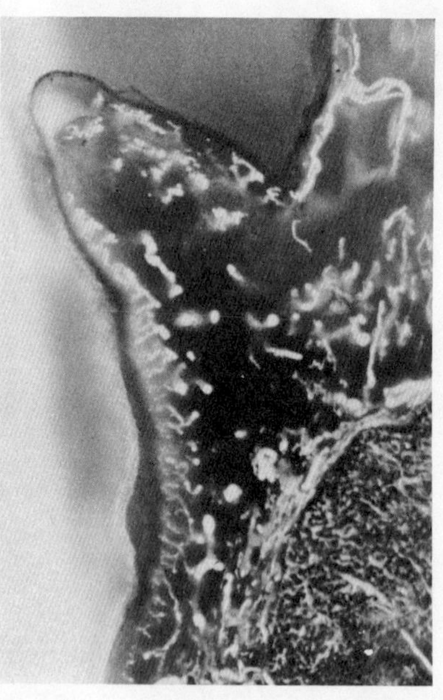

Fig.17. Higher magnification of the specimen in Fig.16.

III. MICROCIRCULATION OF THE CANINE VOCAL FOLD

To determine the direction of the blood flow of the vessels running parallel to the free edge, two different methods were employed.

1. Observation with the Surgical Microscope

When the canine larynx is retracted superiorly as much as possible by the suspension laryngoscope, the blood stream becomes slow, and sometimes a sludging state may be induced. In this condition, the microcirculation of the vessels on the superior surface of the vocal fold could be observed with the surgical microscope (objective lens: 200 mm focal length). The results of the observations are summarized as follows:

1) Microcirculation in the free edge of the vocal fold is scarcely visible under the surgical microscope.
2) Blood flow in the vessels located anterior to the midpoint of membranous portion seems to flow anteriorly and enters the coarse vessels at the anterior end.
3) In the posterior part of the membranous portion, the blood stream tends to flow posteriorly. This directional tendency is especially conspicuous in the vessels located in the deeper layers.
4) In the lateral portion, the blood flow can be observed flowing in various directions.
5) The blood flow of these vessels moves synchronously with the inspiratory phase of respiration.
6) Taking into consideration the fact that the blood flow moves synchronously with inspiration, and the location, diameter, and thickness of the walls of the vessels on the superficial layer of the vocal fold, we conclude that the majority of these blood vessels are venous.

2. Observations of the Direction of the Blood Stream by Dye Infusion

When the dye is injected intra-arterially in one bolus, the area of the nutrient artery can be easily confirmed by the staining, but it is impossible to determine the direction of the coarse vessels. For the purpose of determining the direction of the blood flow in the nutrient arteries, the following procedures are employed.

1) The vocal fold is discolored by washing out the blood perfusion with saline.

2) The venous pressure is increased as much as possible by overfilling the drainage vein of the larynx with saline. The purpose of increasing the venous pressure is to delay the flow of injected dye into the capillary network and veins.
3) A non-extravasative dye is infused into nutrient arteries (flow-rate: 2 mℓ/minute).
4) Observations are carried out, using the surgical microscope, of the superior and inferior surfaces of the free edge of the vocal fold.

The results are summarized as follows:

Observation from above:

1) The dye appears at the anterior end of the vocal fold and spreads posteriorly.
2) The dye appears at the posterior end of the vocal fold and spreads anteriorly.

Observation from below:

1) The dye appears in the subglottic area and proceeds upward towards the anterior and posterior ends of the vocal fold.
2) A faint area of staining is observed at the midpoint of the membranous portion, and at the anterior and posterior end of the vocal fold. The area of faint staining suggests the existence of a reticulated vascular network.
3) When the dye is injected manually in one bolus, the stained area spreads to the middle of the membranous portion from the anterior and posterior ends.

IV. SUMMARY AND CONCLUSION

Based upon these results, the following conclusions can be drawn:

1) The vessels of the free edge run parallel to the longitudinal axis of the vocal fold.
2) The blood stream on the free edge flows posteriorly from the anterior end and anteriorly from the posterior end of the fold.
3) The blood vessels in the mucosa at the free edge are clearly differentiated from those in the mucosa of the upper and lower surfaces of the vocal fold as well as from those in the vocalis muscle.
4) At the midportion of the vocal fold, especially at the lower surface of the free edge, a reticulated vascular network is the characteristic finding.

There is also an abundant direct anastomosis between the arterioles and venules.

5) The distribution and direction of blood flow in these vessels are highly suitable for a structure that must undergo mechanical vibration.
6) It is known that during vibration, the blood volume of the vocal fold decreases markedly. From this point of view the vascular architecture and blood supply of the vocal fold are well suited to prevent the disturbance of the circulation and metabolism of the tissues that may be caused by vibration.

ACKNOWLEDGMENTS

This investigation was supported in part by a Grant-in-Aid for Scientific Research (No.337040, 557402) from the Japanese Ministry of Education, Science and Culture.

REFERENCES

Hirano, M. (1975) Phonosurgery: Basic and clinical investigations. Otologia (Fukuoka) 21, 239-440.

Hiroto, I. (1971) The hemodynamics of the vocal fold and the tympanic membrane during vibration. Otologia (Fukuoka) 17, 1-5.

Hiroto, I., Toyozumi, Y., Tomita, H., Miyagi, T., Kuroki, K., Koike, Y., and Matsushita, H. (1969) An experimental study on the hemodynamics of the vocal fold during vibration. Jap. Jour. Otol. Tokyo 72, 884-888.

Mihashi, S., Okada, M., and Hirano, M. (1976) Distribution and direction of the blood vessel in the canine vocal cord: An X-ray investigation. Jap. Jour. Otol. Tokyo 79, 435-438.

Okada, M. (1978) An investigation of the blood vessels of the vocal fold. Otologia (Fukuoka) 24, 974-994.

Okada, M. Mihashi, S., Ito, T., and Hirano, M. (1978) Distribution and direction of the blood vessel in the canine vocal cord. Otologia (Fukuoka) 24, 225-232.

Okura, B. (1970) An experimental study on blood volume of the tympanic membrane during vibration. Otologia (Fukuoka) 16, (suppl. 3) 185-204.

DISCUSSION

Hirano: I would like to discuss the blood flow of the vocal fold during vibration. Dr. Hiroto and his co-workers in Kurume have demonstrated that during vibration, blood flow is reduced. It has been demonstrated by Dr. Okura that during vibration of the tympanic membrane, the blood flow is also decreased. These findings suggest that the vascular structure of organs that have the capacity to vibrate require a specific structure that is suitable and which also minimizes the possibility of hypoxia of the tissues.

Fujimura: If I understand correctly, the circulatory system not only demonstrates a logical design for mechanical vibration but also reflects the microscopic structure of the anatomical system. One could perhaps go further and say that the blood vessels develop according to the structural orthotropicity, i.e., the lack of isotropicity with respect to the longitudinal direction.

Kirikae: In the case of vocalists, particularly in opera singers, we often encounter acute hemorrhage of the vocal fold which can be seen laryngoscopically. Is the hemorrhage located in the superficial layer or in the deeper muscular layer of the fold?

Mihashi: It is very difficult to be certain regarding the source of bleeding in the vocal fold, but we presume that it takes place in the superficial layer of the vocal fold and arises from the post capillary venules.

CHAPTER 6
PHYSICAL PROPERTIES OF MUSCULAR TISSUE: DETERMINATION OF FIRING RATE, NUMBER, AND SIZE OF MOTOR UNITS

K. Akazawa and K. Fujii

Department of Electrical Engineering, Faculty of Engineering, Osaka University, Suita, Osaka 565, Japan

INTRODUCTION

When an α-motoneuron fires and then an impulse reaches the motor endplate where the axonal branch terminates on a muscle fiber, an electrical action potential (duration of a few msec) propagates along the muscle fiber, and this activity results in a single mechanical contraction or twitch. When the muscle is stimulated for a brief time interval, a chain of twitch contractions is temporally added. As the frequency of the repetitive stimulation increases, greater contraction is developed and finally complete mechanical fusion, or tetanus, is obtained. Contraction properties of the muscle vary depending on the type of muscle fibers.

In general, intrinsic laryngeal muscles can be classified as fast muscles. Sawashima (1974) made a survey of laryngeal research, in which mechanical properties of the laryngeal muscles presented by several authors were summarized. For example, contraction properties of the cricothyroid of the cat reported by Hirose, Ushijima, Kobayashi and Sawashima (1969) are as follows: the contraction time (time from the beginning to the peak of isometric twitch tension) is 44 msec, the tetanus-twitch ratio (ratio of the maximum tetanus tension to the maximum twitch tension in isometric contraction) is 4.3 : 1, and fusion frequency (minimum frequency of repetitive stimulation for complete tetanus) is 44 cps. The muscles of the vocal fold are fast, with a contraction time of 6-10 msec, one-third that of the cricothyroid in rabbit. Similarly, isotonic twitches are twice as fast in the muscles of the vocal fold as in the cricothyroid and the posterior crico-arytenoid muscles in dog (Buchthal and Schmalbruch, 1980).

Each efferent nerve fiber from an α-motoneuron in the spinal cord innervates a number of muscle fibers. Therefore, when an α-motoneuron fires, a group of muscle fibers contracts almost simultaneously. A subsystem which consists of an α-motoneuron, a single efferent nerve fiber, and associated muscle fibers works as one functional unit; this unit is referred to as a motor unit (Fig.1). In general, muscles controlling fine or delicate movements (such as those attached to the eyeball and the larynx) have the smallest number of muscle fibers per motor unit, and large coarse-acting muscles (such as those in the limb) have larger numbers of fibers per motor unit. For example, the number of motor units N_{mu} and the average number of muscle fibers per motor unit N_{mf} in human muscles are as follows; N_{mu}=5 to 6, N_{mf}=1700 in extraocular muscle, N_{mu}=980, N_{mf}=1021 in masseter, N_{mu}=580 and N_{mf}=1720 in medial gastrocnemius muscle (Basmajian, 1974; Buchthal and Schmalbruch, 1980). On the other hand, with respect to the human laryngeal muscles, Faaborg-Anderson (1957) and English and Blevins (1969) reported the numbers given in Table 1.

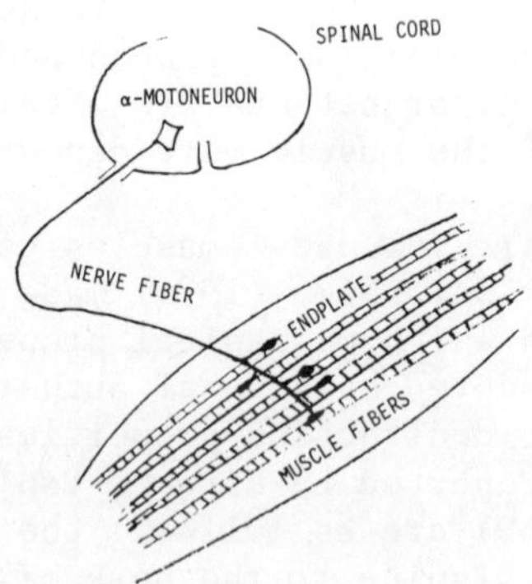

Fig.1. Schematic representation of a motor unit.

Voluntary contraction of the skeletal muscle is characterized basically by two factors relating to motor unit activity: recruitment and firing rate. One factor, then, is the number of active motor units at a given time. Not all the motor units in the muscle are active at the same

Table 1. Number of muscle fibers of human laryngeal muscles

	Muscle	Number of muscle fibers	Calculated number of motor units	Average number of muscle fibers per motor unit
	Cricothyroid	18550	112	166
(A)	Transverse arytenoid	34470	139	247
	Posterior cricoarytenoid	16200	140	116
(B)	Cricothyroid	15693	522	29.8

(A), from Faaborg-Andersen (1957)
(B), from English and Blevins (1969)

time. The other factor is the firing rate (firing frequency) of each motor unit. A motor unit generates a larger force as the firing rate increases. Šram and Syka (1977) analyzed the firing pattern of single or a few motor units in human vocal muscles and found that the firing rate increases with increasing voice pitch. Additionally we have to consider the size of each motor unit. Size differences are observed in the cell body, axon diameter, number of muscle fibers innervated, and sometimes, size of muscle fibers. Roughly speaking, the size can be regarded as the number of muscle fibers of the motor unit. Larger motor units are capable of generating larger force. In addition, contraction times of the larger units are typically shorter. According to the size principle found by Henneman, Somjen and Carpenter (1965), motor units are generally recruited, or begin to contract, in order of their size; that is, the smallest motor units are recruited first. Sussman, MacNeilage and Powers (1977) studied recruitment and discharge patters of single motor units in the anterior belly of digastric during speech and obtained results in accordance with the size principle.

We may depict this situation as in Fig.2, where people are trying to pull a rock with a rope. In the upper figure, smaller motor units are recruited, but larger motor units are not engaged in work. When larger force is required, as shown in the lower figure, those larger motor units are also recruited, and each motor unit fires at a higher frequency. This analogy holds for a typical voluntary isometric contraction.

Fig.2. Schematic illustration of motor unit organization in generating small force (upper figure) and larger force (lower figure).

It is important to provide further experimental and quantitative evidence about such a systematic relationship between the size of motor units, their recruitment and their firing behavior during voluntary isometric contraction in man. So far, much work has been done with respect to the relation between muscle force and firing rate of motor units (Bigland and Lippold, 1954; Milner-Brown, Stein and Yemm, 1973b; Tanji and Kato, 1973b; Kosarov, Gydikov and Tankov, 1976) and the relations between muscle force, number of active motor units and their size (Milner-Brown, Stein and Yemm, 1973a; Tanji and Kato, 1973a; Brody and Scott, 1974; Monster and Chan, 1977). However, because of technical problems, it has been difficult to draw conclusions about this relation for the muscle force range near its maximum, primarily due to interference of action potentials from many motor units at high force levels.

In the present study, the brachialis and extensor digitorum communis (EDC) muscles in man were examined. We first investigated the firing rate of motor units during voluntary contraction with force varying up to the maximum (PART I). Secondly, applying a new method devised by Kanosue, Yoshida, Akazawa and Fujii (1979), we estimated the number of active motor units and the size of the action potential (PART II).

PART I: FIRING RATE OF MOTOR UNITS OF THE BRACHIALIS MUSCLE

Methods

Experiments were carried out on three healthy subjects. Electrical recordings were made from the brachialis muscle. A subject sat on a chair with the upper arm pressed against the body and with the elbow joint fixed at a right angle. The forearm was fixed horizontally on a stiff lever in a spine position. The isometric torque of elbow flexion was measured by a strain gauge attached to the lever. In the following, the force will be expressed in kg measured at the wrist. The subjects were instructed not to move the shoulder and to increase the isometric force of the elbow flexion at a constant rate by tracking a reference displayed on an oscilloscope. The rate of rise of force was set sufficiently slow (12-15 sec/maximum force). The output of the strain gauge amplifier was displayed on one channel of the oscilloscope and a target ramp (reference) was on the second channel.

Action potentials of motor units were recorded by means of bipolar fine wire electrodes made from polyurethane-insulated copper wires 50 μm in diameter. Electrodes were guided into the brachialis muscle through the lumen of a hypodermic needle (27 gauge). The signal was amplified by a low noise differential amplifier with 20 MΩ input impedance.

Signals from the electrodes and the strain gauge were recorded on magnetic tape, and later they were rewritten on recording paper driven at a speed of 320 cm/sec. Individual motor unit discharges could be identified by examining waveforms, amplitudes and intervals of appearance. Figure 3 is a representative record showing action potentials; the discharges which we interpret to be due to the same motor unit are labelled by the same character A, B and C, respectively.

Results

In each subject, about 35 motor units were recorded with contraction force varying over a sufficiently wide range. Figure 4 shows a typical example of the relation between the force of isometric elbow flexion and the firing rate of each motor unit. For a given period of sampling, the firing rate is defined as the inverse of the mean of five consecutive inter-spike intervals for the spikes visually identified to be due to the same unit, and the force is defined as the mean of forces during that period. Large open circles represent the points at which each motor unit was recruited. There is a close similarity among the three subjects' data, two of them being shown, with regard to the distribution and configuration of the force-firing rate curves.

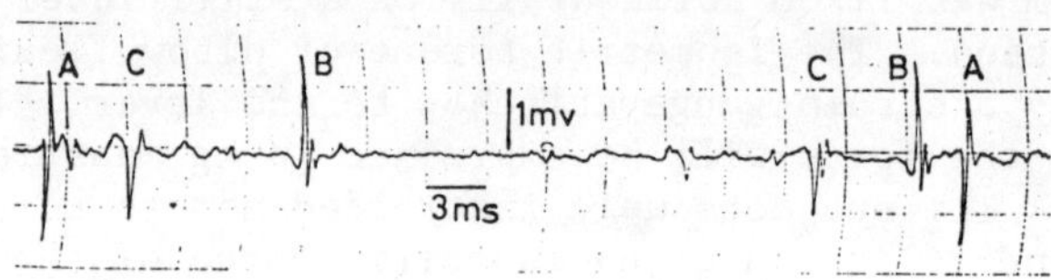

Fig.3. An action potential observed in human brachialis muscle under voluntary isometric contraction. The letters A, B and C identify the individual motor units responsible for the discharge patterns.

For the sake of description, the force-firing rate curves were interpreted to consist of three sections by dividing the abscissa value into three regions, I, II and III, as marked in Fig.4. In region I the force increases from 0 to about 35 % of the maximum. Here the motor units increase their firing rate steeply with force just after recruitment, though the rate of increase progressively decreases. In region II, which covers the force from about 35 to 80 % of the maximum, the firing rates of motor units increase approximately linearly with lower rates of increase than in regions I and III. Solid lines in the middle part (most of them are in region II) are the best fitting lines (correlation coefficients ≥ 0.6; $p < 0.05$). Those solid lines generally show a tendency to have a higher firing rate the lower the threshold force for recruitment. However, the rate of increase of the firing rate is about the same irrespective of the threshold force for recruitment. Finally, in region III where the force is above 80 % of the maximum, the rate of increase of the firing rate becomes steep again; the firing rate often reached values as high as 50 to 60 Hz at the maximum force. As a whole, motor units increase their firing rates with force along a rotated Z-shaped curve.

We also measured the force-firing rate relation of several motor units in the EDC muscle. Since they agree well with the data reported by Monster and Chan (1977), these results are not presented here.

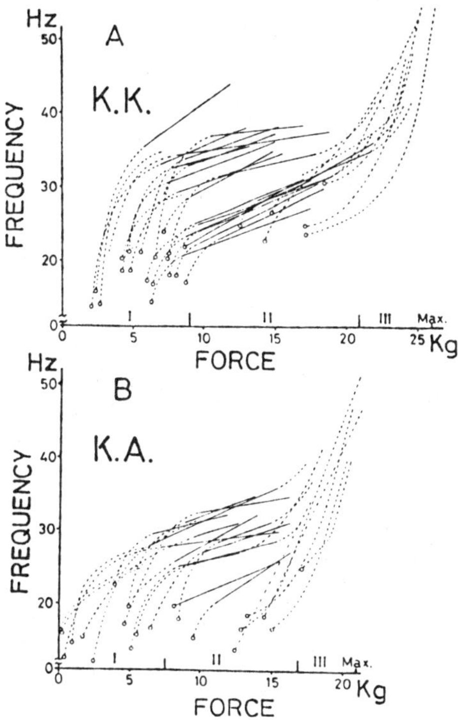

Fig.4. Force-firing rate curves of many motor units obtained from two subjects K.K. (upper panel) and K.A. (lower panel). The maximum force of voluntary contraction was 26 kg for K.K. and 21 kg for K.A. Solid lines are the best fitting lines determined by the least square method for the data in the intermediate force range in which the firing rate varies linearly with force. Open circles indicate the point at which each motor unit was recruited. For Roman numerals I, II and III on the abscissa, see text.

PART II: NUMBER OF ACTIVE MOTOR UNITS AND SIZE OF ACTION POTENTIAL

We have recently developed a method of estimating the number of active motor units and the size of the action potential by statistically processing mass EMGs (Kanosue, Yoshida, Akazawa and Fujii, 1979). First, we shall outline the essentials of the method.

When a nerve impulse in the efferent nerve arrives at a muscle, action potentials develop in a group of muscle fibers of the motor unit and propagate along the muscle fibers. These action potentials are filtered through muscle tissues and then may be measured by surface electrodes as motor unit action potential MUAP. The process can be expressed by a simple linear system in Fig.5. The input is an impulse, the impulse response of the system is represented by K $h(\tau)$, and the output is MUAP, where it is assumed that

$$\int_{-\infty}^{\infty} h^2(\tau)\, d\tau = 1 \qquad (1)$$

$$\int_{-\infty}^{\infty} h(\tau)\, d\tau = 0. \qquad (2)$$

The size of MUAP is defined by K, which is approximately in direct proportion to the twitch force size of the unit (Monster and Chan, 1977), assuming that the transfer characteristics for the signal transmission between origin of the travelling signal of each muscle fiber and the electrode is identical for all muscle fibers (see below).

For the sake of convenience, we divide the force range into segments as shown in Fig.6; segment j extends from P_{j-1} to P_j (j=1,2,3...). We define a motor unit recruited within segment j as a segment-j motor unit. Suppose K_j is the size of a segment-j motor unit, N_j the number of segment-j motor units, and $f_j(P_i)$ the firing rate of any segment-j motor unit at force p_i. We can then obtain a model for generation of the surface-electrode mass EMG as shown in Fig.7. In the figure, $S_i(t)$ denotes the arithmetic sum of the myoelectric signals generated by all segment-i motor units. Hence, the mass EMG at the force level of P_i is given by

$$X(t) = \sum_{\iota=1}^{i} S_\iota(t) \qquad (3)$$

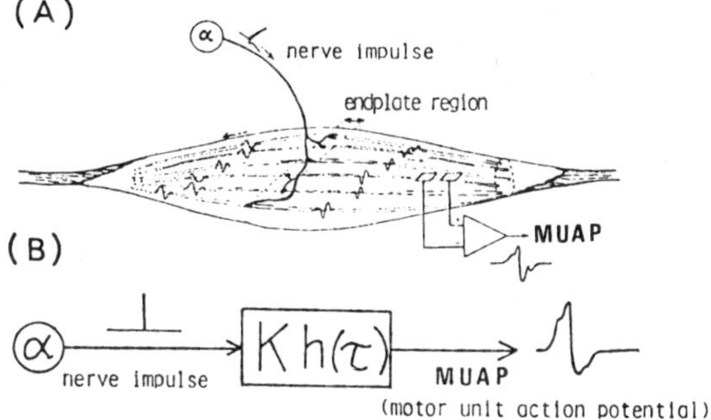

Fig.5. Generation of motor unit action potential MUAP is illustrated in (A) and the process is represented by a simple linear system in (B).

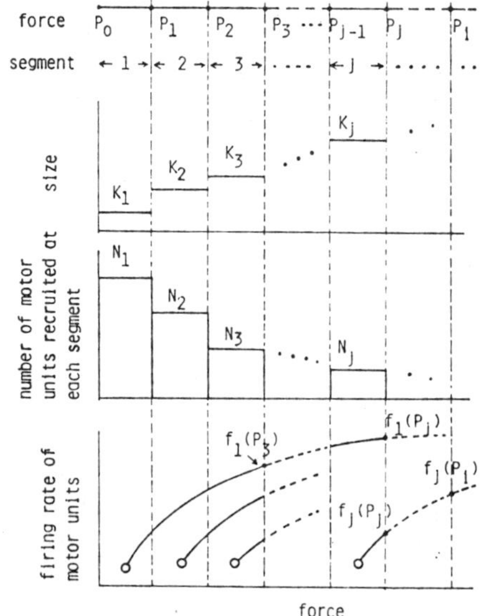

Fig.6. The entire force range is divided into segments for the sake of estimation; segment j includes the range of forces from P_{j-1} to P_j. See text.

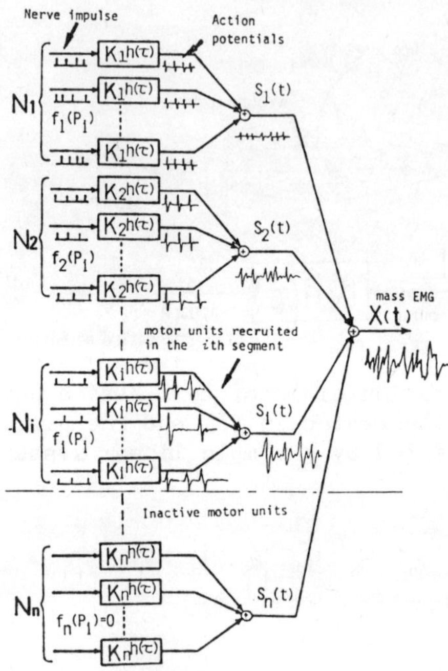

Fig.7. A model for generation of mass EMG.

In the present method, we have made two assumptions:

(1) All motor units show action potentials with identical wave form, $h(\tau)$, as the result of the identical pathway characteristics.

(2) All motor units discharge independently in the statistical sense.

The first assumption is based on the Milner-Brown and Stein's (1975) findings. They determined the waveform contributed by each motor unit to the surface EMG in the first dorsal interosseus (FDI) muscle in man, and concluded that large and small motor units are uniformly distributed through the FDI muscle, and the muscle fibers making up a motor unit may be widely dispersed. The second point has been studied experimentally by using cross-correlation histograms (Kanosue, Yoshida, Akazawa and Fujii, 1979); the cross-correlation histogram indicates the frequency of discharges of a motor unit as a function of time before and after a discharge of another motor unit. We found that individual motor units fire independently (asynchronously) of each other up to intermediate level of force, but they fire somewhat synchronously with each other in a force range close to the maximum.

According to the assumption (1), the EMGs $S_j(t)$ can be considered as the output of a filter, of which the impulse response is $K_j h(\tau)$ where K_j is the mean size of segment j motor units, and the input is an impulse train of the average frequency $N_j f_j(P_i)$ at the force P_i. According to the assumption (2), the input can be regarded as a Poisson impulse train (Cox and Smith, 1954). Hence, by applying theories about "shot noise" such as Campbell's theorem (Papoulis, 1965), one can obtain the second moment m_2 and fourth moment m_4 of mass EMGs X(t) at the force P_j as:

$$m_2(P_j) \triangleq E\{X^2(t)\} = E\{(\sum_{l=1}^{j} S_l(t))^2\} = \sum_{l=1}^{j} E\{S_l^2(t)\} \quad (4)$$

$$= N_j f_j(P_j) K_j^2 + R_j$$

$$m_4(P_j) \triangleq E\{X^4(t)\} = E\{(\sum_{l=1}^{j} S_l(t))^4\} \quad (5)$$

$$= \sum_{l=1}^{j} E\{S_l^4(t)\} + 6 \sum_{\substack{m=1 \\ m>n}}^{j} \sum_{n=1}^{j} E\{S_m^2(t)\} E\{S_n^2(t)\}$$

$$= N_j f_j(P_j) K_j^4 \alpha + 3m_2^2(P_j) + Q_j$$

$$\alpha \triangleq \int_{-\infty}^{\infty} h^4(\tau) d\tau \quad (6)$$

From Eqs. (4)-(5), one can easily obtain

$$\tilde{N}_j \triangleq \frac{N_j}{\alpha} = \frac{\{m_2(P_j) - R_j\}^2}{\{m_4(P_j) - 3m_2^2(P_j) - Q_j\} f_j(P_j)} \quad (7)$$

$$\tilde{K}_j \triangleq \sqrt{\alpha}\, K_j = \sqrt{\frac{m_4(P_j) - 3m_2^2(P_j) - Q_j}{m_2(P_j) - R_j}} \quad (8)$$

where $\tilde{N}_j$ and $\tilde{K}_j$ are the normalized values of N_j and K_j, respectively, superscripts refer to exponents, and

$$Q_j = \sum_{\imath=1}^{j-1} \tilde{N}_\imath \, (\tilde{K}_\imath)^4 \, f_\imath(P_j) \tag{9}$$

$$R_j = \sum_{\imath=1}^{j-1} \tilde{N}_\imath \, (\tilde{K}_\imath)^2 \, f_\imath(P_j) \tag{10}$$

From mass EMGs and the firing rate of individual motor units, therefore, the number of motor units recruited in each segment and the mean size of their action potentials can be calculated. Eqs. (7)-(10) imply that N_j and K_j can be estimated successively from j=1. Additionally $N(P_j)$, the number of active motor units at the force P_j can be obtained by

$$N(P_j) = \sum_{\imath=1}^{j} N_\imath \tag{11}$$

Practically the second moment $m_2(P_j)$ and the fourth moment $m_4(P_j)$ at the force level P_j are calculated as

$$m_2(P_j) = \frac{1}{T} \int_0^T X^2(t)dt \tag{12}$$

$$m_4(P_j) = \frac{1}{T} \int_0^T X^4(t)dt \tag{13}$$

where T is the integration time which is sufficiently long.

The accuracy of this estimation method was examined by computer simulation. It was confirmed that the deviation of the estimated values N_j and K_j from the predicted values decreased as the integration time T increased, and they were about 15 % when T was 100 sec.

Methods

The experimental system was the same as described in PART I. Since the brachialis muscle is located beneath the biceps brachii, its mass EMGs were picked up by means of wire electrodes. The electrodes were made from poly-urethane-insulated copper wires (diameter, 50 μm) whose tips were exposed to the extent of 1 cm by stripping the insulating coat off. A pair of these electrodes was inserted into the muscle 2 cm apart along muscle fibers;

potential differences between them were amplified by a differential amplifier.

The subjects were asked to maintain a constant force. The experiment was repeated at different levels of force with a sufficiently long resting period between each session. The number of active motor units and the size of the resultant potential were calculated by a mini-computer (HITAC 10).

Similar experiments and calculations were made for the EDC muscle, but details are omitted here. Mass EMGs of the EDC muscle were picked up by means of surface electrodes (diameter, 1 cm) and then amplified by a differential amplifier.

Results

For the estimation of the number of active motor units and the size of the action potential, it is necessary to determine the following parameters: (1) the relation between muscle force and firing rate of each motor unit, and (2) the second and fourth moments of mass EMGs. The former was already obtained, as noted in PART I. On the basis of the experimental data as shown in Fig.4, $f_j(P_i)$ was approximated with equations;

$$f_j(P_i)=\begin{cases} c_1(P_i-P_{jo})+d_1[1-\exp\{-\tau_1(P_i-P_{jo})\}]+e_1 & (P_{jo} < 6.6\text{ kg}) \\ c_2(P_i-P_{jo})+d_2[1-\exp\{-\tau_2(P_i-P_{jo})\}]+e_2 & (P_{jo} \geqq 6.6\text{ kg}) \end{cases} \quad (14)$$

where P_{jo} is the threshold force of the segment j motor units and c_1, c_2, d_1, d_2, e_1, e_2, τ_1 and τ_2 are constants. These constants are determined by the experimental data (Table 2). In Fig.8, approximated curves are given with thick solid lines.

The second and fourth moments of mass EMGs were computed by Eqs. (12)-(13). Those moments of the brachialis muscle are plotted against force in Fig.9 and regression curves are expressed by the equations:

$$\log m_2(P_i) = a_0+a_1P_i+a_2P_i^2+a_3P_i^3 \quad (15)$$

$$\log m_4(P_i) = b_0+b_1P_i+b_2P_i^2+b_3P_i \quad (16)$$

They are shown with broken and solid lines, respectively, in Fig.9. The constants a_0, a_1, a_2, a_3, b_0, b_1, b_2 and b_3 are given in Table 2.

Substituting these relations into Eqs.(7)-(10), we obtain N, N_j and K_j at various force levels. Figure 10A shows the results obtained from the brachialis muscle. The results obtained from another subject were found to be similar to the data shown. The total number of active motor units N increases approximately linearly with force at low levels of force; motor units are recruited in succession as the force increases. However, after the force exceeds some intermediate value, say 10 kg, the number of recruited motor units starts to saturate. On the other hand, with regard to the EDC muscle (Fig.10B), the total number of active motor units N increases approximately linearly with force up to the high force level of 300 g, and the number of motor units N_j recruited at the segment j decreases very slowly with an increase in force. It should be noted that the relation between N_j and force in Fig.10B is in close agreement with the result obtained by Monster and Chan (1977) (relation between number of units and unit twitch force in Fig.8 of their paper).

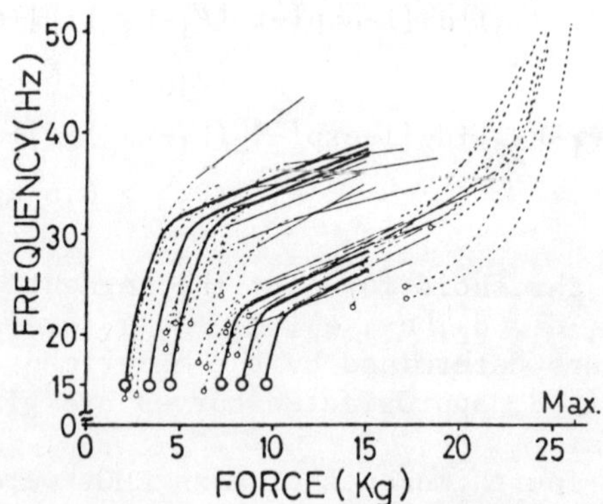

Fig.8. Force-firing rate curves are approximated by thick solid lines. The thin curves are the same as those given in Fig.3A.

The mean size of motor unit action potentials, K_j, becomes large as their threshold force for recruitment becomes higher. These features are seen in both brachialis and EDC muscles. The larger the potentials of a motor unit, the greater the force it exerts (Milner-Brown and Stein, 1975; Monster and Chan, 1977). It can be thus concluded that the "size principle" (Henneman, Somejen and Carpenter, 1965) is valid for voluntary isometric contraction of the human brachialis muscle and EDC muscles.

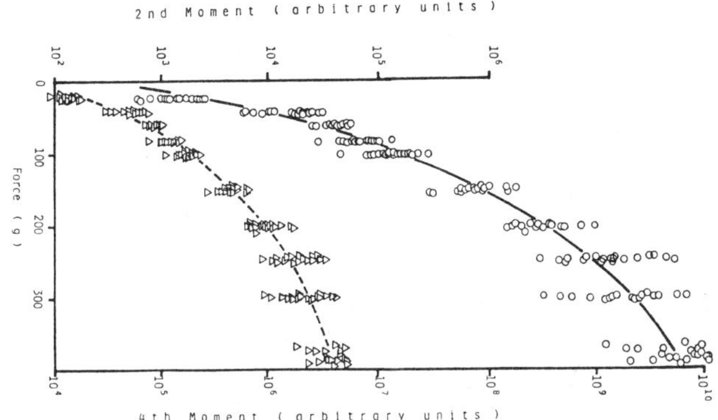

Fig.9. The second and the fourth moments of mass EMGs of the brachialis muscle at different isometric forces. Each point was obtained with the integration time T=4 sec in Eqs. (12) and (13). Regression curves are drawn according to Eq. (15) and the coefficients obtained are given in Table 2.

Table 2. Constants for the relations of force vs. firing rate of motor units (A) and force vs. the second and fourth moments (B).

(A)

Sub.	K.K.	K.A.	Sub.	K.K.	K.A.	
c_1	0.652	0.632	c_2	0.790	0.632	(Hz/kg)
d_1	15.0	7.0	d_2	6.5	7.0	(Hz)
τ_1	0.988	1.98	τ_2	1.98	1.98	(1/kg)
e_1	15.0	15.0	e_2	15.0	15.0	(Hz)

(B)

Sub.	K.K.	K.A	Sub.	K.K.	K.A.	
a_0	1.85	0.611	b_0	4.86	2.73	
a_1	0.396	0.504	b_1	0.603	0.757	(1/kg)
a_2	-0.0256	-0.0354	b_2	-0.0297	-0.0478	$(1/kg^2)$
a_3	0.627×10^{-3}	0.937×10^{-3}	b_3	0.617×10^{-3}	0.122×10^{-2}	$(1/kg^3)$

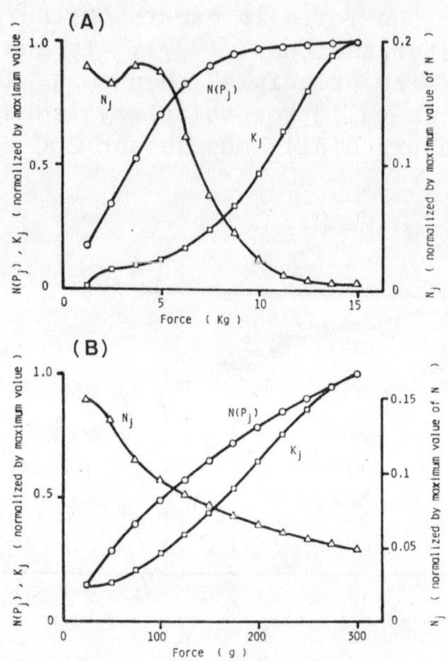

Fig.10. The estimated number N_j of active motor units and the mean amplitude (size) of action potential K_j due to those motor units that are active in each segment of force, j=1,2,3...12. $N(P_j)$ is the estimated total number of active motor units at force P_j. (A) brachialis muscle, subject K.K. (B) left middle finger extensor digitorum communis muscle, subject S. H. The isometric force of the middle finger extension is expressed in g measured at the tip of a finger.

DISCUSSION

One of the difficult problems we had in our experimental procedure was, as Dr. Hirose pointed out in the meeting, that identification of each motor unit becomes considerably difficult in a force range close to the maximum. For low levels of force, it is easy to distinguish individual motor unit discharges by examining action potential waveforms as shown in Fig.3. At high levels of force, however, it is quite difficult to recognize single motor unit discharges because the action potential waveform shows an interference pattern resulting from simultaneous activations of many motor units. We have no powerful pattern recognition technique which can be applied effectively to such a pattern with a high degree of interference, although we (Kanosue, Akazawa and Fujii, 1979) have developed a simple computer-aided technique similar to Prochazka and Kornhuber's (1973) method. In this area, according to Dr. Fujimura, De Luca has worked out a sophisticated analysis of interference EMG patterns by assuming linear superposition of elementary waveforms. This is a sort of analysis-by-synthesis, and seems to be effective for detailed analyses of EMG waveforms.

There is an effect of increase in the speed of contraction on motor unit firing patterns. Tanji and Kato (1973b) pointed out that the rise in discharge frequency was steeper and the peak value of frequency was higher when the contraction was faster. Therefore, we had the subject repeat the voluntary isometric contractions with varying rates of increase in force, and confirmed that when it took more than 10 seconds to reach the maximum force, the relations between the firing rate and the force were quite the same. Subsequently, in the present experiments we employed a rate such that maximum force was reached in 12-15 sec, which was sufficiently slow.

It is generally believed that a small size motor unit is composed of slow type muscle fibers and a large motor unit is composed of fast type muscle fibers. By judging from the configuration of force-firing rate curves as shown in Figs.4 and 8, a clear separation of the two types of motor units is suggested in the brachialis muscle. Identification of the two types, however, could not be made explicitly by examining electrical recordings as we used. Dr. Hirano pointed out that distributions of fast and slow muscle fibers in the laryngeal muscles have been observed by Dr. Ryu at Kyushu University.

As Dr. Fujisaki pointed out, it is of interest to examine the motor unit activities during the transient phase of movement or muscle contractions. In particular, one needs to examine how the onsets of fast and slow fiber activities are temporally distributed (or synchronized) in starting sudden movements (twitches), and how the offsets of their activities are distributed over time at sudden relaxation (i.e. sudden decrease of muscular activity). So far there has been very little research dealing with such problems, since it is quite difficult to separate discharges of the fast and slow fibers, and almost impossible in fast movements. We have observed motor unit activities without separating slow and fast muscle fibers, and found that when the voluntary isometric force increases steeply, many motor units begin to discharge approximately at the same time; the temporal pattern of motor unit firing looks like bursting. We have not measured the motor unit activities during a sudden decrease in isometric force.

On the other hand, Kosarov, Gydikov and Tankov (1976) studied the discharge pattern of tonic (small, with low threshold) and phasic (large, with high threshold) motor units in human muscles upon stretch reflex caused by sudden load change. They found essential differences in the discharge patterns of the tonic and phasic motor units. The tonic motor units show relatively small deviations during repeated stretch reflex and also all units of this type behave in a similar manner. On the contrary, the phasic motor units show a greater dispersion of the interimpulse intervals, greater variety of the discharge patterns upon repeated stretch, and independence of the discharge characteristics within this type.

On the other hand, Desmedt and Godaux (1978) recorded single motor units from fast or slow human muscles (the masseter, soleus, and first dorsal interosseous muscles). For each muscle, the rank order for recruitment of different motor units recorded from one electrode position was virtually identical in slow ramp voluntary contractions versus brisk ballistic voluntary contractions of different force.

ACKNOWLEDGEMENTS

We would like to thank Dr. O. Fujimura for his helpful comments of the manuscript, and Dr. H. Hirose for his teaching and sending us some papers about laryngeal muscles. The present work has been carried out in collaboration with Mr. K. Kanosue, Department of Physiology, Osaka University School of Medicine, and Mr. M. Yoshida, Department of Electrical Engineering, Faculty of Engineering, Osaka University.

REFERENCES

Bigland, B. and Lippold, O.C.J. (1954) Motor unit activity in the voluntary contraction of human muscle. J.

Physiol. (London), 125; 322-335.

Brody, G. and Scott, R.N. (1974) A model for myoelectric signal generation. Med. Biol. Eng., 12; 29-41.

Buchthal, F. and Schmalbruch, H. (1980) Motor unit of mammalian muscle. Physiological Review, 60; 90-142.

Cox, D.R. and Smith, W.L. (1954) On the superposition of renewal process. Biometrika, 41; 91-99.

De Luca, C.J. (1979) Physiology and mathematics of myoelectric signals. IEEE Trans. Biomedical Engineering, BME-26; 313-325.

Desmedt, J.E. and Godaux, E. (1978) Ballistic contractions in fast and slow human muscles: Discharge patterns of single motor units. J. Physiol., 285; 185-196.

English, D.T. and Blevins, C.E. (1969) Motor units of laryngeal muscles. Arch. Otolaryng., 89; 778-784.

Faaborg-Andersen, K. (1957) Electromyographic investigation of intrinsic laryngeal muscles in humans. Acta Physiol. Scand., 41: suppl. 140; 1-147.

Freunt, H.J., Büdingen, H.J. and Dietz, V. (1975) Activity of single motor units from human forearm muscle during voluntary isometric contractions. J. Neurophysiol., 38; 933-946.

Gydikov, A. and Kosarov, D. (1974) Some features of different motor units in human biceps brachii. Pflügers Arch., 347; 75-88.

Henneman, E., Somejen, G. and Carpenter, D.O. (1965) Functional significance of cell size in spinal motoneurons. J. Neurophysiol., 28; 560-580.

Hirose, H., Ushijima, T., Kobayashi, T. and Sawashima, M. (1969) An experimental study of the contraction properties of the laryngeal muscles in the cat. Ann. Otol. Rhinol. Laryngol., 78; 297-307.

Kanosue, K., Akazawa, K. and Fujii, K. (1979) Method of recognizing motor units and its application to analysis of the force-position control mechanism. 6th Domestic Biomechanism Symposium (SOBIM Japan), 1979, July.

Kanosue, K., Yoshida, M., Akazawa, K., and Fujii, K. (1979) The number of active motor units and their firing rates in voluntary contraction of human brachialis muscle. Japan. J. Physiol., 29; 427-443.

Kasarov, D., Gydikov, A. and Tankov, N. (1976) Discharge pattern of tonic and phasic motor units in human muscles upon stretch reflex. Progress in Brain Research, 44; 355-365.

Milner-Brown, H.S., Stein, R.B., and Yemm, R. (1973a) The orderly recruitment of human motor units during voluntary isometric contractions. J. Physiol. (London), 230; 359-370.

Milner-Brown, H.S., Stein, R.B., and Yemm, R. (1973b) Changes in firing rate of human motor units during linearly changing voluntary contractions. J. Physiol. (London), 239; 371-390.

Milner-Brown, H.S. and Stein, R.B. (1975) The relation between the surface electromyogram and muscular force. J. Physiol. (London), 246; 549-569.

Monster, A.W. and Chan, H. (1977) Isometric force produced by motor units of extensor digitorum communis muscle in man. J. Neurophysiol., 40; 1432-1443.

Papoulis, A. (1965) Probability, Random Variables and Stochastic Processes, New York: McGraw-Hill, p.569.

Prochazka, V.J. and Kornhuber, H.H. (1973) On-line multi-unit sorting with resolution of superposition potentials. EEG & Clin. Neurophysiol., 34; 91-93.

Sawashima, M. (1974) Laryngeal research in experimental phonetics, in Current Trends in Linguistics, vol.12, Linguistics and Adjacent Arts and Sciences, T.A. Sebcok (ed.), Paris: Mouton, 2303-2348.

Šram, F. and Syka, J. (1977) Firing pattern of motor units in the vocal muscle during phonation. Acta Otolar-

yngol., 84; 132-137.

Sussman, H.M., MacNeilage, P.F. and Powers, R.K. (1977) Recruitment and discharge patterns of single motor units during speech production. _J. Speech Hearing Res_., 20; 616-630.

Tanji, J. and Kato, M. (1973a) Recruitment of motor units in voluntary contraction of a finger muscle in man. _Exp. Neurol_., 40; 759-770.

Tanji, J. and Kato, M. (1973b) Firing rate of individual motor units in voluntary contraction of abductor digiti minimi muscle in man. _Exp. Neurol_., 40; 771-783.

II. OBSERVATION OF VOCAL FOLD VIBRATION

Section Editor: Thomas Baer

Haskins Laboratories, New Haven,
Connecticut, USA

CHAPTER 7
DATA FROM HIGH-SPEED MOTION PICTURE STUDIES

M. Hirano*, Y. Kakita*, H. Kawasaki*,
W.J. Gould**, and A. Lambiase**

*Department of Otolaryngology, Kurume University, Japan
**Lenox Hill Hospital, New York, USA

In this paper, vibratory patterns of selected surface points of the vocal fold are discussed.

I. SUBJECT AND METHOD

A 22-year-old bass singer of an amateur choir served as the subject. His vocal folds were photographed on color film at a film speed of approximately 5,000 frames per second during phonation in a modal register at a fundamental frequency of 128 Hz. One vibratory cycle was selected for frame-by-frame analysis. For the analysis, we used a computer system developed by Baer (1977) and Gay (1977) enabling us to measure and store in computer memory the x-y coordinates of selected points.

We selected seven points along a horizontal line drawn through the vocal folds at a point of maximum lateral excursion as shown in Fig.1. Points 1 and 7 were located on the edge of the left and right ventricular folds; points 2 and 3, on the edge of the left and right vocal folds; and points 4, 5 and 6, on three blood vessels (vessels 1, 2 and 3). In order to minimize the error in locating each point on the images projected, we repeated the procedure of data input into the computer five times with the same vibratory cycle, and obtained values averaged over the five repetitions.

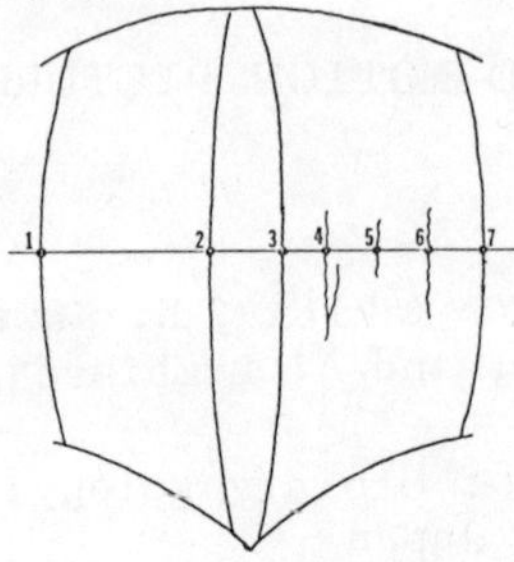

Fig.1. Points for measurements. Point 1: Edge of the left ventricular fold. Point 2: Edge of the left vocal fold. Point 3: Edge of the right vocal fold. Point 4: Vessel 1. Point 5: Vessel 2. Point 6: Vessel 3. Point 7: Edge of the right ventricular fold.

II. RESULTS

Figure 2 depicts the pattern of the horizontal excursion of each point and the glottal width waveform. Figure 2A shows traces of the five repetitions which were superimposed on each other. The variation between the repetitions was small enough to indicate that errors in locating each point on the projected images were negligible. Figure 2B presents traces averaged over the five repetitions. Since our separate investigation revealed that the average distance between the bilateral ventricular folds during easy phonation was approximately 6 mm in normal Japanese adults (Kakita et al. 1976), we assumed the distance from point 1 to point 7 in the present case to be 6 mm. Figure 3 shows a horizontal excursion pattern of the three vessels and the edge of the right vocal fold with greater scale magnification than that used in Fig.2.

In the glottal width waveform, the maximum amplitude, open quotient, and speed quotient were 1.9 mm, 0.72, and 0.65 respectively. The edges of the bilateral vocal folds presented almost symmetrical movements. The maximum amplitude of the excursion of each vocal fold edge was approximately 1 mm. Since the edge represented mainly the so-called upper lip during the opening phase and the so-called lower lip during the closing phase, the value does not indicate the maximum amplitude of a definite point. The maximum amplitude of the upper lip should be greater than that of the effective glottal border.

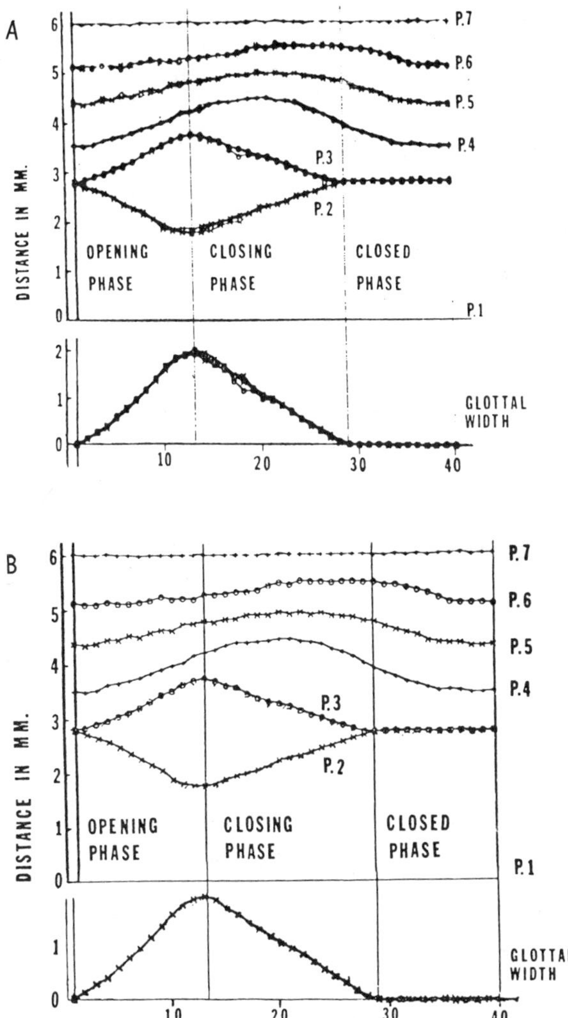

Fig.2. Pattern of the horizontal excursion of each point and glottal width waveform. A: Five measurement repetitions superimposed on each other. B: Average over the five repetitions. The abscissa is the frame number, each frame being about 0.2 msec.

The waveform for the edges resembled a triangular wave, whereas that for the vessels was more like a trapezoid. As the point of measurement became more laterally located, there were delays in the occurrence of the maximum lateral excursion, i.e. the first apex of the trapezoid. These delays seemed to indicate the time span required for wave propagation through the tissue. The propagation speed from vessel 1 to vessel 2 was measured at approximately 2.5 m/sec, and that from vessel 2 to vessel 3 approximately 1.5 m/sec. The decrease in speed in the more lateral portion of the vocal fold may be attributed to an increase in mass of tissue.

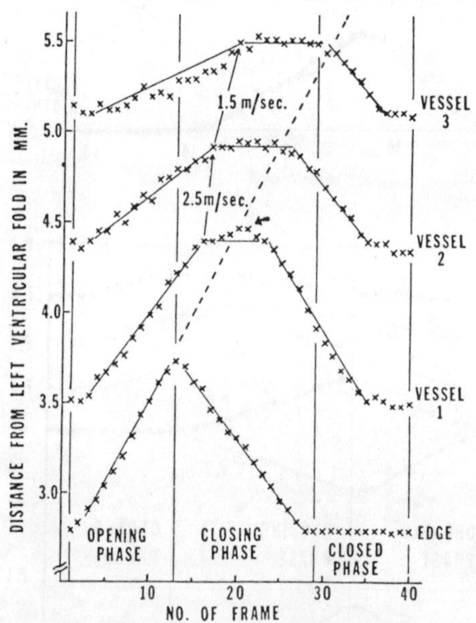

Fig.3. Pattern of the horizontal excursion waveform of the vessels and edge of the right vocal fold with greater magnification. Piecewise linear functions are fitted to the data. The arrow on the curve for vessel 1 shows a ripple caused by a travelling wave on the mucosal surface, and the dashed line indicates the direction of this wave.

The second apex of the trapezoid, i.e. the beginning of the medial excusion, occurred also with a certain delay as the vessel became more laterally located. The delay for the second apex was greater than that for the first apex. This indicates that the factors which determine the propagation characteristics for the medial excursion are not the same as those for the lateral excursion.

An additional small ripple was observed on the upper side of the trapezoid for vessel 1 (Fig.3). This ripple was located on the dashed line which was an extension of the opening section of the edge of the vocal fold where the movement traced was primarily that of the so-called upper lip. Therefore, we assumed that this ripple resulted from a traveling wave on the surface of the mucosa. This interpretation was made after repeated observations of the film which was again projected at a normal speed after the frame-by-frame analysis. There was no such ripple on the trapezoid for vessel 2 and for vessel 3. The traveling wave was diminished markedly at these points. Furthermore, it presented greater vertical than horizontal movement at these points.

Table 1 shows the maximum amplitude and speed of excursion for the edge and the three vessels of the right vocal fold. The speed was calculated at an almost linear portion of the lateral and medial excursions. Among the three vessels, the more medially the point of measurement was located, the greater was the amplitude of movement. The amplitude for the edge was almost the same as that for vessel 1. However, the amplitude for the upper lip should be greater than that for the edge, as described earlier.

Table 1. Maximum amplitude and speed of excursion for the edge and the three vessels of the vocal fold.

	Maximum amplitude in mm.	Speed of lateral excursion in m/sec.	Speed of Medial excursion in m/sec.
Point 3(Edge)	0.96	0.50	0.33
Point 4(Vessel 1)	0.98	0.33	0.38
Point 5(Vessel 2)	0.63	0.19	0.31
Point 6(Vessel 3)	0.44	0.11	0.31

The speed of the lateral excursion was greatest at the glottal edge, and it decreased as the point of measurement became more laterally located. The speed of the medial excursion did not show much difference between the points of measurement. It was slightly greater for vessel 1 than for vessels 2 and 3. The speed of the medial excursion was greater than that of the lateral excursion for all vessels studied in the present case. The opening speed of the edge of the vocal fold was greater than the closing speed.

An additional interesting finding in the present investigation was the fact that the vessels became obscure in some frames, whereas they were clearly visible in most frames. The obscurity occurred primarily toward the end of the lateral excursion, where the distance between the vessels became smaller. The possible reasons for this phenomenon appear to be the following:

1) A blur caused by very fast movements. This is unlikely because the speed was much faster in the medial excursion (where the vessels were clearly visible) than in the lateral excursion. There may be some very rapid and minute vibrations superimposed on the nearly linear lateral movement, but we are not sure whether such vibration can occur.
2) Changes in the angle of the upper surface of the vocal fold to light. Since the distance between the vessels is decreased, the angle of the upper surface of the vocal fold to the light may deviate from a right angle. This change in angle may cause a change in reflection, and less visibility of the vessels which lie underneath the epithelium.
3) A compression of the vessels associated with a decrease or cessation of the blood flow. Hiroto et al.(1969) reported a decrease in total blood flow of the larynx during vibrations of the vocal folds. A decrease in the blood flow of the ear drums in response to sound input was also experimentally presented by Ohkura (1970). Therefore, it is evident that the average blood flow is decreased when tissue begins to vibrate. It is, however, not clear whether blood flow is equally decreased throughout an entire cycle of vibration or decreased particularly during a certain phase within a cycle. If the obscurity is really caused by a compression of the vessels, one could say that the local blood flow is particularly decreased when deformation of the vocal

folds is great.

At this point in the investigation, we are not yet able to determine which of the three possible explanation offered above is correct.

ACKNOWLEDGMENTS

The authors are greatly indebted to Dr. Thomas Baer for his valuable contribution in conducting the present investigation. This investigation was supported in part by a Grant-in-Aid for Scientific Research (No. 337040, 557402) from the Japanese Ministry of Education, Science and Culture.

REFERENCES

Baer, T. (1977) Personal communication

Gay, T. (1977) Articulatory movements in VCV sequences, J. Acoust. Soc. Am. 62; 183-193.

Hiroto, I., Toyozumi, Y., Tomita, H., et al. (1969) An experimental study on the hemodynamics of the vibrating vocal fold. J. Otolaryngol. Jpn. 72; 884-888.

Kakita, Y., Hirano, M., Kawasaki, H., and Matsushita, H. (1976) Schematical presentation of vibration of the vocal cords as a layer-structured vibrator. Normal larynges. J. Otolaryngol. Jpn. 79; 1333-1340.

Ohkura, B. (1970) An experimental study on blood volume of the tympanic membrane during vibration. Otologia (Fukuoka) 16; 185-204.

DISCUSSION

Titze: Why did you choose to approximate the waveforms with a trapezoid rather than a sinusoid or some other function?

Kakita: The trapezoid was chosen because the waveforms are asymmetric in time, and they demonstrate a saturation effect.

Rothenberg: It seems likely to me that your results do represent an approximation to the traveling-wave speed. However, one must be careful in interpreting the details of the waveform, since in a steady-state, repeating motion the waveform is the sum of the propagated motion of the lip and a small amount of energy reflected in the opposite direction from the previous waves. Also, the motion shown can be thought of as the sum of the surface wave and the motion of the entire vocal fold. Perhaps a component representing the entire fold motion should be subtracted before the surface wave can be seen.

Baer and Saito: These measurements only indicate the lateral component of movement. There may also be a vertical component.

Baer: In Fig. 3, an apparent propagation delay can also be seen in another aspect of the curves--the point at which they return to their baseline during the closed period. At least this is true when comparing the data for vessel 2 and vessel 3.

Kakita: Possibly the differences in speed for lateral and medial excursions can be explained on the basis of differences in tissue properties. The stiffness of the epithelium is larger than that of the lamina propria. If the epithelium is tenser during the medial excursion, the speed may be greater.

Titze: One explanation for the difference in velocity of the lateral and medial surface waves may be that upon return (medial movement) the wave has been dispersed and damped sufficiently to have become an integral part of the body of the vocal fold. In other words, a true surface wave exists only after closure, as a result of the collision between the folds. Upon returning to the medial edge, the surface wave effect may be minimal.

Hirano: We think that there are at least three possible surface waves: (1) waves produced by air pressure acting on the inferior surface of the vocal fold; (2) waves produced by collision of the bilateral vocal folds, and (3) waves reflected from the lateral wall of the ventricle.

CHAPTER 8
X-RAY STROBOSCOPY

S. Saito, H. Fukuda, Y. Isogai, and H. Ono

Department of Otolaryngology, School of Medicine, Keio University, Japan

Up to the present time, movement of the vocal fold during phonation has been observed perorally by use of high speed motion picture photography or by laryngo-stroboscope. In order to examine the vibratory pattern of the vocal fold from different directions, we have developed a method of observing the vocal fold vibration by using an X-ray system. Voice-synchronized X-ray can be obtained by using a pulse signal from a laryngo-stroboscope as a trigger to a pulsed X-ray unit. The block diagram of this system is shown in Fig.1.

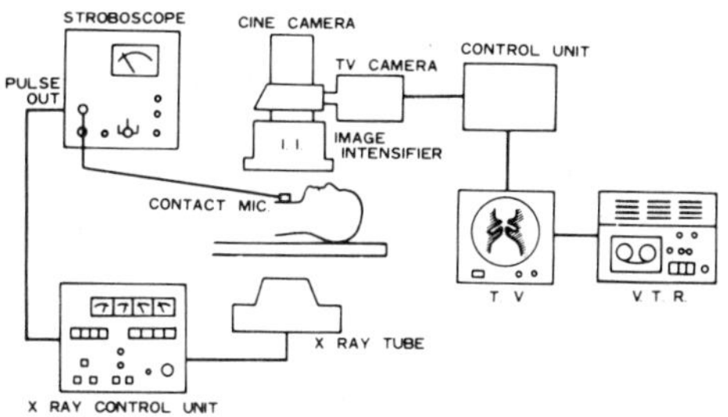

Fig.1. Block diagram of the system.

An experimental sound was obtained by use of the excised larynges of a human and canine, and vibratory patterns of their vocal folds were observed by use of the

X-ray system. Moreover, in order to observe the movement of the various parts of the vocal fold, tiny lead particles (0.5 mm diameter) were inserted into the vocal fold and the movements of these lead particles were observed at the time of phonation. These movements were recorded on a videoscope or on 35 mm or 16 mm film.

FRONTAL VIEW: EXCISED LARYNX

Figure 2 shows the frontal plane view of the vocal fold vibration photographed by stroboscopic X-ray. The corresponding schematic representation of the folds (Fig.3) was obtained by frame-by-frame analysis of the film using a

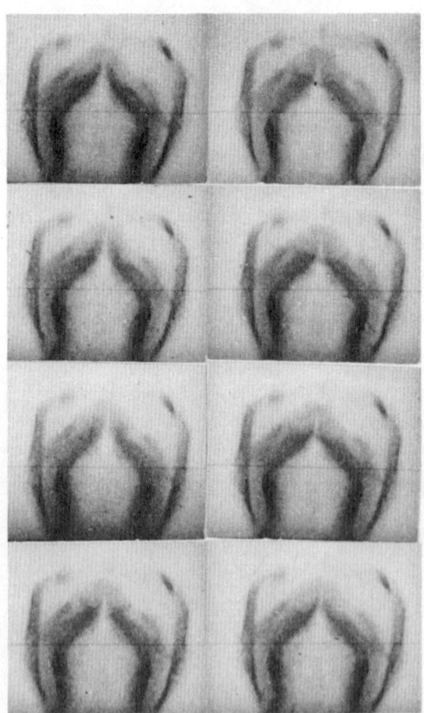

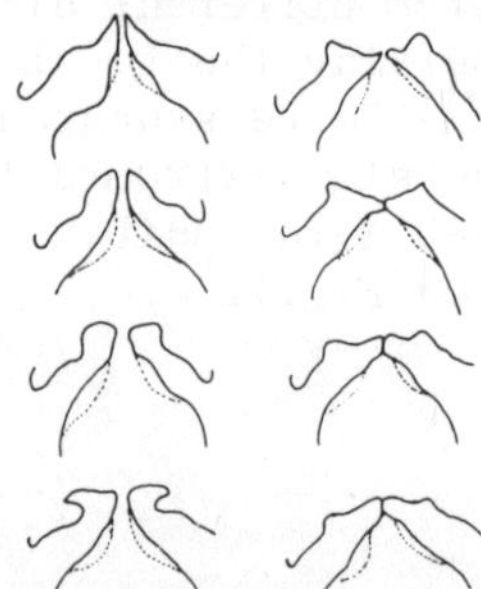

Fig.3. Schematic representation traced from the pictures in Fig.2.

Fig.2. Successive stroboscopic X-ray pictures for one cycle of vibration, frontal plane view. Time proceeds from the lower right frame upwards, then to the lower left frame, and finally to the upper left.

film analyzer. It is most likely that the air flow pushes out the free edge of the vocal fold, and that the wave motion of the mucous membrane travels to the upper surface of the vocal folds and transmits laterally. In addition, it is revealed that at the same time, the lower surface begins to partially protrude and a wave travels upward on this surface toward the free edge.

TRAJECTORIES OF POINTS IN VOCAL FOLD

In order to get an overall idea of the vibration of the vocal fold, tiny lead particles were placed as shown in Fig.4. Particle A is within the vocal muscle, particle B is in the mucous membrane of the free edge, and particle C is also in the mucous membrane but more lateral and deeper than particle B.

The trajectories for each of the particles during experimental phonation, labeled with eight points throughout a vibratory cycle, are shown in Fig.5. Particle B on the free edge moves in nearly circular motion. The particle in the central part of the mucous membrane of the upper surface of the vocal fold (particle C) travels in an elongated ellipse with the long axis about 45 degrees from the horizontal. Particle A in the lateral and upper part of the vocal muscle moves in an elongated ellipse whose long axis is near 80 degrees from the horizontal. The side-to-side movement of particle A in the upper part of the vocal muscle is much smaller than the up-and-down movement.

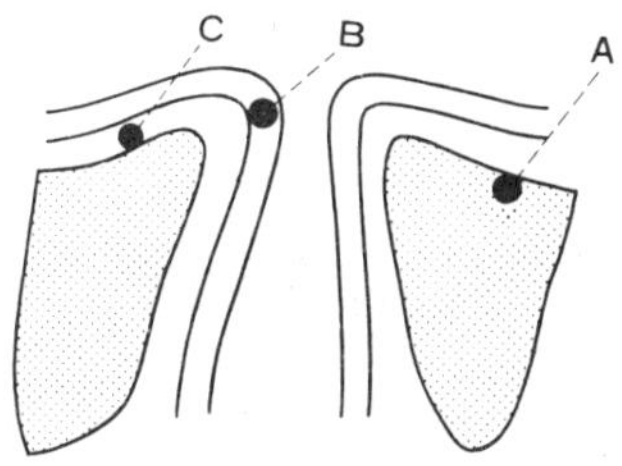

Fig.4. Location of lead particles used for tracing trajectories of points on vocal fold.

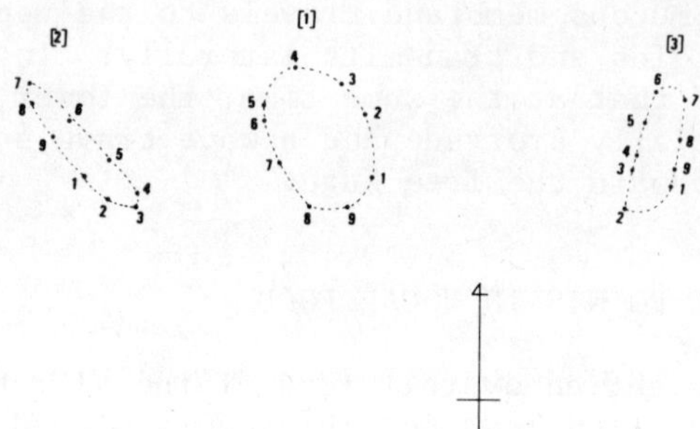

Fig.5. Trajectories of the lead particles in Fig.4, labeled with eight points throughout a vibratory cycle.

In order to observe the movements of the various parts of the subepithelial region of the vocal fold, many more lead particles were inserted into the subepthelial area than in the experiment mentioned above. As seen in Fig.6, six tiny lead particles were inserted into the subepithelial region and the movements of each of the lead particles were observed and analyzed during experimental phonation. Moreover, in order to examine the influence of changes in pitch and intensity on vocal fold vibration during experimental phonation, these two factors, i.e., the pitch and intensity, were changed, and the vocal fold vibration was observed by X-ray stroboscopy.

The relationship between the trajectory and the phase of each of the particles is shown in Fig.7. Here a sound

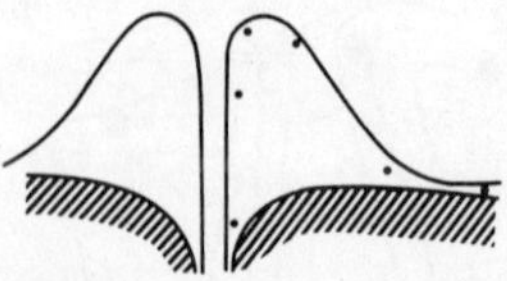

Fig.6. Location of lead particles for study of movements in subepithelial region.

with a fundamental frequency of 200 Hz and middle-range intensity was produced. The phases in the movements of each of the particles are delayed relative to one another along the surface. The movements of the particles are greatest at the free edge. The vibratory pattern of the vocal fold obtained by sketching contours through the particles at each phase of vibration is shown in Fig.8.

Fig.7. Trajectories of lead particles in Fig. 6 for phonation in middle range of intensity at 200 Hz.

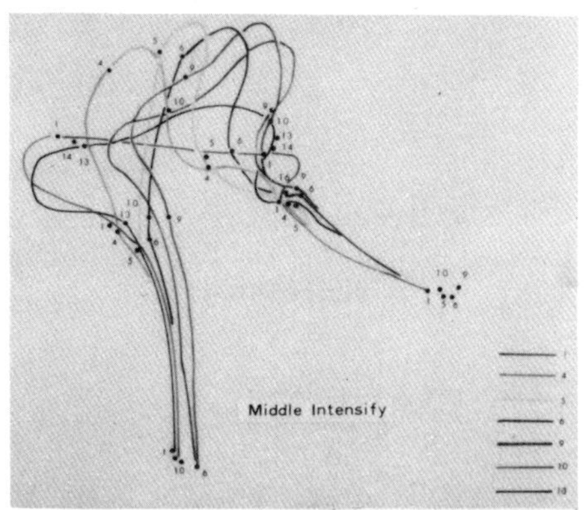

Fig.3. Sketches of shapes of vocal fold surface at different times in a vibratory cycle from observation of movements of lead particles for phonation in middle range of intensity at 200 Hz.

Next, the posterior commissure of the excised larynx was pushed down, thus increasing the intensity and raising the pitch. The trajectories of the particles and the estimated vocal fold shapes are shown in Fig.9. The movements of the lead particles become greater, and the portion of the vocal fold which vibrates increases. The phases of the movements of the particles are again delayed relative to one another.

The upper edge of the thyroid cartilage was pushed down and the long axis of the vocal fold was lengthened, thus raising the fundamental frequency to 400 Hz. The movement of the particles, shown in Fig.10, grows much smaller, and the portion of the vocal fold which vibrates decreases.

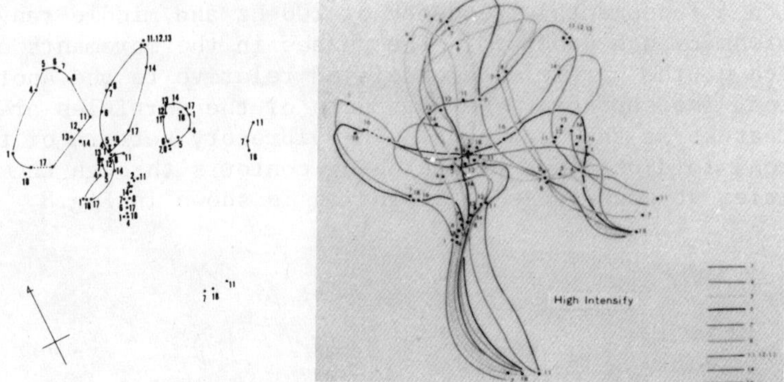

Fig.9. Trajectory of lead particles and vibratory pattern for phonation in a high intensity range.

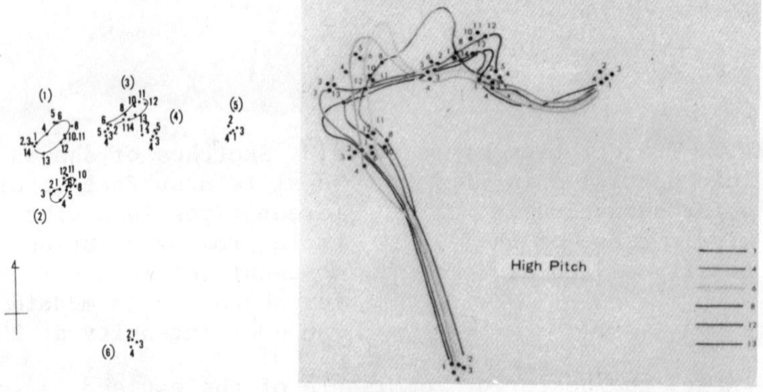

Fig.10. Trajectory of lead particles and vibratory pattern for phonation at a high pitch (400 Hz).

The results from these observations of the trajectories are summarized in Table 1. This table indicates how the sizes of the trajectories and the extent of the vibratory portion change with increasing pitch and intensity.

If the vocal fold vibration is considered as the collective movements of consecutive points, each point moves in an ellipse. The phases lag behind one another as the points move from inferior to superior locations. The closer the point is to the free edge of the vocal fold, the more the shape of the trajectory approaches a circle.

From the facts mentioned above, it can be said that

the vibration of the vocal fold is made up of travelling waves which move from the lower part of the vocal fold via the free edge to the upper part of the vocal fold. But we have observed that there are cases in which the particle in the lower portion of the vocal fold and especially in the deeper layer is rotating in the opposite direction from the lead particle at the free edge. This finding has not yet been shown to be consistent. If this result is confirmed, then it appears that the vertical component precedes the horizontal one at the free edge, and the opposite events happen at the inner layer. That is, the directions of the vertical motion are opposite to each other. These problems must await further data, however, for satsifactory resolution.

Table 1. Summary of how the sizes of the trajectories and the extent of the vibratory portion change with increasing pitch and intensity.

	Size of trajectory	Vibratory portion
Pitch↑	↓	↓
Intensity↑	↑	↑

FRONTAL VIEW: HUMAN LARYNX

Having experimentally examined excised larynges, we now observed vocal fold vibration in a normal adult from the frontal view. The case of a human being is different from that of excised larynges because the cervical vertebrae, laryngeal cartilages, and cervical muscles surround the vocal fold with matter which has a poor X-ray penetration rate. However, in actuality, picture quality sufficient to capture the vocal fold vibration as a pattern of movement was obtained.

The X-ray image of one vibratory cycle of the vocal fold is shown in Fig.11. In frame-by-frame images, the outline of the vocal fold is not very clear, mainly because it overlaps with the shadow of the cervical vertebrae. Therefore, improvement of the picture quality by such means as computer image processing would be desirable. Figure

12 depicts the traces of the frontal view of the vibration obtained from the X-ray image in Fig.11.

These preliminary observations show that vocal fold vibration in a human being can now be observed from a frontal view without the necessity of any special procedure such as the insertion of a laryngoscope, without giving any discomfort to the examinee, and without restricting his phonation in any way. However, since this is X-ray examination of soft tissue, it is rather difficult to differentiate between the vocal fold and other tissue, and the quality of the X-ray image of the vocal fold movement shown on the T.V. screen is not always good. Consequently, we are currently attempting to improve the quality of the image by using contrast media or by performing automatic extraction of the contour of the image by means of a computer system.

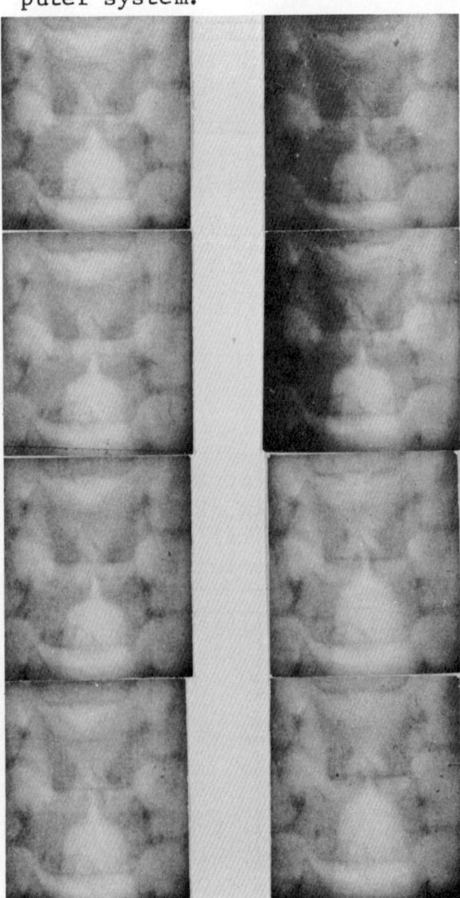

Fig.11. X-ray image of one vibratory cycle of the vocal fold in man.

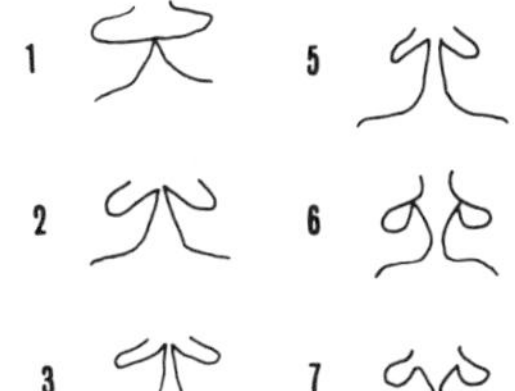

Fig.12. Traces of the image of the vibratory pattern in Fig.11. The numbers indicate successive frames.

SUMMARY

1) The vibratory pattern of the vocal folds was observed from the frontal view by use of a newly designed stroboscopic X-ray method both in an excised larynx and in a human being.
2) Not only the surface vibratory pattern but also that of the inner layer of the vocal folds can be detected experimentally.
3) Stroboscopic fluorocinematography was phototechnically analyzed, and the mode of the vibration of the vocal folds was considered as a travelling wave which consists of rotatory movements of individual points on the vocal fold with differentially shifted phases along the vibratory line of the fold.

DISCUSSION

Fujimura: I have been considering this approach for studying the vocal fold vibration mechanism in connection with the cover-body theory, but I did not expect this could be done so soon. I am impressed by your success. The pellet should be as small as possible, in order to avoid artifacts due to the disturbed mass distribution. I have an impression, seeing your film, that the 1/2-mm pellets could be further reduced in size and still they could be identified accurately. We also need to make the X-ray generating spot as small as possible for this purpose. Also a statement of the X-ray dose would be appreciated in the case of human subjects.

Saito: We also consider that the pellet should be as small as possible for avoiding artifacts. However, a pellet smaller than the 1/2 mm one used may not be adequate for clear identification by the film analyzer. But we think that much smaller pellets should be used in the near future. The spot size was 0.6 mm, and the X-ray unit was operated at 50 kV, 2 mA.

Baer: I am very impressed by this work, and I am looking forward to further results with your improved image quality. With excised larynges, it is unnecessary to use an automatic phase advance when triggering the strobe. Since these preparations can maintain steady phonation, better picture quality could be obtained by taking successive frames using synchronous stopped-motion stroboscopy and advancing the phase manually frame-by-frame.

Saito: Your idea is correct. However, it would be said that automatic phase advance by triggering the strobe is much easier than manual advance frame-by-frame especially in our systems. And in our laboratory, the phonatory mechanism in gradual changing pitch or vocal register has been also experimentally studied. In such a case, automatic phase advance is absolutely necessary.

Koike: From my own experience, the best material for the X-ray marker is pure gold.

Fujimura: Depleted uranium may be even better.

Strong: Stroboscopic laminography is extremely useful to the surgeon who must decide whether to perform vocal surgery or refer a patient to a voice therapist. X-ray stroboscopy may prove to be even more useful in this regard.

Titze: As a statement of confirmation, we have observed rotary motions in our simulated vocal fold movement. I believe your explanation for this occurrence is quite correct.

Saito: Your comment encourages us very much. In addition to our study presented here today, we are going to investigate rotary movement in various situations of phonation as pitch or intensity varies.

Kirikae: I was very much impressed by your excellent and precise observations of the trajectories of movement of points located on the vocal fold seen in the frontal plane. According to my previous study of the trajectory of a given point on the margin of the vocal fold by means of stroboscopy, I found that the long axis of the elliptic trajectory is tilted from inferior-lateral to superior-medial. The same opinion was also reported by other authors at that time. On the other hand, Nagel claimed that the long axis of the ellipsoid tilted from inferior-medial to superior-lateral, which is perpendicular to the direction mentioned above. Dr. Saito's finding seems to support Nagel's observation. Do you think that the apparent difference comes from the difference in the materials used? In other words, would there be a possible difference between the living human larynx and the excised canine larynx? I also want to ask Dr. Hirano's opinion on this matter.

Saito: At this time, we cannot explain the exact reason for this difference. To obtain a clear answer to this question, painstaking effort must be carried out because the elliptic movement may vary depending on frequency-intensity and on the vocal structure itself, and also with the presence or absence of muscular activities of the vocal cord.

Hirano: The cadaver experiments are important, but we must

remember that there are differences between the excised canine larynx and the live human one. Like the human infant, the canine larynx has no vocal ligament and a relatively thick mucosa. In addition, the vocalis muscle in the excised larynx cannot contract, so the balance of forces between the cover and body may be very different. Nevertheless, the vibratory mechanisms probably still share a common basic principle.

Baer: Because the anatomical structure of canine larynges differs from that of humans, experiments with excised canine larynges have limited application to study of human phonation. However, it is still a useful exercise to develop a model for the excised canine larynx, since very comprehensive data can be obtained on the anatomy, the mechanical properties, and the vibratory patterns in these preparations.

CHAPTER 9
ULTRASONIC OBSERVATIONS OF VOCAL FOLD VIBRATION

T. Kaneko, K. Uchida, H. Suzuki, K. Komatsu,
T. Kanesaka, N. Kobayashi, and J. Naito

Department of Otolaryngology,
School of Medicine, Chiba University,
Japan

In the head and neck, pulsed ultrasound has come into wide use in the diagnosis of tumors of the maxillary sinus, parotid gland, and thyroid gland, but few applications to laryngeal diseases have been reported thus far. Ultrasonic examination in the larynx is mainly performed for two purposes. One is diagnostic, using ordinary equipment, and the other is for phonetic examination using specially devised equipment. We have performed various studies as shown in Table 1.

Table 1. Summary of studies involving ultrasonic examination of the larynx.

I. Diagnostic application to the larynx
II. Observation of glottal movements during phonation using Ultrasonoglottography
   1) Horizontal and vertical components of the vibration of a vocal fold
   2) Phase difference between the movements of the upper and lower margins of a vocal fold
   3) Influences of vocal tract shape on the glottal movement
   4) Influences of pitch and loudness on the glottal movement
   5) Change of contact area of both vocal folds during one vibratory cycle
   6) Simultaneous recording of the contact area curve and ultrasonoglottogram
   7) Measurement of the phonation neutral area and build-up time

DIAGNOSTIC APPLICATION TO THE LARYNX

In the larynx, ocular inspection and histological examination are relatively easy, and it may be said that ultrasonic diagnosis does not play such an important role. However, ultrasonic examination is useful for estimating the submucous extension of laryngeal tumors.

The transducer is placed on the thyroid lamina, and its ultrasonic beam is set up to irradiate the margin of a vocal fold perpendicularly. Using A-mode, we can find a characteristic echo, namely the vibration echo, from the margin of a vocal fold during phonation. This is shown on the upper right of Fig.1. On the upper left, a tomoechographical image of the normal larynx by B-mode display is shown in horizontal section, together with a sketch showing anatomical landmarks. On the lower left of the same figure, supraglottic cancer by B-mode display is demonstrated in horizontal section and glottic cancer on the lower right in vertical section. In each of these images the degree of infiltration can be estimated from the presence of spot-shaped tumor echoes infiltrating the pre-epiglottic space or submucous layer.

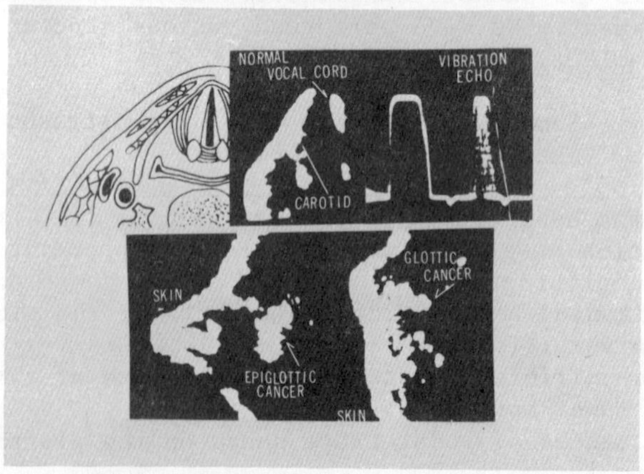

Fig.1. Displays obtained from ultrasonic observation of the larynx. See text.

Figure 2 shows an example of glottic cancer located in the anterior half of the left vocal fold. Even such a small tumor can be detected by ultrasonic examination.

Figure 3 shows a B-mode horizontal section at the level of the vocal fold together with the anatomical structures of the anterior part of the neck cross-section at the same level. The black areas represent echoes from boundary surfaces of the cartilage, muscle, and free margin of the vocal fold.

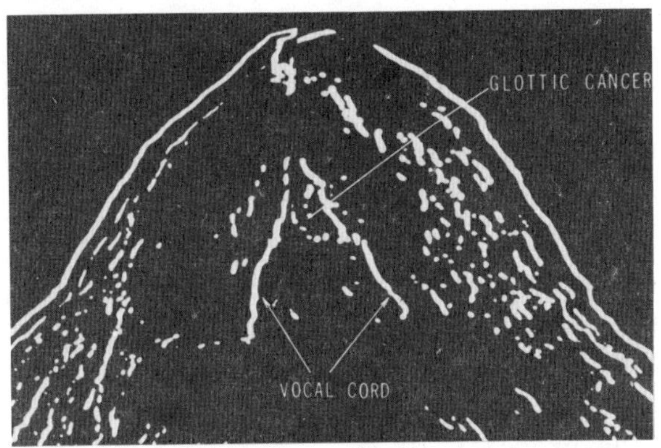

Fig.2. B-mode horizontal section of vocal fold examined with ultrasound, showing the location of a small tumor.

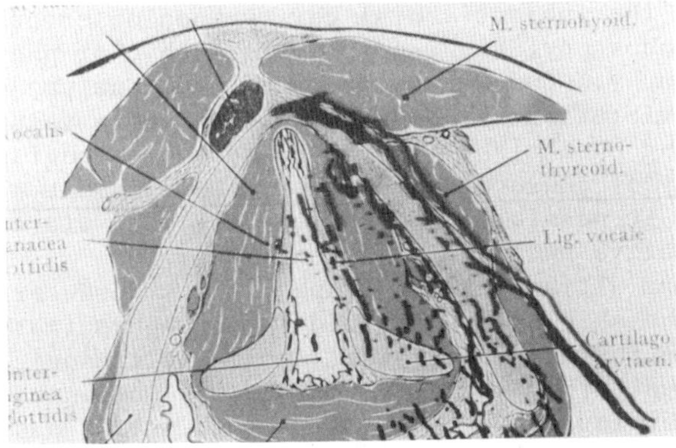

Fig.3. B-mode horizontal section of vocal fold (as in Fig.2) together with sketch of anatomical structures.

TECHNIQUE FOR ULTRASONIC OBSERVATION OF GLOTTAL MOVEMENTS

As mentioned before, the other way of applying ultrasonics to the larynx is by phonetically examining the vocal fold vibration. This procedure, named ultrasonoglottography, was developed in our department. Figure 4 shows the equipment we are using routinely.

This apparatus consists mainly of five units:

1) high speed multivibrator SSZ-30, the repetition frequency of which is 5000 Hz
2) slow sweep generator SSD-II, the frequency of which is variable from 10 to 140 Hz
3) echo selector SSZ-43
4) ultrasonic reflectoscope
5) oscilloscope VC-7

The ultrasonic frequency being used is 2.25 MHz and the diameter of the probe is 10 mm.

There are several methods for observing vocal fold vibration during phonation. For instance, stroboscopy and high speed photography are optical methods, and photoelectroglottography and electroglottography utilize the changes in the quality of light or in electric resistance due to vocal fold vibration. However, each method has its advantages and disadvantages. A mirror or a rod must be inserted into the subject's oral cavity when observation is made by stroboscopy, high speed photography, or photoelectroglottography. Consequently, one cannot analyze natural vocal fold vibration or measure the expiratory volume velocity during phonation. Use of ultrasonoglottography does not have any of these disadvantages. Development of this method made it possible to observe vocal fold vibration in a more objective and natural manner.

To perform ultrasonoglottography, the transducer is placed on the skin of the thyroid lamina approximately 1 cm below the thyroid prominence, and the ultrasonic beam is irradiated perpendicularly to the free margin of the vocal fold during phonation. Ultrasonic pulses pass from the skin through prelaryngeal muscles, thyroid cartilage, and vocal muscles, and they reach the free margin of a vocal fold. When they reach the margin, most of the ultrasonic energy is reflected at the boundary surface and returns the same way to the transducer. The pulses are received by the same probe and are represented as an echo of the vocal fold. This is the vibration echo. Then the vibration echo from the margin of the vocal fold is modulated according to its intensity and expressed as a spot on the screen. The spot is swept vertically in M-mode. We have named this wave pattern "ultrasonoglottogram" or U.G.G.

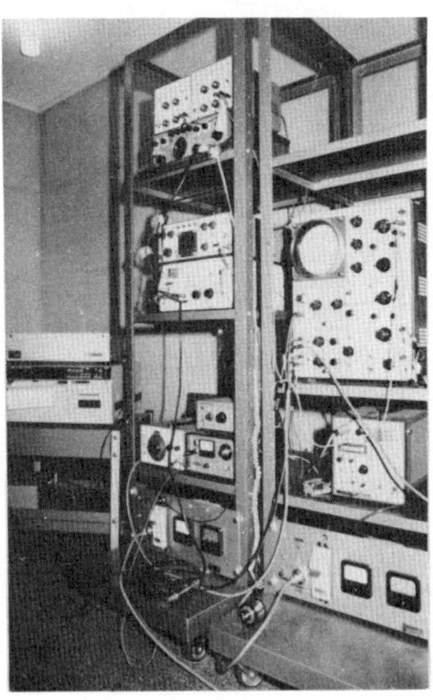

Fig.4. Equipment used for ultrasonoglottography

As shown in Fig.5, two probes are used. One probe is placed directly on the skin over the thyroid lamina. A 3 cm balloon is fixed on the tip of the other probe, and this probe is placed on the skin over the opposite thyroid cartilage, the balloon making actual contact with the skin. Because of the different distances from the tips of the two probes to the closed free margin of the vocal folds, we could successfully record a U.G.G. of the right and left vocal folds simultaneously.

OBSERVATION OF GLOTTAL MOVEMENTS DURING PHONATION USING ULTRASONOGLOTTOGRAPHY

1. Horizontal and Vertical Components of the Vibration of a Vocal Fold (Fig.6)

The vocal fold vibrates not only horizontally but also vertically and in other directions. In order to record the horizontal and vertical movements of a vocal fold

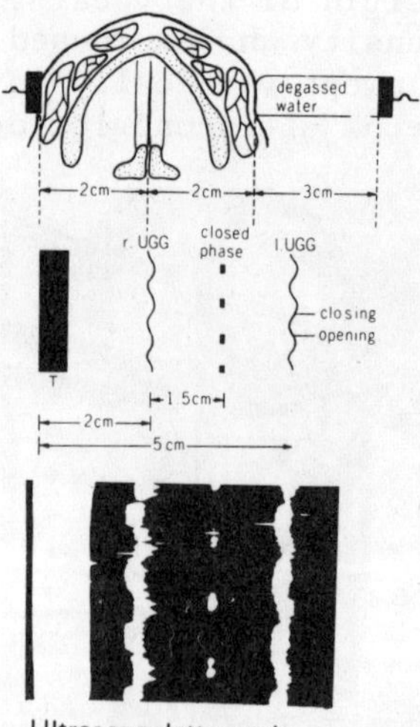

Fig.5. Illustrating the use of ultrasonoglottography to examine the vibration of the margins of the two vocal folds. The arrangement of transducers is shown at the top, a typical recording is displayed at the bottom, and a schematization of the recorded signals is given in the middle.

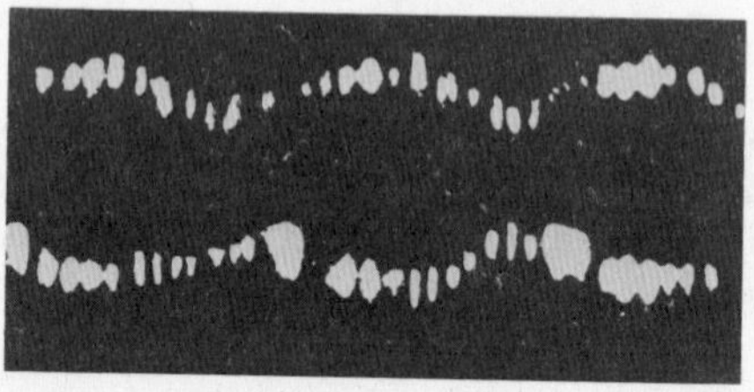

Fig.6. Ultrasonoglottogram showing the horizontal (upper trace) and vertical (lower trace) components of the vibration of a vocal fold.

simultaneously, one probe is placed on the skin on the thyroid lamina and the other is placed on the skin on the midline over the cricothyroid membrane.

2. Phase Difference of the Movements between the Upper and Lower Margins of a Vocal Fold (Fig.7)

As clearly seen by high speed cinematography, there is a phase difference in movement between the upper part and the lower part of the free margin of the vocal fold. These two waves can be recorded on the cathode ray display when two probes 5 mm in diameter are placed to irradiate the upper and lower part of a margin respectively. Figure 7 shows the vibration curves of the two parts. The phase difference is about 60° and vibration of the upper part is larger in amplitude than that of the lower part. The movement of the upper part gradually becomes difficult to distinguish from that of the lower part as the pitch increases, and the phase difference between the two parts diminishes and disappears.

Fig.7. Ultrasonoglottogram showing the phase difference of the movement between the upper and lower margins of a vocal fold.

3. Influences of the Vocal-Tract Shape on the Glottal Movement (Fig.8)

In order to examine the influence of change in the shape of the vocal tract on the waveform of vocal fold vibration, we examined the U.G.G. obtained by articulating /a/, /i/, /u/, /e/, /o/, avoiding vertical shift of the thyroid cartilage as much as possible. Little difference was observed in waveform among the pronounciation of these vowel sounds, as shown in Fig.8. However, the waveforms for /pa/ and /ba/, i.e. when occlusive consonants precede the vowels, are remarkably different. These results show that the mode of vocal fold vibration during a vowel can be influenced appreciably by an adjacent consonant.

4. Influences of Fundamental Frequency and Intensity on the Glottal Movement (Fig.9)

The ascending curve in the opening phase has a tendency to become steeper as the pitch increases. On the contrary, the descending curve in the closing phase remains unchanged or slightly moderates. When amplitude increases, the vibration increases in amplitude, and the descending curve in the closing phase becomes steeper.

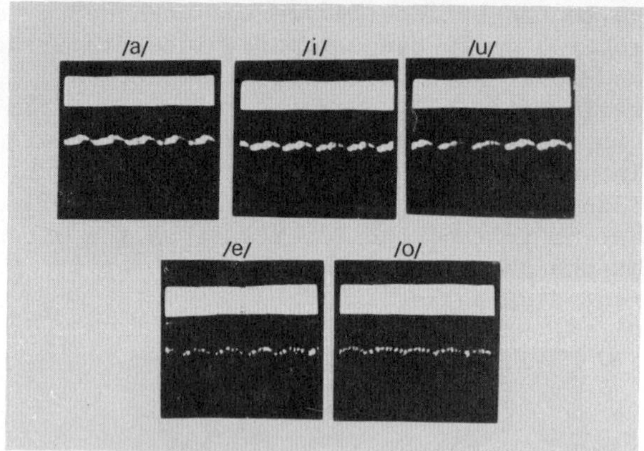

Fig.8. Ultrasonoglottograms showing vocal fold vibration for different vowels. There appears to be little influence of the vowel on the waveform.

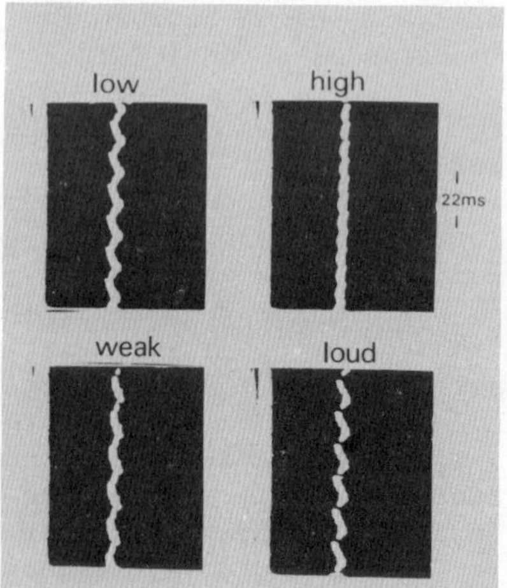

Fig.9. Influences of fundamental frequency and intensity on glottal waveform.

5. Change of Contact Area of both Vocal Folds during One Vibratory Cycle (Fig.10)

A transducer is placed on each side of the thyroid lamina. The ultrasonic beam is irradiated from one probe, and the transmitted pulse is received by the other only when the glottis is closed. The height of the echo expresses the size of the contact area. In the open phase, while both vocal folds do not contact each other, the beam is not transmitted, so the signal remains on the base line. Once the vocal folds begin to contact, the waveform increases and reaches a plateau instantly. The plateau represents the closed time. When the closed phase is over, the waveform returns to the base line instantly. In the case of low pitch, a trapezoid-shaped wave is observed. When the pitch is high, the wave is rather triangular.

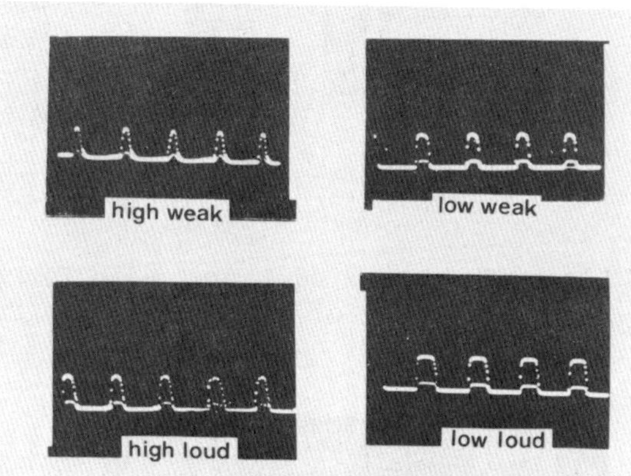

Fig.10. Waveforms of transmitted ultrasound through the glottis, showing the time of contact of the vocal folds during one vibratory cycle under various conditions of pitch and intensity.

6. Simultaneous Recording of U.G.G. and Contact-Area Curve. (Figs.11, 12)

Two probes are placed on the thyroid lamina, as shown in Fig.11. One of them is used as a transmitter and receiver, and the U.G.G. is shown in channel A of an oscilloscope. The other probe is used only as a receiver for the contact-area curve demonstrated in channel B. In this way the U.G.G. and the contact-area curve can be seen on the same screen simultaneously. Thus we can analyze the relationship between U.G.G. and closed time more clearly. Furthermore, we can analyze the onset of voicing and measure the phonation neutral area and buildup time for steady-state oscillation. The buildup of oscillation at onset of voicing is illustrated in Fig.12.

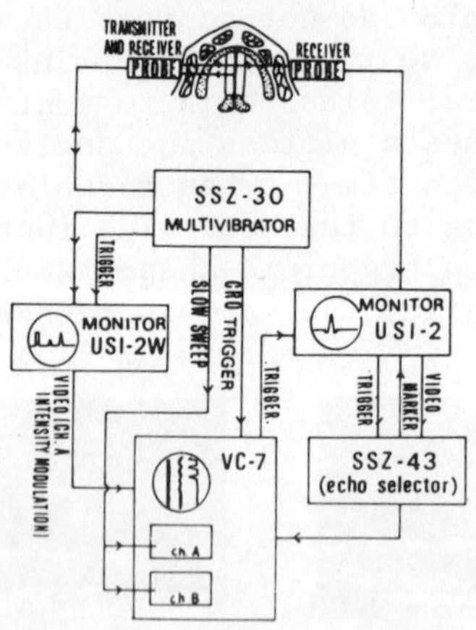

Fig.11. Block diagram of equipment used for simultaneous recording of ultrasonoglottogram and time interval of contact of vocal folds.

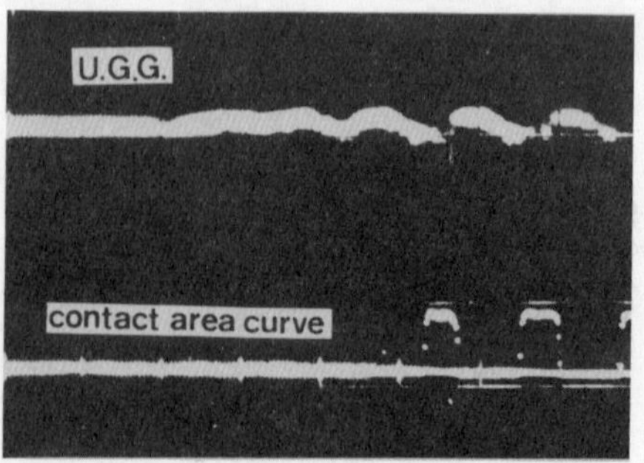

Fig.12. Simultaneous recording of U.G.G. and curve showing times of vocal fold contact, as vocal fold vibration builds up at onset of voicing.

CONCLUDING REMARKS

In the beginning of this paper we referred to the use of ultrasonics for the diagnosis of laryngeal tumors. It is difficult, so far, to differentiate if a tumor of the larynx is malignant or benign. However, ultrasonics is a useful method to find out the degree of the submucous extension of the tumor.

Next, we described the methods used to examine the vibration mode of the vocal folds during phonation, using ultrasonic reflection and transmission methods. The advantages of the ultrasonic method over other methods are:

1) continuous recording of the vibrating vocal folds;
2) no interference with the articulatory movements of the tongue and the mandible;
3) no discomfort to the patients and simplicity of application.

ACKNOWLEDGEMENT

This research was partially supported by a Grant-in-Aid for Co-Operative Research (No. 337040), The Ministry of Education, Science and Culture, Japan.

DISCUSSION

Baer: How small can the ultrasonic field be made in the vertical dimension? The beam width would affect the ability to resolve tissue movement along this dimension.

Kaneko: Although the diameter of the transducer is about 10 mm, the dimension of the echo source on the free surface of the vocal fold will be limited to a small rectangular surface (ca. 1 mm thick, 5 - 6 mm length) according to geometrical consideration on the propagation of the ultrasonic beam. To obtain high resolution in future work, a concave probe will be available, and this probe will enable the ultrasonic beam to be focused to one point on the free surface.

Fujimura: Discussion on the spatial resolution is important. Can we differentiate the measurements at different parts of the vocal fold along the longitudinal direction?

Kaneko: If a small transducer of 5 mm diameter is used, the vibration modes of the anterior part and posterior part of a vocal fold can be recorded simultaneously.

Kakita: We might also consider resolution along the lateral dimension. This is limited by the wavelength, which is 0.3 mm for 5 MHz ultrasound.

CHAPTER 10
OBSERVATION OF VOCAL FOLD VIBRATION: MEASUREMENT OF EXCISED LARYNGES

Thomas Baer

Haskins Laboratories, New Haven,
Connecticut, U.S.A.

INTRODUCTION

Recent empirical and theoretical studies of laryngeal anatomy, of laryngeal biomechanics, and of glottal aerodynamics have contributed substantially to the development of a detailed quantitative model of phonation. However, progress toward this end has been seriously hampered by the sparcity of detailed descriptions of phonatory vibration patterns, especially in the frontal plane. Studies with excised larynges can help substantially in this regard, since such preparations are accessible for observations and measurements that are not possible with the intact larynx. A particular advantage is that vibrations can be observed from the inferior aspect (Matsushita, 1969, 1975; Baer, 1975) or the medial aspect (Matsushita, 1969, 1975), as well as from the normal superior aspect. Measurements can even be made within the folds, with the aid of novel x-ray techniques (Saito, 1977; also Chapter 8 of this book). An additional advantage is that laryngeal configuration and subglottal pressure can be maintained in steady state for extended durations while the vibrations are studied, and these (and other) parameters may be manipulated systematically and independently.

Usefulness of data obtained from excised-larynx studies is, of course, somewhat limited, since the death of the tissues undoubtably changes their mechanical properties. More significantly, activity of the vocalis muscle, which forms part of the body of the vocal folds and which is normally active during phonation, cannot be adequately simulated. Nevertheless, development of a comprehensive, testable model for the vibratory mechanics of the excised larynx on the basis of detailed data is a useful first step toward the development of a model for the intact larynx.

In the study reported here, an optical technique was used to observe and measure mechanical vibrations from the superior and inferior aspects. Observations from the inferior aspect were made through a subglottal window, which afforded a direct view of the subglottal surface of the vocal folds. Particles attached to the vocal folds were optically tracked throughout the glottal cycle, using stroboscopic illumination while the larynx maintained steady state phonation. By tracking several particles "simultaneously", it was possible to estimate the detailed frontal-plane configuration of one vocal fold throughout a glottal cycle. Canine (rather than human) larynges were used, because human preparations were unavailable. This factor further limits the usefulness of the data as a it applies to human laryngeal mechanics, since there are significant differences between canine and human laryngeal anatomy which are expected to affect their vibratory performance (Hirano, 1975). However, since similar experiments are feasible with live-animal preparations, techniques developed in this study could be extended toward further studies with both excised human preparations and live animal preparations, to investigate the significance of both the canine-human and excised-live distinctions.

METHODS

The method for preparing the larynges in this study was modelled after that of van den Berg, as described in his later publications (van den Berg, 1960). Larynges were stripped of their extrinsic structures, except for a short section of trachea. A small rigid bar was attached to the lamina of the cricoid cartilage, and was then used to fix the cartilage to the apparatus. Three sets of threads were then attached to simulate the activity of the lateral adductor muscles, the interarytenoid muscle, and the cricothyroid muscle. The trachea was clamped to the pseudo-subglottal system.

A schematic drawing of the apparatus is shown in Fig.1. The apparatus contains components for actuating the larynges, for observing them under stroboscopic light, and for measuring the three-dimensional trajectories of individual fleshpoints during phonation.

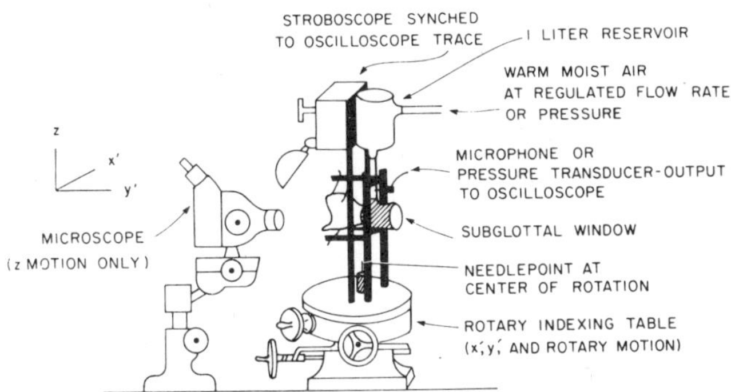

Fig.1. Schematic sketch of the apparatus.

The larynx was supported in a horizontal configuration, to facilitate measurements. Tension was applied in appropriate directions to the threads simulating the intrinsic muscles to maintain a stable phonatory configuration. Warm, moist air was supplied to a reservoir and length of flexible tubing which were intended to simulate the tracheo-bronchial tree. In early experiments, this air was delivered at regulated flow rate, but later experiments employed a pressure-regulated source. The effective flow resistance of this source was about 15 to 20 cm H_2O/lps, or roughly ten times that of the human subglottal tract. Thus, improvements in the design of this system would be desirable.

A modified brass plumbing "tee" was used to attach the larynx to the subglottal system. Air was supplied through the flexible tubing to the base of this "tee" and the larynx was clamped to one of the branches. The other branch of the tee was sealed by an optical glass window. Thus, the airway made a right angle turn before entering the glottis, and the window supplied a direct view of the subglottal laryngeal surface. This apparatus was heated to prevent condensation. Because this subglottal fitting did not significantly constrict the airway, the right-angle bend did not affect the patterns of glottal airflow during phonation.

The apparatus for supporting the larynx was mounted on

the top of a rotary indexing table. The tabletop could be translated along two horizontal rectangular axes and could be rotated, so that observations could be made from any aspect. Observations could be made either with the naked eye or through a stereo microscope. The microscope's working distance was sufficiently long to focus on the vocal folds through the subglottal window.

As shown in Fig.1, the larynx was illuminated from the anterior-superior aspect by a stroboscope, which was suspended above the specimen. A mirror was placed below and in front of the specimen to improve the illumination of the glottis. The stroboscope could be operated asynchronously, to show the vibrations in apparent slow motion, or synchronously, to stop the motion at an arbitrary phase in the glottal cycle. Synchronization was derived from the output of a pressure transducer coupled to the pseudotrachea.

Small (.08 mm) carborundum particles were placed on the vocal fold surface to serve as landmarks for measurement. In most cases, the particles appeared to move with the tissues throughout the vibratory cycle, rather than sliding across them. Using synchronous stroboscopic illumination, the particles could be apparently stopped at any point along their trajectories, so that their positions could be measured using the microscope and rotary table apparatus. Particle trajectories were measured by repeating this procedure at different phases throughout the cycle.

Measurements of particle position could be made while the tabletop was rotated to any angle convenient for observation, and then referred to a coordinated system fixed with respect to the tabletop. To make these measurements, the microscope and rotary table were both fixed to a rigid base. The microscope could move only in the vertical direction (i.e. along the anterior-posterior axis), as indicated in Fig.1. All other motion was provided by the rotary table, whose translation axes were oriented parallel and perpendicular to the optical axis of the microscope. Measurements were made through only one eyepiece of the stereo microscope, using the highest available magnification. Position along the dimension prependicular to the optical axis was measured with the aid of an eyepiece reticle. Position along the other frontal-plane dimension was measured by utilizing the limited focal depth of the microscope.

Two rectangular coordinate systems were defined. One

was the frontal plane coordinate system (X-Y) attached to the tabletop and thus fixed with respect to the larynx. Another, primed coordinate system (X'-Y'), was defined by the translation axes of the table. Both coordinate systems had a common origin, which was fixed to the center of rotation of the tabletop. The angle of rotation, θ, between them, was read from the rotation dial of the table.

The measurement system was initialized by translating the tabletop until its center of rotation was centered in the eyepiece reticle and was also centered within the depth of focus. A telescoping needlepoint was accurately aligned with the rotation axis for this purpose. With the tabletop in this position, the adjustable translation dials were set to zero. The X'-Y' position of any point could then be measured by translating the tabletop until the point was similarly centered in the microscope's field. The coordinates were then simply read off the axis dials. The angle θ was also recorded, and this information was used to transform the measurements to the common X-Y coordinate system. Thus, measurements could be made from any angle for which the point was visible, including through the subglottal window.

Measurement accuracy along the X' (lateral-medial) axis was about .05 mm. Accuracy along the Y' (superior-inferior) axis was limited by the optics to about .13 mm. Measurement accuracy along the X and Y axes then depends on the value of θ, but is not worse than about .13 mm.

RESULTS

General Observations: As noted by others, excised larynges were able to produce vibration patterns typical of normal chest-voice phonation. Falsetto phonation could also be produced, but the ability to vibrate in this mode was dramatically impaired when the larynges became desiccated or when their condition otherwise deteriorated. Thus, the conditions for producing falsetto, more than those for producing chest voice, appear to be constrained by the mechanical properties of the vocal folds. Apparent vocal fry could be produced when both vertical tension and subglottal pressure were low and the vocal folds were fairly tightly adducted. Within the mid range, two distinct modes of vibration were observed, and sometimes there were spontaneous shifts between them. In one mode, the rate of vibration was generally lower, and the amplitude of vibration in the subglottal tissues was greater than in the other. It is still unclear whether these represent intrinsically distinct vibration modes, such as chest- vs. mid-register, or whether the phenomenon results from an acoustic interaction with the subglottal tract.

The minimum subglottal pressure for which phonation was spontaneously initiated was about 3 cm H_2O. However, vibrations could then be sustained as the pressure was reduced to about 2 cm H_2O. The values for both initiating and sustaining vibrations increased as the surface tissues desiccated, and the separation between these values also increased. Thus, the phonatory ability of the larynx appears to be very sensitive to the mechanical properties of the laryngeal cover.

Detailed Measurements: All detailed measurements of vibrations were made during apparent chest-register phonation. In a given run, measurements were all in about the same frontal plane, which was located along the anterior-posterior axis at about the point of maximum vibration amplitude. Some initial measurements were made to determine the envelope of vibrations in this mode. Results are shown in Fig.2. The total vertical extent in the frontal plane of "large" (greater than 0.3 mm) vibration was 5 to 7 mm. However, the vertical extent over which bilateral contact between the folds occurred was smaller (3 to 4.5 mm). The maximum instantaneous depth of closure was, in general, still smaller (about 3 mm). The minimum instantaneous depth of closure usually occurred just before the end of the closed period, and was almost infinitesimally small.

Measurements of particle trajectories in the frontal plane formed the main source of quantitative results in this study. For each particle measured, its position in the frontal plane was determined at 8 phase increments uniformly distributed through the glottal cycle. Because the larynges would maintain a vibratory steady state for only a limited time, the number of particles that could be simultaneously tracked was limited to 2 or, in one case, 3. Some sample results of these measurements are shown in Fig.3. Each part of this figure contains, in addition to the trajectories themselves, an inset showing schematically the gross orientation (in static, non-phonatory condition) of the particles being tracked and a list of notes, including a record of the table angle,

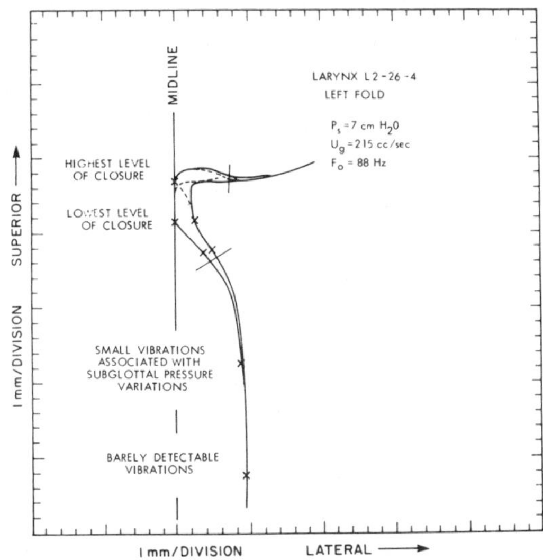

Fig.2. Outline of the frontal section of a vocal fold based on measurements from the inferior aspect. Measured points are indicated by symbols. The estimated envelope of vibrations is indicated by solid lines. Estimated shapes at two instants during the cycle are indicated by broken lines. Two tick marks delimit the region of large vibration amplitude. All subsequent measurements on different larynges were limited to such a region.

θ, for which each measurement was made. An angle of 0° implies measurement from the supraglottal aspect, while an angle of 180° implies a measurement from the subglottal aspect. Thus, these data carry some information about the particles' orientation with respect to the overall vocal fold shape.

In general, the shapes of the particle trajectories were not simple, but could be roughly characterized as elliptical with perturbations. Movement around the main parts of the trajectories was always clockwise in the coordinate system shown, with lateral to the right and superior toward the top of the page. That is, the lateral-going parts of the trajectories were superior to the medial-going parts. Particles furthest from the midline had the flattest trajectories, which most nearly approximated perfect ellipses. Trajectories of particles nearest the midline had the most nearly circular ellipses, but also had the greatest perturbations. General properties of trajectories for particles in three different regions - on the lateral supraglottal surface, near the free edge of the folds, and on the subglottal surface - are described further below, using Fig.3 for examples:

Lateral supraglottal surface (particle 1, Fig.3B); Trajectories are mostly elliptical with relatively small minor axes. The orientation of the major axes are nearly vertical. According to available data, movements are primarily upward during the closed period and downward during the open period.

Near the midline (particles 1 and 2, Fig.3A; particle 2, Fig.3B): These trajectories are more complex. The "elliptical" parts are more nearly circular, but the perturbations are also more dramatic, sometimes forming secondary loops or more complex shapes. These pertur bations are usually near the most medial parts of the trajectories. When the particle is near the subglottal edge of the glottis (particle 2, Fig.3A), the perturbation occurs near the moment of closure. For these particles, movements are generally upward and lateral during the closed period, downward and medial during the open period. When the particle is near the supraglottal edge (particle 1, Fig.3A; particle 2, Fig.3B), the perturbation occurs near the moment of opening. For these particles, movements are generally lateral and downward during the open period, upward during the closed period. Medial movements may occur during either phase, appatently depending on the particle's distance from the midline.

Subglottal surface (particle 3, Fig.3B): Trajectories are again ellipses with relatively small minor axes. The major axes are tilted from the horizontal, and are probably perpendicular to the tissue surface. Movements are generally lateral during the closed period and medial during the open period.

The sketches in Fig.3A indicate a phenomenon that was often noted. Particle 1 was on the superior surface of the vocal fold in the static configuration and during much of the vibratory cycle, but was at an apparent corner at phase 3. In Fig.3B, a more dramatic example of the same phenomenon can be noted. Particle 2 is on the superior surface in the static configuration and during much of the vibratory cycle, but it is actually below the region of glottal closure at phase 2. Thus, the apparent location of the "corner" of the vocal fold seems to change throughout the cycle, due to tissue movements on the superior surface toward the midline. The complex nature of the vibrations can also be highlighted by noting that the trajectories of particles 1 and 2 in Fig.3B intersect each other. These two particles are essentially in horizontal alignment for part of the cycle (e.g., at phases 6 and 0), but they are essentially in vertical alignment at phase 4. A straight line drawn between these particles rotates counterclockwise during the closed period and the early part of the open period, and then clockwise during the remainder of the open period. Such rotations of the tissues near the edge of the fold were often noted.

As the result of vertical phase differences, horizontal excursions of some particles are often greater than the total excursions of "glottal width". For example, the excursion of particle 2 in Fig.3B is from the midline to its position at phase 4. However, at this phase, particle 3 is moving medially, and is already closer to the midline.

Some aspects of glottal wall vibrations appear to be describable as displacement waves propagating in the superior direction. Propagation velocity was found to be about 1 m/sec, and this is consistent with the phase delays between the horizontal movements of particles at different vertical levels. For example, for the particles in Fig.3A, the vertical separation is about 3 mm, and the phase delay corresponds roughly to 3 msec. Because of the elliptical shapes of the trajectories, the propagating disturbances are presumed to be surface waves. Waves also propagate in the lateral direction on the superior surfaces of the vocal folds, as is often noted in high speed films of normal larynges. Propagation usually begins with the open period of the cycle. The velocity of this wave is smaller - about 0.3 to 0.5 m/sec.

Properties of glottal closure were studied. This phenomenon also shows evidence of a propagating wave. After the tissues from the opposite folds first come into contact, tissues at the lower border of this region continuously separate, while tissues at its upper border continue to come into contact. Thus, glottal closure itself

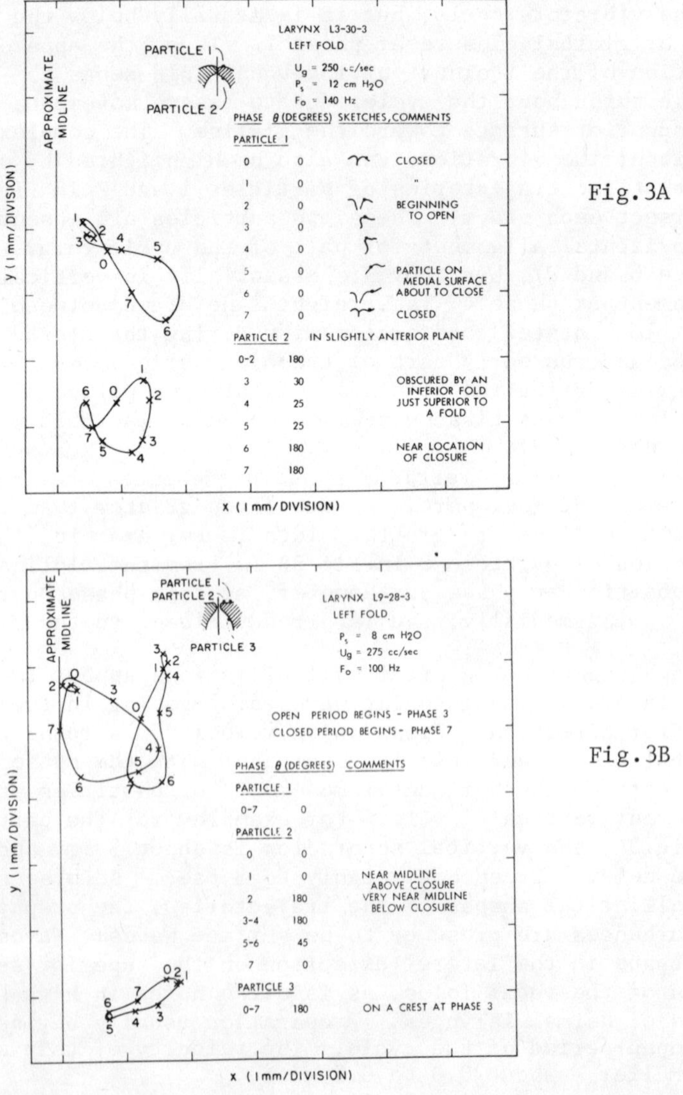

Fig.3. Measured trajectories from two different runs. Measurements, indicated by symbols, were made at 1/8-cycle intervals, numbered 0-7. Trajectories are arbitrarily drawn by hand, and midline positions are drawn from

estimates or approximate measurements. The inset to the right of each panel contains additional qualitative information. The schematic sketch at the top shows the orientation of the measured particles on the static vocal fold. Additional notes and sketches associated with individual measurements are tabulated below (see text).

3A: Simultaneous trajectories of two particles.

3B: Simultaneous trajectories of three particles.

propagates upward as a wave. The wavelike nature of glottal closure is emphasized by the fact that closure itself can propagate past a particle. This was noted already in the discussion of Fig.3B. Particle 2 is above the region of closure during the early part of the closed period, but below it at phase 2.

When the vocal folds first come into contact during a cycle, they often form the shape of an inverted V at the subglottis. Just before opening, when the depth of the closure is often almost infinitesimally small, they form a smooth dome (inverted U) shape.

We have noted that several aspects of the vibration patterns seem to be describable on the basis of propagating surface waves. Even the phase delay between the medial parts of the trajectory for particle 3 and the superior parts of the trajectory for particle 1 in Fig.3B could be accounted for in this manner, assuming propagation along the surfaces and past the corner at a velocity of 1 m/sec. However, these same data could be used to argue for the influence of bulk deformations of the vocal folds. If the lateral parts of the trajectories for particle 3 are compared with the superior parts of the trajectory for particle 1, the latency between them is only about 1 msec. Thus, perhaps tissues are displaced laterally from the subglottal surfaces, causing vertical deformations of the supraglottal surface during the closed period. To summarize, some aspects of the vibrations are explainable on the basis of surface waves in the vocal fold cover, while some can also be explained on the basis of bulk deformations of the body. There may in fact be contributions from both mechanisms.

Analysis of Vocal Fold Silhouettes in the Frontal Plane: The data in Fig.3B, along with more general observations of vibration patterns in these excised-larynx experiments, were used to estimate the frontal-plane shape of the vocal fold at each of the eight phase increments. The resulting sketches are shown, both separately and superimposed, in Fig.4. In the sketch for each of the eight phase increments, the three particle trajectories have been superimposed, and the instantaneous position of each of the three particles is indicated by an asterisk. The shape to the left of the midline is not based on separate data, but is a reflection of the shape to the right. The digit in the upper left part of each panel indicates the phase, as numbered in Fig.3B, and the corner in the upper right indicates 1 mm scales along the vertical and horizontal dimensions.

Useful measurements can be made from these sketches that cannot be made on the preparation itself. These measurements include distance along the surface of the silhouette and its area. Measurements of the surface distances between particles 1 and 2 and between particles 2 and 3 from each of the sketches were made. The area of each silhouette was also measured.

The measurements of surface length indicate that the surface tissues are stretched significantly during the cycle. For particles 3-2, the change of distance is about 30% of its average value. For particles 2-1, it is over 50%. In both cases, the waveform showing the surface length as a function of time is near a maximum when the glottis opens and near a minimum when the glottis closes. Therefore, to the extent that vertical stiffness of these tissues is significant, mechanical energy is stored during the closed period and released during the open period.

The area measures show changes of about 20% during the cycle. Because of tissue incompressibility, the area of the vocal folds might be expected to remain constant. This apparent change in area suggests either that there are inaccuracies in the sketches, or that there are additional area variations outside the regions of the sketches.

The superimposed sketches at the top of Fig.4 show a systematic, nearly circular pattern of movements of the vocal fold edge throughout the vibratory cycle. The significance of this pattern is unclear. We have already noted that the edge is not stable with respect to individual particles on the surface tissues. Thus, the apparent movements might be a wave phenomenon or might, alternatively be due to circular (string) vibrations of some underlying fibrous tissues across which the surface tissue slide. Hirano's (1975, 1979) anatomical investigations apparently militate against the latter hypothesis. However, investigations with x-ray stroboscopy (Saito, 1977; Chapter 8 of this book) may help to determine whether the data themselves are realistic, and to elucidate the nature of the vibrations if these results are replicated.

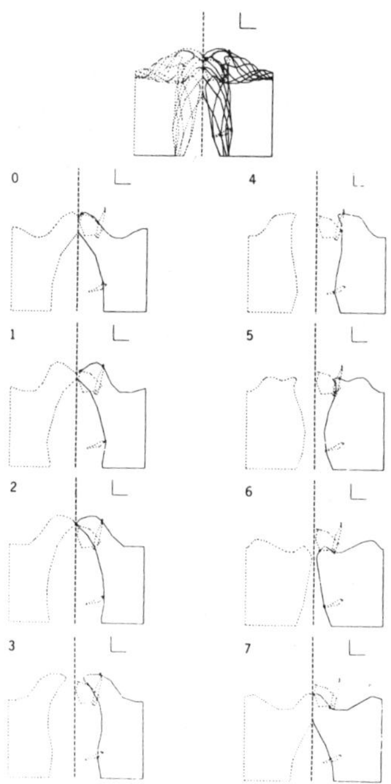

Fig.4. Estimates of the vocal fold shapes based on the data in Fig.3B. The top part shows all eight shapes superimposed. Below are the individual shapes associated with each of the eight phase increments, superimposed on the particle trajectories. The shape to the left of the midline is a reflection of the shape to the right. The scales on the upper right of each part indicated 1 mm in the vertical and horizontal dimensions.

Other Measurements: In another series of experiments, the entire vocalis muscle was unilaterally or bilaterally removed. Excised larynges that had been modified in this way were still able to produce nearly-normal chest-voice vibrations. Trajectories of particles near the superior borders of these vocal folds were similar to those from preparations with intact muscles, except that the major axes of the ellipses were tilted differently. With these preparations, vibration patterns of the vocal fold cover could be observed on the lateral sides of these membranes. Apparent waves, with a propagation velocity of about 1.1 m/sec were observed. This value is similar to that derived for the "intact" excised preparations. These results are especially intriguing, since they suggest that the body of the vocal fold plays a relatively unimportant role in maintaining the vibrations. When the region of the vocal ligament was impaired, on the other hand, phonatory vibrations could no longer be sustained. Thus, this structure seems to play an important role in the phonatory mechanism.

A seemingly counterintuitive result was obtained when falsetto phonation was attempted with these preparations. Falsetto could not be produced. A possible explanation for this result is that the muscle was needed to damp vibrations of the surface tissues at the lower parts of the folds.

REFERENCES

Baer, T. (1975) Investigation of phonation using excised larynxes, Ph.D. thesis, M.I.T.

Hirano, M. (1975) Phonosurgery: Basic and clinical investigations. Otologia (Fukuoka) 21, 239-440.

Hirano, M. (1979) Structure of the vocal fold in normal and disease states. Anatomical and physical studies. Paper presented at the Conference on the Assessment of Vocal Pathology, Bethesda, Md.

Matsushita, H. (1969) Vocal cord vibration of excised larynges - a study with ultra-high speed cinematography. Otologia (Fukuoka) 15, 127-142.

Matsushita, H. (1975) The vibratory mode of the vocal folds in the excised larynx. Folia Phoniatrica 27, 7-18.

Saito, S. (1977) Phonosurgery. Otologia (Fukuoka) 23, 171-384.

van den Berg, Jw. (1960) Vocal ligaments versus registers. Current Problems in Phoniatrics and Logopedics 1, 19-34.

III. CONTROL OF THE PHYSIOLOGIC PARAMETERS FOR SPEECH AND SINGING

Section Editor: James H. Abbs

Speech Motor Control Laboratories,
Waisman Center, University of Wisconsin,
Madison, Wisconsin, USA

CHAPTER 11
FUNCTIONS OF THE LARYNGEAL MUSCLES IN SPEECH

Hajime Hirose and Masayuki Sawashima

Research Institute of Logopedics and
Phoniatrics, Faculty of Medicine,
University of Tokyo, Japan

It has generally been recognized that the primary function of the larynx is sphincteric in nature. However, particularly in humans, the larynx has also been regarded as the organ of voice production. Indeed, with its abundant endowment of intrinsic and extrinsic laryngeal muscles, the human larynx is able to play an inportant role in speech production. The muscles underlying the movements of the laryngeal cartilages and of the larynx as a whole usually are divided into several groups including the adductor muscles, abductor muscle, tensor muscle, and strap mucles.

Introduction of electromyographic (EMG) approaches to laryngeal physiology provided new perspectives for modern laryngology and experimental phonetics, and a large number of EMG studies have been reported since the classic and pioneering work of Faaborg-Andersen (1957). Recent advances in both EMG recording and data processing techniques have enhanced our capability to further explore unanswered questions regarding active laryngeal adjustments in speech. The aim of the present paper is to describe our electromyographic data assessment technique and to present some recent findings on the laryngeal muscle actions associated with segmental as well as prosodic aspects of speech.

LARYNGEAL EMG - TECHNICAL ASPECTS

For the acquisition of laryngeal EMG data, electrodes must be inserted into the pertinent muscles. Since many of the laryngeal muscles are situated deep in the laryn-

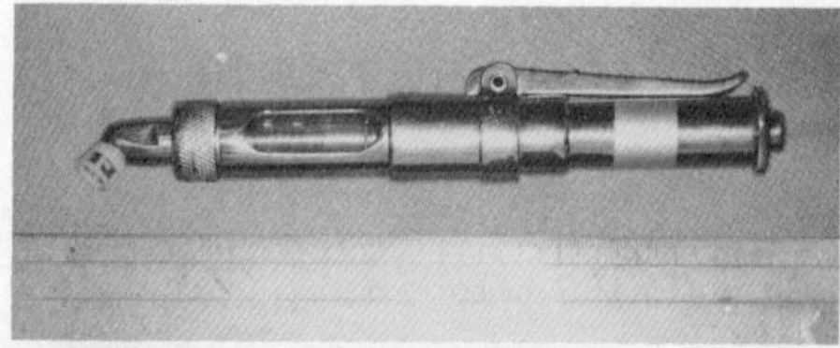

Fig.1. (a) Panjet

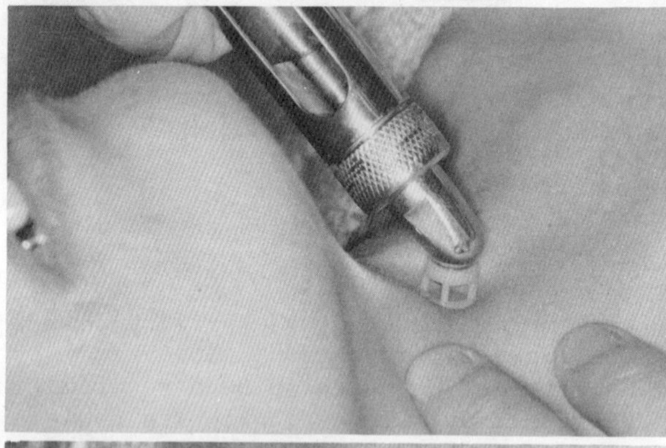

Fig.1. (b) Use of Panjet before electrode insertion

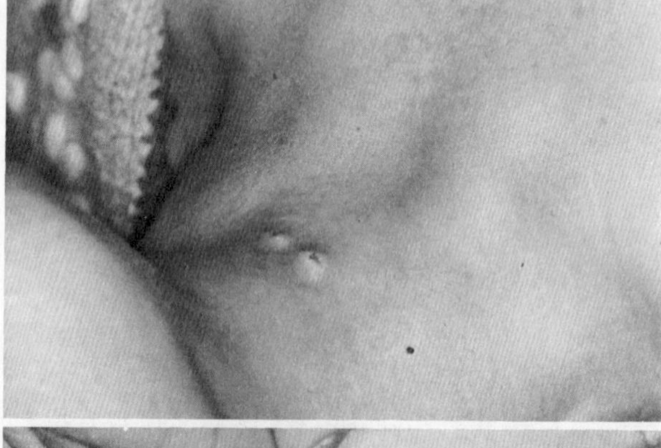

Fig.1. (c) Circumscribed swellings following intradermal administration of Xylocaine solution

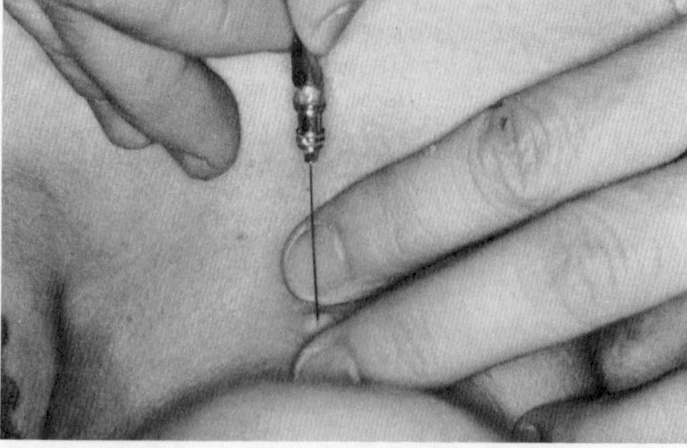

Fig.1. (d) Insertion of a needle electrode.

geal framework, their access often is difficult unless the examiner has a good knowledge of laryngeal topographic anatomy and physiology. In clinical laryngology, concentric needle electrodes are used widely for diagnostic purposes. From a kinesiological viewpoint, however, conventional needle electrodes are inadequate for speech research because the needle may hinder natural articulatory and phonatory performance. Thus, the use of hooked-wire electrodes (Basmajian and Stecko, 1962) was introduced (Hirano and Ohala, 1969) and further elaborated (Hirose, 1971; Hirose, Gay and Strome, 1971), making it possible to obtain multichannel recordings from the laryngeal muscles with minimum performance artifact or discomfort to the subject. We are now using either platinum-iridium or platinum-tungsten alloy wires with polyester coating for these electrodes.

In the preparation of hooked-wire electrodes, attempts have been made to adhere the two wires to each other as a means of minimizing recording artifacts due to mechanical contacts between the wires and to maximize the stability of the EMG signals. In some cases, a third wire is attached to provide the stabilizing hook, and the other two wires are used exclusively as electrodes. Unless we are interested in the discharge pattern of a single motor unit, the area of removal of polyester insulation at or near the tip of the wire must be large enough to pick up an appropriate number of motor unit discharges to reflect the pattern of EMG activity of a muscle as a whole. If adequately prepared, the input impedance of the electrode is found to be lower than several hundred kilohms.

The intrinsic laryngeal muscles can be reached via two different routes: percutaneous and peroral. In the percutaneous approach, prefabricated wires are threaded into a 26 or 27 gauge hypodermic needle and sterilized before experimental sessions. The insertion of the wire-carrying needles is preceded by the intradermal administration of a small amount of 0.5% Xylocaine solution through a Panjet at the site of needle insertion (Fig.1). The percutaneous approach is selected to reach the thyroarytenoid (VOC), lateral cricoarytenoid (LCA), and cricothyroid (CT).

Directions of needle insertion are schematically shown in Fig.2. To reach the thyroarytenoid, the needle is passed through the cricothyroid space near the midline and advanced cranially and slightly laterally in the submucous tissues near the anterior commissure. In order to avoid bringing the needle too close to the mucosal surface the subject is asked to phonate during insertion so as to bring the vocal cords to the midline. For the cricothyroid, insertions are made at the level of the lower edge of the cricoid ring and 5 mm lateral to the midline. The needle is advanced postero-laterally and slightly upward aiming toward the inferior tuberculum of the thyroid cartilage. Penetration of the fascia is often felt when the tip of the needle reaches the muscle (Hirose, 1979)

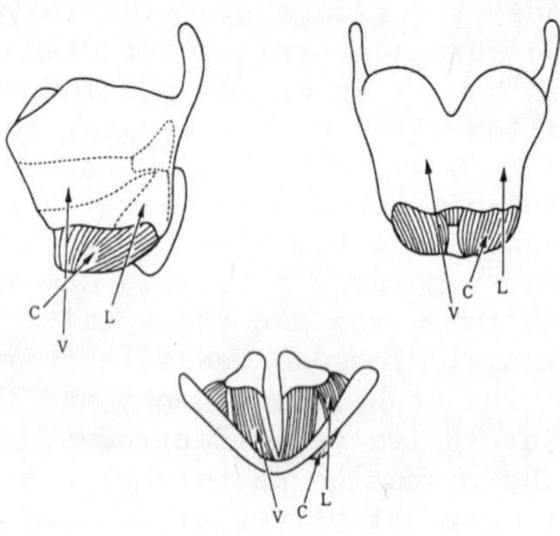

Fig.2. Directions of insertion of the needle electrode into the thyroarytenoid (V), cricothyroid (C) and lateral cricoarytenoid (L).

The peroral approach is taken to reach the posterior cricoarytenoid (PCA) and interarytenoid (INT). For peroral insertion under indirect laryngoscopy, a specially designed curved probe is used (Fig.3a) and wire electrodes are directed to the insertion points, as illustrated in Fig.3b (Hirose, 1976).

Recorded EMG data are reproduced and computer-processed with reference to simultaneously recorded acoustic signals. In our present system, the high-pass filtered and amplified EMG signals are full-wave rectified and integrated over an effective 10 millisecond interval; the integrators are reset at the end of each interval. In a recent comparison (using a computer simulation) between the integration method and the level-cross-count (LCC) method we found that the LCC method appears to have inherent difficulties in threshold setting and saturation characteristics

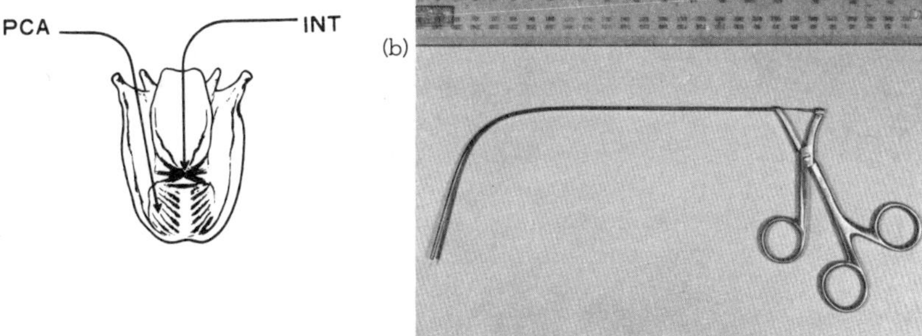

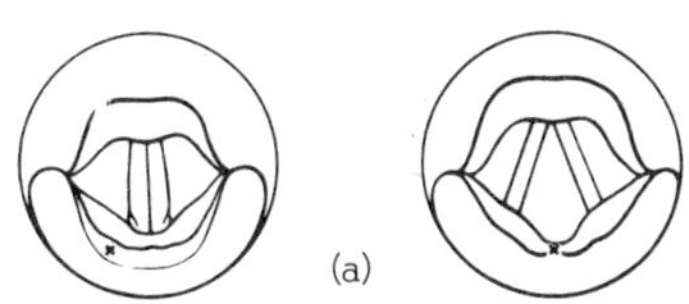

Fig.3. (a) Insertion of wire electrodes into PCA and INT, shown by arrows in upper sketch and by x's in lower sketch; (b) a curved probe for peroral insertion.

which might result in nonlinearity between the muscle activity and the obtained LCC value. Therefore, we are exclusively using the integration method.

Following this analog processing the EMG signals are digitized and displayed on an oscilloscope screen with appropriate smoothing and averaging (in most cases) to provide a graphic representation of the obtained results. When we wish to compare EMG activity and the corresponding movement data for the production of a single repetition, no averaging of the EMG is done (see infra).

LARYNGEAL EMG FINDINGS WITH REFERENCE TO SEGMENTAL ASPECTS OF SPEECH

As reported earlier (Hirose and Gay, 1972), EMG findings about glottal adduction-abduction indicate that there is active participation of the intrinsic laryngeal muscles in the control of laryngeal articulatory gestures. In particular, PCA, the only abductor of the vocal folds, is found to play a subtle role in speech glottal opening gestures, provided that there is simultaneous supression of the adductor muscles. Among the adductors, INT most clearly shows a reciprocity with the PCA in relation to the voicing feature in such languages as American English, French, Danish, and Japanese (Hirose, Yoshioka, and Niimi, 1979).

Figure 4 shows examples of computer-averaged EMG curves

obtained from the five intrinsic laryngeal muscles of a Japanese subject for paired test words of meaningful Japanese embedded in a frame sentence "sorewa____desu" (that is ____). It can be seen that PCA and INT show reciprocity regardless of the phonetic environment. The degrees of PCA activation for voiceless portions of the test utterances and corresponding INT suppression do vary somewhat depending upon the environment. A statistical test revealed that there is a significant negative correlation between the magnitudes of PCA and INT activity, thus supporting the above observation of their reciprocity (Hirose and Ushijima, 1978). A similar relationship between PCA and INT was also revealed in other phonetic conditions including voiced-voiceless contrasts in initial and final positions (Hirose and Gay, 1972; Sawashima, Hirose, Ushijima, and Niimi, 1975).

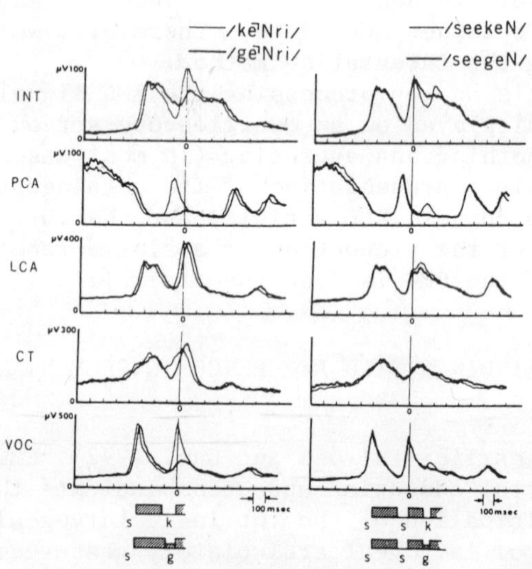

Fig.4. Averaged EMG curves of five intrinsic laryngeal muscles for test utterances comparing /k/ to /g/ in Japanese in the word-initial (left) and medial (right) positions. The line-up point for averaging was the onset of vowel after /k/ or /g/, as shown by the schematized acoustic time patterns at the bottom.

It was also found that there is a significant positive correlation between peak values of averaged PCA activity and maximum glottal width as measured by means of a fiberoptic technique (Hirose, 1976). In general, the averaged PCA curve corresponds to the time course of the glottal aperture change (arytenoid separation) for various voiceless sounds and other sound sequences, with an expected time delay. For example, PCA activation is accompanied by arytenoid separation throughout the voiceless sound sequences including geminates or devoiced vowel segments. Similar observations were made for voiceless segments in French in the three-way contrast between liaison, non-geminated, and geminated conditions (Benguerel, Hirose, Sawashima, and Ushijima, 1978).

The glottal opening gesture and its timing were studied further in clusters of voiceless obstruents of American English with a combination of EMG, fiberoptics, and transillumination techniques (Yoshioka, Löfqvist, and Hirose, 1979). In this study, two distinct peaks in the PCA activity waveform were observed for the [sk] sequence when a word boundary intervened, but only one PCA peak for the same sequence without the boundary (Fig.5). This finding, together with parallel data on glottal separation, would suggest that each voiceless obstruent with aspiration or frication requires a separate opening gesture.

When we examine Fig.4 further, it is obvious that there are differences in the activity patterns between the three adductors (INT, LCA, and VOC). For both LCA and VOC, muscle activity increases for initiation of each utterance and decreases for word initial consonants, and the degree of reduction is comparable for both voiced and voiceless consonants. The activity increases again after the suppression, apparently for the nuclear vowel following the initial consonant. In the case of VOC, muscle activity sharply increases after the voiceless consonant, particularly when the accent kernel is attached to that mora, whereas the increase is less marked after the voiced pair. The pattern of LCA activity in terms of suppression for the initial consonant and increase for the following vowel essentially is the same regardless of voicing distinction of the initial consonant. For the consonant segment in the word-medial position, LCA and VOC curves generally show the pattern of suppression after the activation for the vowel segment of the preceding mora.

In the study of other languages, it has been revealed that LCA appears to provide supplementary adduction con-

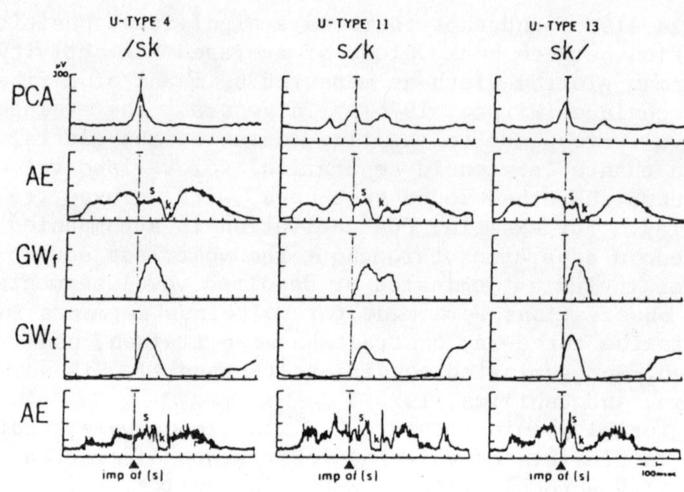

Fig.5. Averaged EMG of PCA, averaged audio envelopes (AE), representative plots of glottal width using fiberoptics (GW_f), corresponding glottograms (GW_t), and audio envelopes (AE) for three utterance types: "I may scale" (type 4), "my ace caves" (type 11), and "I mask adi" (type 13). (From Yoshioka et al., 1979.)

trol (Hirose, Lisker, and Abramson, 1972; Fischer-Jørgensen and Hirose, 1974a; Benguerel et al., 1978). As Dixity (1975) has claimed and other anatomical studies have indicated (Hirano, 1975), the INT action alone does not seem to result in full adduction of the vocal folds. For this reason, it may be plausible to consider that INT provides the finer adjustments of the glottal aperture for various speech sounds possibly with supportive action of LCA, after the larynx is once geared to "speech mode" by the activation of all the adductors and the suppression of PCA.

The general pattern of CT activity in Fig.4 is characterized by two peaks separated apparently by suppression at the initial consonant of the test words, presumably as a boundary effect of the test utterances. At least in the word-initial position, this suppression is less marked for the voiceless cognate than for the voiced. Our previous studies did not reveal any significant difference in CT activity with reference to the voicing distinction, and pitch control has been considered the primary role of CT. Although the apparent difference in the degree of CT suppression can also be attributed to the difference in dynamic control of the pitch contour, as reported elsewhere (Hirose and Ushijima, 1978), the possibility of CT contribution to facilitating devoicing by increasing the longitudinal tension of the vocal fold needs to be investigated further (Hirose, 1977a).

In a recent study, the EMG patterns for each of the utterance samples containing voiceless sounds were examined in Japanese subjects (Sawashima, Hirose, and Yoshioka, 1978). Figure 6 shows examples of EMG patterns of PCA and INT for a single token of a test word [siQseH] embedded in a carrier "sore o___to yuu" (we call that ___), obtained from two Japanese subjects. The data are displayed together with the temporal course of the glottal width (measured at the vocal processes) by means of fiberoptics. Here also, at least qualitatively, the opening-closing gesture of the glottis apparently is controlled by a reciprocal pattern of PCA and INT activity. It should be noted that there is intersubject variation in the mode of the laryngeal control for these two muscles. In MS, the long period of voicelessness is associated with a slow closing movement of the glottis, which appears to be controlled mainly by gradual reactivation of INT accompanied by continuous suppression of PCA. In HH, on the other hand, the glottal time curve consists of two smoothed peaks with steep slopes both at the beginning and end of the glottal opening. The time course appears to be controlled mainly by PCA. Thus, it can be said that the relative contribution of PCA and INT differs between the two subjects at least in this experimental condition.

As illustrated in Fig.7, the reciprocal relationship between PCA and INT was maintained even for labial stops of five phonetic types as produced by a phonetician. An additional EMG-fiberoptic study of glottal opening for the third, fourth, and fifth types of stops (in Fig.7) revealed that there was good agreement in both magnitude and timing between the opening gesture of the glottis and muscle activity patterns (Hirose, Lisker, and Abramson, 1972). The data from these observations also suggested that the timing of the glottal gesture interacted with the supralaryngeal articulation to determine the phonetic characteristics of each stop type. In particular, the degree of aspiration was considered to be controlled by the timing relation between the glottal opening and the movement of the upper articulators.

As for voicing, there are certain situations where

vocal fold vibration continues with an open glottis, as often observed for voiced [h]. In order to clarify the mechanism of voicing in these cases, more data about laryngeal, supralaryngeal and aerodynamic variables are necessary.

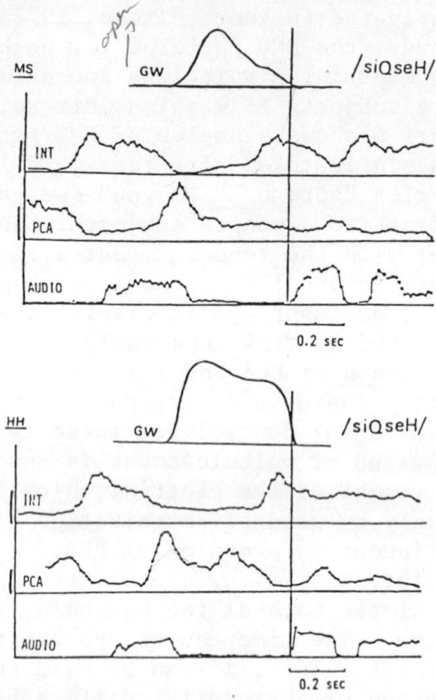

Fig.6. Time curves of the glottal width (GW), smoothed and integrated EMG of INT and PCA, and audio envelope for /seQseH/. Vertical line indicates the onset of vowel /e/.

It must also be noted in Fig.4 that the difference in the vowel carrier does not result in any appreciable difference in the activity patterns of PCA and INT. Also, as indicated in Fig.8, vowel differences do not appear to influence VOC and CT patterns.

In Fig.8, averaged EMG activities of VOC and CT for the production of three types of Korean stops are shown. In this experiment, test words of a CV1-type are embedded in a carrier sentence [ikəsi___ita]. As can be seen, there is a sharp peak of VOC for the forced [P] production. This VOC activity presumably results in an increase in the tension of the vocal fold body as well as constriction of the glottis during or immediately after the articulatory closure; this VOC gesture can be considered as a physiological correlate of so-called 'laryngealization' (Hirose, Lee, and Ushijima, 1974). In these cases, in addition to opening-closing of the glottis, these other physiological dimensions should be taken into consideration for specifying consonant distinctions (Hirose, 1977b).

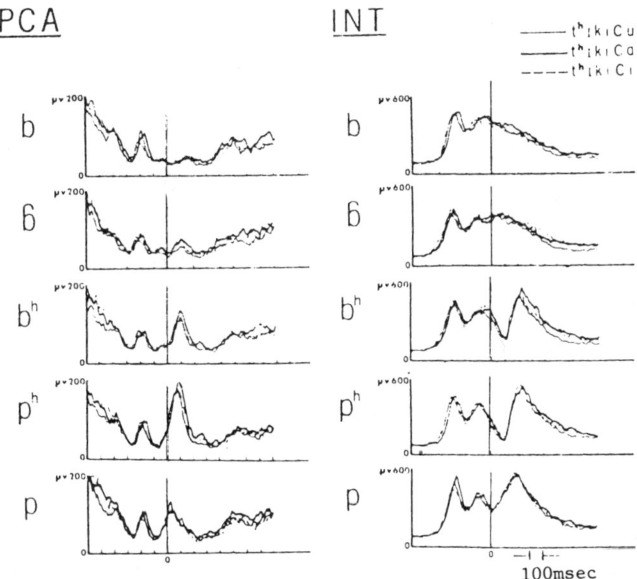

Fig.7. Averaged EMG curves of PCA and INT for test utterances containing five phonetically different labial stops embedded word medially. For each type, three curves are superimposed, each of which represents a different vowel carrier following the stop consonant. The line-up point is the instant of release of the stop consonant. The utterances were produced by a phonetician.

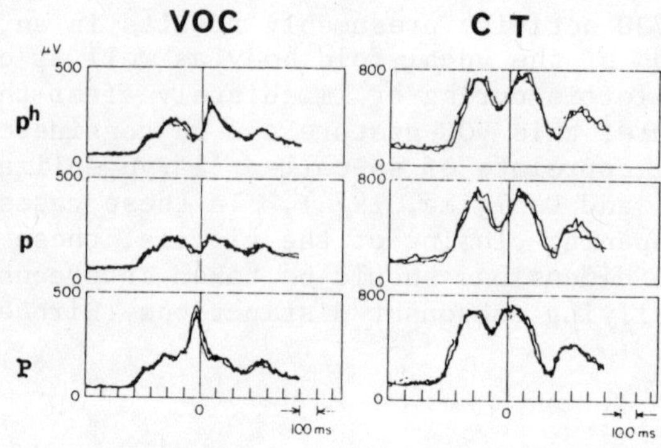

Fig.8. Averaged EMG curves of VOC and CT for the three bilabial stops of Korean in word-medial position. In each type, three curves are superimposed for the postconsonantal vowel /i/, /a/ and /u/. The zero on the abscissa marks the line-up for averaging, which corresponds to the stop release.

LARYNGEAL EMG FINDINGS WITH REFERENCE TO PROSODIC ASPECTS OF SPEECH

EMG studies of the laryngeal muscles during speech in a variety of languages have shown that the laryngeal muscles are primarily responsible for pitch (F_0) control, no matter what type of pitch change is involved (Ohala, 1977). In particular, in agreement with the earlier findings for singing, CT has been found to be the primary muscle for raising pitch, although LCA and VOC may also assist in pitch raising. It has also been suggested that the strap muscles are active during pitch lowering.

The principal mechanism for pitch change is to increase or decrease the longitudinal tension of the vocal folds, and the function of CT is related to this process. On the other hand, the possibility that the strap muscles contribute to pitch control is not as straightforward as in the case of CT, since activity in strap muscles often appears to be a response to change in conditions rather than the cause, i.e., changes in strap muscle activity appear to follow rather than precede the pitch changes (Collier, 1975; Fujimura, 1977).

Figure 9 shows examples of EMG curves of LCA, CT and sternohyoid (SH) for single tokens of isolated two-mora

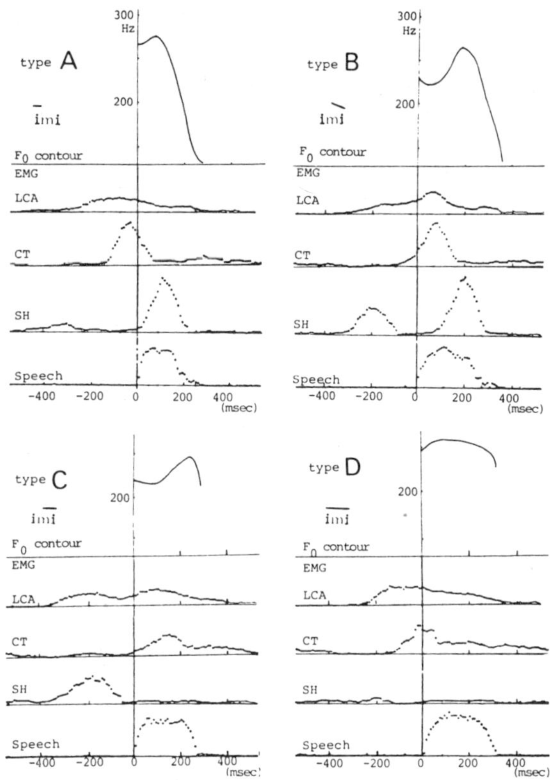

Fig.9. Integrated and smoothed EMG curves of LCA, CT and SH and F_0 contours for single tokens of two-mora words of Japanese having four different accent patterns of the Kinki dialect. The vertical bar indicates the onset of voicing.

words of Japanese with four contrasting accent patterns of the Kinki dialect (Sugito and Hirose, 1978). It is obvious that CT activation is related to pitch rise with some lead in time. As for pitch descent, the decrease in CT activity and increase in SH appear to correlate with the F_0 contour, particularly in types A and B. However, there is an obvious time-lag between the onset of decline of CT activity and that of the elevation of SH activity in type A. Thus, SH seems to play a role in assisting or enhancing a sharp descent of F_0 as seen in these cases, but it is not likely that SH acts as the primary pitch lowering muscle.

It is interesting to note that there is SH activation before the voice onset in the so-called "low-start" types (types B and C). The increase in SH activity before the voice onset has been found in other cases as well and interpreted as an indication that SH helps in preparing the larynx for the "speech mode". The nature of SH activation in cases such as these needs further investigation.

Based on his study of laryngeal control in the production of various types of intonation patterns of American English, Atkinson (1978) claimed that different physiological factors served to control F_0 over different F_0 regions. In particular, he suggested that SH was the major factor at mid F_0 range (100-120 Hz in his male subject). It seems possible that there are distinct regions of F_0 within the normal speech range that correspond to different laryngeal states, and the strap muscles may play an important role in producing the different laryngeal states.

The physiological correlates of stress appear to be very complex. For the production of stress effect, as the so-called "extra effort" model suggests, extra energy can be applied to the stressed vowel, with the result that it lasts longer and is further from a neutral vocal tract position (Öhman, 1967). At the same time, as many acoustical studies indicate, a rise in pitch appears to be one of the most important correlates of stress (Lieberman, 1960).

Figure 10 compares averaged EMG curves of CT, INT, and LCA together with F_0 contours for meaningful words of English, which differ from each other in lexical stress. The two stress patterns show differences in F_0 contour, and the pattern of CT activity seems to be related to this adjustment. In addition, the other two muscles also appear to be activated in the production of stress, although it is not possible to determine whether the activation is related to the rise in F_0 or, rather, to the general increase in EMG activities that can be regarded as evidence of "extra effort". Further studies are needed for elucidating the physiological mechanism underlying stress production, particularly from the viewpoint of laryngeal physiology.

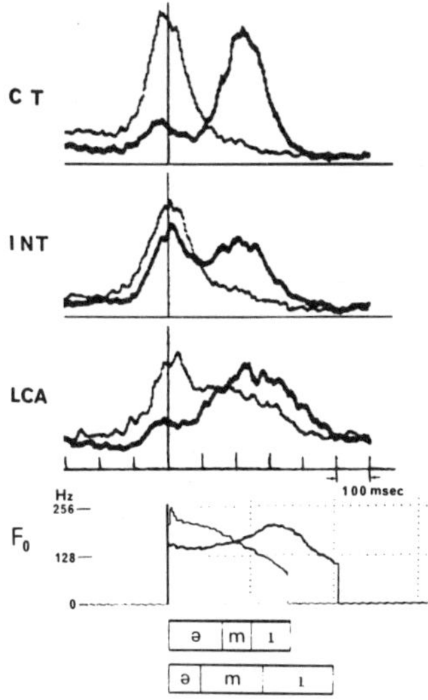

Fig.10. Averaged EMG curves of CT, INT and LCA and pitch contours for the pair of "pérmit" and "permít" produced by an American English speaker. Locations of boundaries of phonetic sequents are shown at the bottom.

ACKNOWLEDGMENT

The preparation of this paper was made possible in part by support under a Grant-in-Aid for Scientific Research (No. 337040, 349008, 410207, 448322), Ministry of Education, Japanese Government.

REFERENCES

Atkinson, J.E. (1978) Correlation analysis of the physiological factors controlling fundamental voice frequency. J. Acoust Soc. Am., 63; 211-222.

Basmajian, J.L. and Stecko, G. (1962) A new bipolar electrode for electromyography. J. Appl. Physiol. 17; 849.

Benguerel, A.P., Hirose, H., Sawashima, M. and Ushijima, T.

(1978) Laryngeal control in French stops: A fiber-optic, acoustic and electromyographic study. Folia Phoniat., 30; 175-198.

Collier, R. (1975) Physiological correlates of intonation patterns. J. Acoust. Soc. Am., 58; 249-255.

Dixit, R.O. (1975) Neuromuscular aspects of laryngeal control: With special reference to Hindi. Ph.D. dissertation presented to the Faculty of Graduate School of the University of Texas at Austin.

Faaborg-Andersen, K. (1957) Electromyographic investigation of intrinsic laryngeal muscles in humans. Acta physiol. Scand., 41; suppl. 140.

Fischer-Jørgensen, E. and Hirose, H. (1974a) A preliminary electromyographic study of labial and laryngeal muscles in Danish stops consonant production. Haskins Laboratories Status Report on Speech Research, SR-39/40; 231-254.

Fischer-Jørgensen, E. and Hirose, H. (1974b) A note on laryngeal activity in the Danish "stød": Haskins Laboratories Status Report on Speech Research, SR-39/40; 255-259.

Fujimura, O. (1977): Control of the larynx in speech. Phonetica 34; 280-288.

Hirano, M. (1975) Phonosurgery: Basic and clinical investigations. Otologia (Fukuoka) 21; 239-440.

Hirano, M. and Ohala, J.J. (1969) Use of hooked-wire electrodes for electromyography of the intrinsic laryngeal muscles. J. Speech Hearing Res., 12; 362-373.

Hirose, H. (1971) Electromyography of the articulatory muscles: Current instrumentation and technique. Haskins Laboratories Status Report on Speech Research 25/26; 73-86.

Hirose, H. (1976) Posterior cricoarytenoid as a speech muscle. Ann. Otol. Rhinol. Laryngol., 85; 334-343.

Hirose, H. (1977a) Electromyography of the larynx and

other speech organs. In Dynamic Aspects of Speech Production, (M. Sawashima and F.S. Cooper (eds.), Tokyo: University Tokyo Press. pp. 49-67.

Hirose, H. (1977b) Laryngeal adjustments in consonant production. Phonetica 34; 289-294.

Hirose, H. (1979) Laryngeal EMG. Ann. Bull. RILP 13; 13-22.

Hirose, H. and Gay, T. (1972) The activity of the intrinsic laryngeal muscles in voicing control - an electromyographic study. Phonetica, 25; 140-164.

Hirose, H., Gay, T. and Strome, M. (1971) Electrode insertion techniques for laryngeal electromyography. J. Acoust. Soc. Am., 50; 1449-1450.

Hirose, H., Lee, C.Y. and Ushijima, T. (1974) Laryngeal control in Korean stop production. J. Phonetics, 2; 145-152.

Hirose, H., Lisker, L. and Abramson, A. (1972) Physiological aspects of certain laryngeal features in stop production. Haskins Laboratories Status Report on Speech Research, SR-31/32; 183-191.

Hirose, H. and Ushijima, T. (1978) Laryngeal Control for voicing distinction in Japanese consonant production. Phonetica, 35; 1-10.

Hirose, H., Yoshioka, H. and Niimi, S. (1979) A cross language study of laryngeal adjustment in consonant production. In Current Issues in the Phonetic Sciences. (H. Hollien and P. Hollein (eds.), Amsterdam John Benjamins, B.V., pp. 165-179.

Lieberman, P. (1960) Some acoustic correlates of word stress in American English. J. Acoust. Soc. Am. 32; 451-454.

Ohala, J.J. (1967) The production of tone. Report of the Phonology Lab. Berkeley, 2; 63-117.

Öhman, S. (1967) Word and sentence intonation; a quantitative model. QPSR 2-3, Royal Inst. Tech., 20-54.

Sawashima, M., Hirose, H., Ushijima, T. and Niimi, S. (1975) Laryngeal control in Japanese consonants, with special reference to those in utterance-initial position. Ann. Bull, RILP., 9; 21-26.

Sawashima, M., Hirose, H. and Yoshioka, H. (1978) Abductor (RCA) and adductor (INT) muscles of the larynx in voiceless sound production. Ann. Bull. RILP., 12; 53-60.

Sugito, M. And Hirose, H. (1978) An electromyographic study of Kinki Accent. Ann. Bull. RILP., 12; 35-52.

Yoshioka, H. Löfqvist, A. and Hirose, H. (1979) Laryngeal adjustments in the production of consonant clusters and geminates in American English. An extended version of the paper presented at the 97th ASA Meeting, Cambridge, Mass. (June, 1979)

CHAPTER 12
THE FUNCTION OF THE INTRINSIC LARYNGEAL MUSCLES IN SINGING

M. Hirano

Department of Otolaryngology, Kurume University, Kurume, Japan

The purpose of this paper is not to present new data but to summarize the results of our work conducted during the past decade so that these findings can be related to the other studies to be presented in this conference.

I. SUBJECTS AND METHOD OF INVESTIGATION

Five adult singers (three males and two females) and four untrained male adults served as the subjects. Bipolar hooked wire electrodes were inserted into the intrinsic laryngeal muscles through the skin of the neck (Hirano and Ohala, 1969). Evaluation of muscle activity was based chiefly on visual observations of raw EMG recordings, viz., the degree of muscular activation was evaluated from observation of action potential amplitudes and frequencies. Only with some selected singing samples for which repeated utterances were available, was a computer averaging technique employed.

II. VOCAL REGISTER

There appear to be three main vocal registers: falsetto or light register, modal or heavy register, and vocal fry. Falsetto is characterized by the absence of complete glottal closure. The modal register is accompanied by complete glottal closure for each vibratory cycle, and it is traditionally subdivided into head, mid, and chest registers. Vocal fry is characterized by an extremely long closed phase relative to one vibratory cycle. Our investigations have focused primarily on the falsetto and modal registers.

1. Comparison of Muscular Activity among Different Registers at the Same Pitch

Muscular activity was compared among sustained tones produced in different registers, but at the same pitch. Four singers were capable of performing this task. The results of these comparisons are summarized in Table 1. Figure 1 illustrates muscle activity and acoustic recordings from one subject (W.V.).

Table 1. Degree of muscular activity as shown in rank order. The activity of each muscle is compared among different registers at the same fundamental frequency.

Subject	Fundamental pitch	Register	CT	LCA	VOC	IA
J. R. (Soprano)	G_4	Head	2	3	3	
		Mid	3	2	2	
		Chest	1	1	1	
M. M. (Tenor)	C_4	Falsetto	2	3	3	
		Head	2	2	2	
		Chest	2	1	1	
T. M. (Tenor)	C_4	Falsetto	3	3	3	
		Mid	1	1.5	2	
		Chest	2	1.5	1	
W. V. (Bass)	G_3	Falsetto	3	3	3	
		Head	1.5	2	1.5	
		Chest	1.5	1	1.5	
	C_4	Falsetto	2.5	2.5	3	3
		Head	1	1	2	2
		Chest	2.5	2.5	1	1

As is apparent from Table 1, the activity of the vocalis muscle (VOC) was markedly greater for the heavier register in all four subjects. The only exception was observed at pitch G_3 of subject W.V., in which the VOC activity was approximately the same for the head and chest registers. The lateral cricoarytenoid muscle (LCA) tended also to be more active for the heavier register, but not as consistently as VOC. In addition, the difference in LCA activity was not as marked as in VOC activity. The activity of the interarytenoid muscle (IA) (investigated only in one subject) also was slightly greater for the heavier register. The activity of the cricothyroid muscle (CT) did not show any consistent relationship to variations in vocal register.

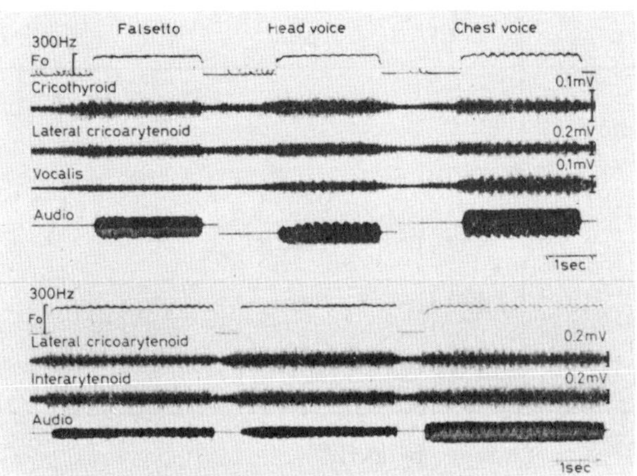

Fig.1. Activity of CT, LCA, VOC and IA in different vocal registers at the same pitch (C_4). Two series of sounds are shown for subject W.V.

2. Muscular Activity Pattern in Response to Register Shift

The muscular activity pattern was investigated when the vocal register was shifted during singing. Five singers were subjects for these tasks. Table 2 summarizes the results from this experiment. Figures 2, 3, 4 and 5 provide examples of raw EMG recordings of changes in muscular activity associated with these register shifts.

As shown, VOC always presented a significant change in activity in response to register shifts. Register shifts from heavy to light were associated with a decrease in VOC activity, whereas shifts to heavier registers were accompanied by VOC increases. The direction of the changes in the LCA, CT and IA activity were the same as in the case of the VOC. However, in the LCA, changes in activity associated with register shifts were observed less frequently, and changes in CT activity were even less consistent. IA activity (investigated in one subject) also changed with register shifts. There were no examples where muscular activity became greater when the register was shifted from a heavier to a lighter one, unless the shift was accompanied by a significant increase in pitch.

Table 2. Changes in muscular activity in response to register shift during singing.

Subject	CT	LCA	VOC	IA
L. C. (Soprano)	(+)or-	+or-	+	
J. R. (Soprano)	(+)or-	+		
M. M. (Tenor)	(+)or-	+or-	+	
T. M. (Tenor)	(+)or-	+or-	+	
W. V. (Bass)	(+)or-	+or-	+	+

+ : Change found.
( ): Not frequent.
- : Change not found.

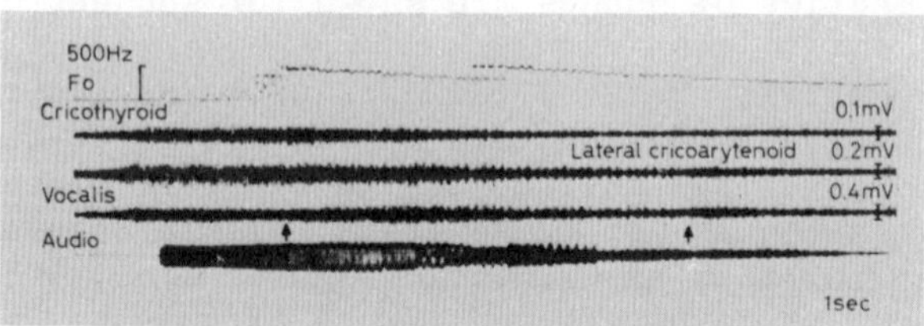

Fig.2. Activity of CT, LCA and VOC during singing a descending three-octaves scale ($E^b{}_6$-$E^b{}_3$). Subject L.C. At the left arrow the voice was shifted from falsetto to head, and at right arrow, from mid to chest.

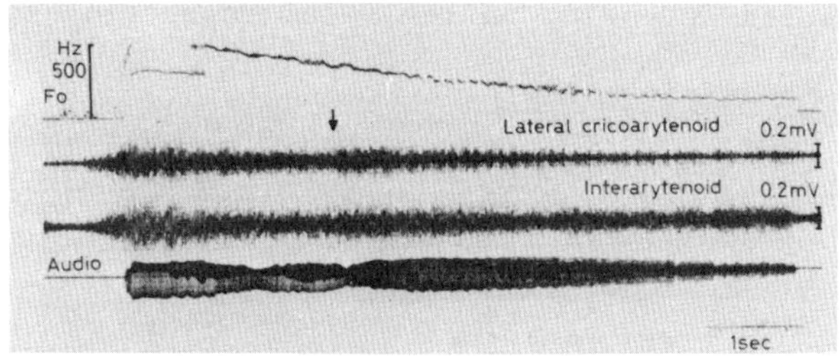

Fig.3. Activity of LCA and IA during singing a descending three-octave scale (D_5-D_2). Subject W.V. At the arrow the voice was shifted from falsetto to head.

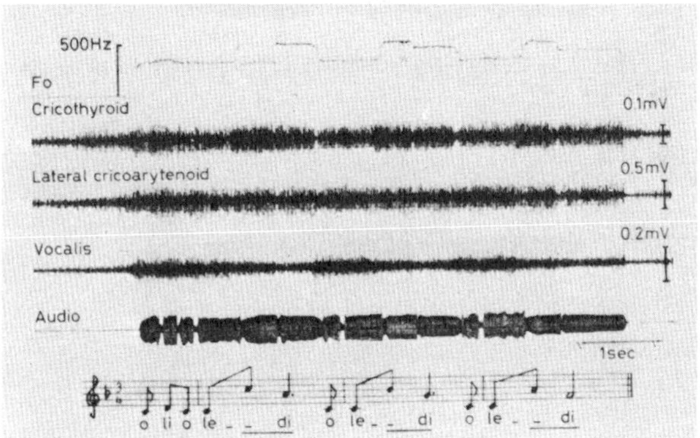

Fig.4. Activity of CT, LCA and VOC during yodeling. Subject M.M. The underlined parts were yodeled (in falsetto).

3. Summary
   (1) VOC participates in regulating vocal register most significantly.
   (2) LCA and IA appear to assist VOC in regulating register.
   (3) CT activity shows no systematic relationship to the register. However, since it has an antagonistic function to VOC, it should influence register regulation significantly.

III. VOCAL PITCH (FUNDAMENTAL FREQUENCY)

The function of the laryngeal muscles in regulation

of pitch varied depending on the vocal register.

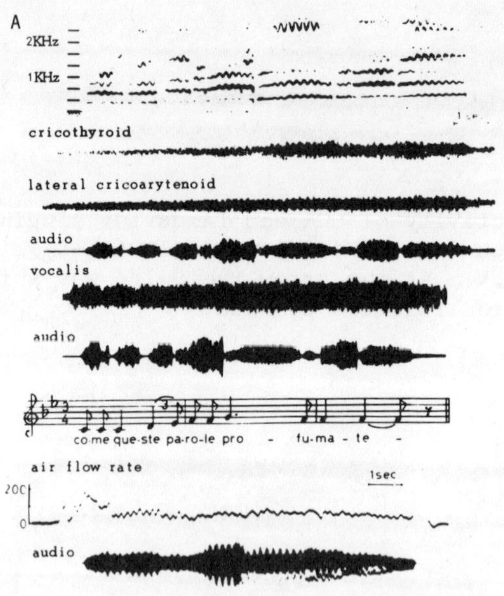

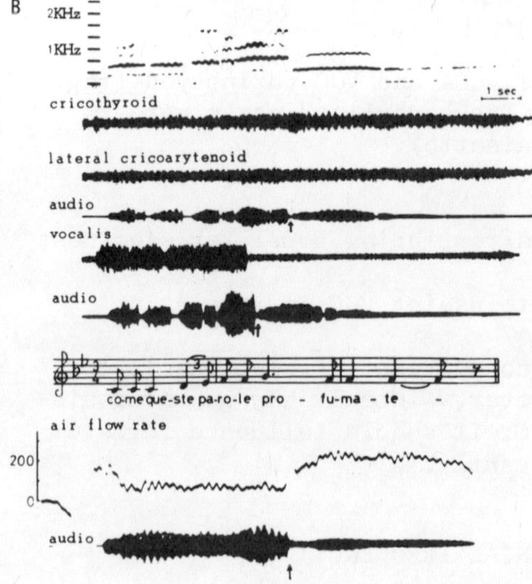

Fig.5. Activity of CT, LCA and VOC when the phrase shown was sung in two different ways: in modal register throughout (A) and with a register shift into falsetto at the arrow (B). A narrow-band spectrogram of the phrase is shown at the top of each section. Subject T.M. Note the inactivation of VOC and the marked increase in airflow for falsetto.

1. Pitch Regulation in the Modal Register

The relationships between the muscular activities and pitch are demonstrated in Figs.2, 3, 4, 5 and 6, and summarized in Table 3. In the modal register, the activity of CT, LCA and VOC were always positively related to the pitch. IA presented greater activity at the higher pitches. There were, however, no gradual activity changes closely related to the pitch (as shown in Fig.3). The posterior cricoarytenoid muscle (PCA) is usually inactive during phonation, with the exception of high tones in the modal register (illustrated in Fig.6). This activity of PCA may be required in order to brace the arytenoid cartilage against the strong anterior pull of the CT.

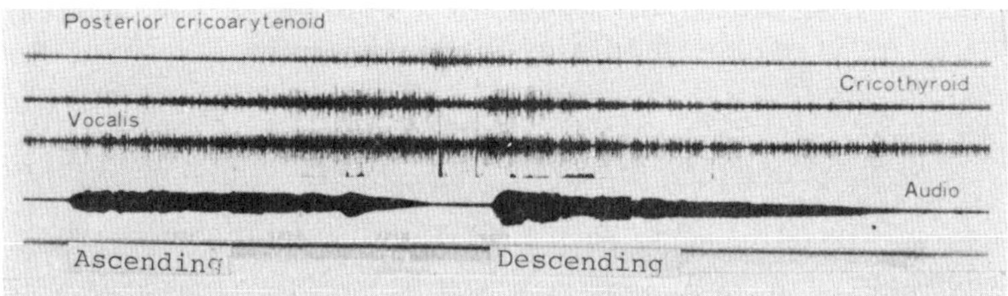

Fig.6. Activity of PCA, CT, and VOC during singing an ascending scale followed by a descending scale in modal register. Subject H.H.

Table 3. Relation of muscular activity to fundamental frequency in the heavy register.

	Subject	CT	LCA	VOC	IA	PCA
Professional singer	L. C. (Soprano)	+	+	+		
	J. R. (Soprano)	+	+			
	M. M. (Tenor)	+	+	+		
	T. M. (Tenor)	+	+	+		
	W. V. (Bass)	+	+	+	+ or 0	
Un-trained	J. O.	+	+	+	+ or 0	
	D. B.	+	+			
	J. A.	+	+			
	H. H.	+	+	+	+ or 0	+ or 0

+: Positively related. 0: Not related.

2. Pitch Regulation in Falsetto

Falsetto pitch regulation also was investigated in the five singers. Table 4 summarizes these results. The activity of CT, LCA and VOC was not always positively related to the pitch in falsetto. However, in a given singing sample, it was rare if the activity of one of these three muscles did not show a positive relation to pitch. It is worth noting that CT, which plays the most important role in pitch control in the modal register, did not always contribute in falsetto. The activity of IA was greater at the higher pitches but it was not closely related to the pitch.

Table 4. Relation of muscular activity to fundamental frequency in the light register.

Subject	CT	LCA	VOC	IA
L. C. (Soprano)	+ or 0	+	+ or 0	
J. R. (Soprano)	+ or 0	+		
M. M. (Tenor)	+ or 0	+ or 0	+ or 0	
T. M. (Tenor)	+	+	0	
W. V. (Bass)	+ or 0	+	+	+ or 0

+: Positively related. 0: Not related.

3. Summary

(1) CT raises the pitch directly

(2) LCA and VOC present greater activity for higher pitch. This pattern of activity appears significant not only for raising pitch but for other purposes. When the CT is activated, the edge of the vocal folds tend to be positioned along the line between the anterior commissure and the posterior cricoarytenoid ligament. In other words, CT has the function of abducting the vocal fold when in the median position. This abduction, in turn, would appear to require compensation by the adductor muscles. Furthermore, CT has an antagonistic function to VOC with respect to the vocal register. In order to maintain register conditions, the

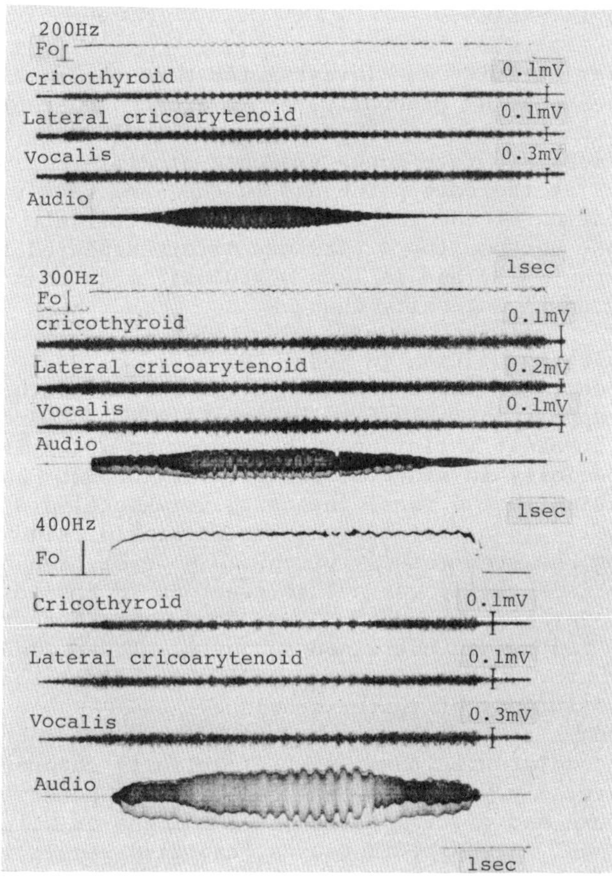

Fig.7. Activity of CT, LCA and VOC during swelltone singing.
A: at pitch G_3 in chest; B: at pitch C_4 in head; C: at pitch G_4 in falsetto. Subject W.V.

activity of VOC should increase in parallel with CT activity.

(3) Participation of CT, LCA and VOC in pitch control is more dominant in the modal register than in falsetto.

(4) IA presents greater activity only for higher pitches, probably to compensate for the abduction influence of CT.

(5) PCA braces the arytenoid cartilage against the strong anterior pull of CT.

IV. VOCAL INTENSITY

Muscular activity was investigated when the vocal intensity was changed gradually, as in crescendo, decrecendo and swelltone. In some subjects, comparisons were attempted among separate tones produced at different intensities but at the same pitch and in the same register. Interpretation of the EMG data was often difficult in this latter case because the expiratory effort appeared to vary more substantially and in less systematic ways than in the case of gradual intensity changes.

1. Intensity Regulation in Modal Register

The results of the regulation of intensity in the modal register appear in Table 5. The muscle that appeared to show the greatest variation with changes in intensity was VOC. Especially in singers, the activity of VOC changed in proportion to the vocal intensity irrespective of the pitch level. In untrained subjects, a similar kind of change was observed for low pitches. However, the degree of change in activity was not so great as in the case of singers. For high pitches, VOC did not contribute to intensity control in untrained subjects. These findings suggest that VOC control is one of the important factors in the proficiency of voice technique.

LCA and IA activity increased with the vocal intensity, but less consistently than VOC. CT activity changes often varied inversely with the vocal intensity. The expiratory air pressure and glottal resistance, changes of which accompany vocal intensity increases, can also result in a rise in pitch. As such, the CT activity may have to be proportionally reduced to maintain a constant pitch level. PCA was activated only at high pitches and had activity level changes similar to CT.

2. Intensity Regulation in Falsetto

Table 6 summarizes the results for falsetto intensity regulation. In falsetto, none of the muscles showed any indication of a significant contribution to intensity regulation. This finding indicates that the vocal intensity is controlled almost exclusively by the expiratory air pressure in falsetto. As in the modal register, CT activity was inversely related to the vocal intensity, probably to maintain pitch, as mentioned earlier.

Table 5. Relation of muscular activity to intensity of voice in the heavy register.

	Subject	Fundamental pitch	CT	LCA	VOC	IA	PCA
Professional singer	L. C. (Soprano)	D_4	–	0	+		
		G_4	–	–∿+	+		
		D_5	–	–∿+	+		
	J. R. (Soprano)	C_4	– or 0	+ or 0			
		G_4	–	+ or 0			
		C_5	–	–			
	M. M. (Tenor)	C_4	–	+	+		
		G_4	–∿+	+	+		
	T. M. (Tenor)	F_3	–	–	+		
		F_4	–	–	+		
		A_4	–	–	+		
	W. V. (Bass)	C_3	0	+	+	–	
		G_3	0	+	+	+	
		C_4	–	– or 0	+	0	
Un-trained	J. O.	C_3			+	+	
		G_3			+ or 0	+	
		C_4			0	+	
	H. H.	low	0		+		0
		high	–		0		–

+: Positively related.
0: Not related.
–: Negatively related.
–∿+: Negatively related at a lesser intensity, and positively related at a greater intensity.

3. Summary

(1) In the modal register, among the laryngeal muscles, VOC participates in intensity regulation most significantly. LCA and IA assist VOC in regulating the vocal intensity.

(2) In falsetto, none of the laryngeal muscles contributes to intensity control significantly.

(3) CT presents a compensatory action in order to keep the pitch adequate.

Table 6. Relation of muscular activity to intensity of voice in the light register.

	Subject	Fundamental pitch	CT	LCA	VOC	IA
	L. C. (Soprano)	E_6	–	0	0	
Profession-al singer	J. R. (Soprano)	C_6	-or 0	+		
	M. M. (Tenor)	G_4	–	0	+ or 0	
		C_5	–	0	0	
	T. M. (Tenor)	F_4	–	–	0	
	W. V. (Bass)	C_4	–	–	0	
		G_4	–	–	–	–
Untrained	J. O.	A_4				0

+: Positively related. 0: Not related.
-: Negatively related.

ACKNOWLEDGMENT

This investigation was supported in part by a Grant-in-Aid for Scientific Research (No. 337040, 557402), the Ministry of Education, Science and Culture.

REFERENCES

Hirano, M. (1970a) Regulatory mechanism of voice in singing. J. Logoped Phoniat. Jpn. 11, 1-11.

Hirano, M. (1970b) Regulatory mechanism of voice in singing. 16 mm Film.

Hirano, M. (1971) Laryngeal adjustment for different vocal onsets. J. Otolaryngol. Jpn. 74, 1572-1579.

Hirano, M. (1972) Physiological aspects of laryngeal adjustments. J. Logoped. Phoniat. Jpn. 13, 63-66.

Hirano, M. (1975) Phonosurgery. Basic and clinical investigations. Otologia (Fukuoka), 21, 239-440.

Hirano, M., Miyahara, T., Miyagi, T. et al. (1971) Vocal regulation in singing. An experimental study in a professional singer. J. Otolaryngol. Jpn. 74, 1189-1201.

Hirano, M. and Ohala, J. (1969) Use of hooked-wire electrodes for electromyography of the intrinsic laryngeal muscles. J. Speech Hearing Res. 12, 362-372.

Hirano, M., Ohala, J. and Vennard, W. (1969) The function of laryngeal muscles in regulating fundamental frequency and intensity of phonation. J. Speech Hearing Res. 12, 616-628.

Hirano, M., Vennard, W. and Ohala, J. (1970) Regulation of register, pitch and intensity of voice. An electromyographic investigation of intrinsic laryngeal muscles. Folia Phoniat. 22, 1-20.

DISCUSSION

Baer: Are registers defined perceptually or on the basis of their physiology?

Hirano: Perceptually.

Strong: Do you think that we need to define the terms more clearly? I refer particularly to: (1) the registers, and (2) the subdivisions of the modal register. Then we can all use the same terms.

Hirano: The registers of voice were first defined perceptually by singers. But it has been revealed that the registers can be defined on the basis of the vibratory pattern of the vocal fold, which is determined chiefly by laryngeal adjustment. There are three major registers: vocal fry, modal, and falsetto registers. The vocal fry is characterized by an extremely long closed phase relative to one vibratory cycle. For the modal register there is a moderate length of the closed phase. In falsetto, there is no closed phase or complete glottal closure. The modal register, in turn, is classified into three subdivisions: chest, mid, and head registers.
There are, however, conflicting opinions about classification of voice register. There are also different terminologies. I think the following classification appears to be most agreeable:

1. Vocal fry register (glottal fry)
2. Modal register (heavy register)
   a. chest register
   b. mid register
   c. head register
3. Falsetto register (light register)

Titze: Within the major laryngeal registers chest (modal), falsetto, and fry, there seem to be secondary registers that are governed by acoustic loading of the vocal folds by the vocal tract. Such secondary registers are very important to voice teachers in voice classification and modification of the sound in different frequency ranges. Secondary registers are often elicited by vowel modification. Much research is needed to identify the acoustic and physiologic difference of these minor registers.

While we are talking about conventions, is there any evidence that spelling out the first two letters AB and AD in "abduction" and "adduction" is associated with a perceptual advantage? Would it not be as effective to articulate a little clearer?

Hirano: I learned the way to spell out the first two letters two days ago from Dr. Strong. For me, this is easier than to articulate carefully and clearly.

Hirose: Most of your figures, we can observe small perturbations of F_0 which seem to indicate the phenomenon of "vibrato". It also appears that there are fluctuations of EMG activities of CT, VOC and LCA, corresponding to F_0 perturbations. Do you think that "vibrato" is controlled by these muscles?

Hirano: Yes. The periodic changes in F_0 represent vibrato. All of the muscles CT, LCA and VOC present periodic changes in their activity corresponding to the F_0 changes in the samples you referred to. I believe that the vibrato is produced by intrinsic laryngeal muscles. But the muscle(s) involved in vibrato production may vary.

Fujimura: Strap muscles seem to function cooperatively in the sense that, even when individual muscles within the group do not show consistent activities, we seem to find that either of them (e.g., the sternothyroid or the sternohyoid) shows some activity for lowering pitch. My conjecture has been that there is a balance function of the complex of the muscles with respect to, let us say, the position of the hyoid bone, based on afferent feedback, and this is reflected in the timing relation between EMG patterns and physical consequences like pitch change (no delay indicates indirect casual relation). Are there any timing data of strap muscles in singing concerning sudden pitch change in connection with removals of such muscles?

Hirano: Several investigators, including ourselves, have revealed electromyographically that many extrinsic laryngeal muscles present an increase in activity for very low and very high pitches. The mechanism of how the extrinsic muscles affect the fundamental frequency, however, is not very clear yet. We have no data with respect to timing as you suggested, but this point is worth investigating.

Isshiki: Thank you for your very clear-cut explanation for pitch and intensity control by the laryngeal muscles. What is not very clear to me is the pitch control in falsetto. You mentioned that the cricothyroid muscle, lateral cricoarytenoid muscle and vocalis muscle are not contributing much to pitch change at falsetto. What is the rank order of these muscles in the control of vocal pitch at falsetto? Do you find that the individual variation is great?

Hirano: As described in the paper, in any sample at least one of the three muscles presented activities positively relates to pitch. There seemed to be not only individual variations but also intra-subject variations as far as pitch control in falsetto is concerned.

CHAPTER 13
THE FUNCTION OF THE EXTRINSIC LARYNGEAL MUSCLES

T. Shin, M. Hirano, T. Maeyama, I. Nozoe, and H. Ohkubo

Department of Otolaryngology, Kurume University, School of Medicine, Kurume, Japan

OUTLINE OF THE EXTRINSIC LARYNGEAL MUSCLES

Recently there has been a considerable advance in studies of laryngeal physiology. It is generally agreed that the movements of the entire larynx are performed by the intrinsic laryngeal muscles in cooperation with the extrinsic laryngeal muscles.

With regard to the "extrinsic" laryngeal muscles, the literature on laryngeal physiology is not specific as to which muscles are to be considered in this category. From our perspective, a large number of muscles participate either indirectly or directly in the functioning of the larynx. These are listed in Table 1, and include:

1. infrahyoid muscles (sternohyoid, sternothyroid, thyrohyoid, omohyoid)
2. suprahyoid muscles (digastric, stylohyoid, mylohyoid, geniohyoid)
3. pharyngeal constrictor muscles (superior pharyngeal constrictor, hyopharyngeal, thyropharyngeal, cricopharyngeal)
4. extrinsic tongue muscles (styloglossus, hyoglossus, genioglossus).

In addition to these muscles (detailed in Table 1), the intrinsic tongue muscles, masseter and facial muscles and others might also be included.

In spite of the importance of the extrinsic laryngeal muscles for the function of the larynx, they have been given little consideration. The animal experiments reported in this paper were designed to determine the influence of activation or deletion of selected extrinsic laryngeal muscles upon laryngeal movements.

Table 1. Extrinsic laryngeal muscles.

1. Infrahyoid muscle	Sternohyoid M. Sternothyroid M. Thyrohyoid M. Omohyoid M.
2. Suprahyoid muscle	Digastric M. Stylohyoid M. Mylohyoid M. Geniohyoid M.
3. Pharyngeal constrictor muscle	Superior pharyngeal constrictor Hyopharyngeal M. Thyropharyngeal M. Cricopharyngeal M.
4. Extrinsic tongue muscle	Styloglossus Hyoglossus Genioglossus

INFLUENCES OF ACTIVATION OF EXTRINSIC LARYNGEAL MUSCLES ON POSITION AND SHAPE IN THE LARYNX

Larynges of mongrel dogs were used as the experimental material. A vertical midline incision was introduced to permit adequate exposure of some selected muscles and their neural supply. Laryngeal movements were observed by means of a suspension laryngoscope. Because the tip of a suspension laryngoscope was placed on the vallecula, it was necessary to take especial care not to disturb the natural movement of the larynx. After the identification of the motor nerves, a supramaximal stimulus was applied directly to each nerve. The laryngeal movements elicited by this stimulation were recorded by use of a movie camera for later detailed examination.

A part of the findings from the first experiment is shown in Table 2. Although different states of movement were observed, stimulation of the suprahyoid muscles and the thyrohyoid muscles caused the larynx to move upward and in a ventral direction. By contrast, stimulation of the sternohyoid and sternothyroid caused the larynx to move downward and in either a dorsal or a ventral direction. On the other hand, the vocal folds were lengthened and hence tensed slightly when the thyrohyoid and sternothyroid were stimulated individually. Stimulation of the inferior pharyngeal constrictor resulted in only slight changes of the larynx; the epiglottis moved backward, and the vocal folds moved somewhat toward the midline.

INFLUENCES OF DELETION OF EXTRINSIC LARYNGEAL MUSCLES ON LARYNGEAL MOVEMENTS

In this series of experiments, we studied how the laryngeal elevation and closure during reflex swallowing is affected by deletion of given muscle(s). The swallowing was induced by either stimulation of the internal branch of the superior laryngeal nerve or by pouring a small amount of water on the epiglottis. The related muscles were denervated in various combinations. Reflex swallowing movements elicited by stimulation were extremely consistent. The same surgical procedure was performed in this experiment as in the first series presented above.

1. Effects of the Deletion of Extrinsic Laryngeal Muscles on Elevation of Hyoid Bone and Thyroid Cartilage during Deglutition.

Measurements of thyroid cartilage and hyoid bone elevation during deglutition before and after functional deletion of selected muscles were obtained from polygraph recordings. The results from this series of experiments are shown in Figs.1, 2, and 3, and are also summarized in Table 3. The apparent function of each of the mucles listed in Table 3 is indicated by the influence of their removal upon laryngeal elevation. That is, a plus (+) indicates that removal of a muscle resulted in an increase in thyroid cartilage and hyoid bone elevation, and hence the normal function of that muscle is presumed to be one of providing a downward force on these structures. Conversely, a minus (-) reflects a muscle function of elevating the thyroid cartilage or hyoid bone. Zero (0) indicates that laryngeal elevation occurs in a way similar to that in the control, viz., no significant change was observed. The results of this series of experiments, as summarized in Table 3 and Figs.1-3, yield the following conclusions:

Table 2. Movements of the larynx and the vocal fold caused by electrical stimulation of extrinsic laryngeal muscles observed under a suspension laryngoscope. A + indicates a significant movement, and a (+) indicates a smaller, less consistent movement.

Muscle Stimulated	Entire larynx				Vocal cord			
	Up	Down	Fore	Back	Elong.	Shorten.	Adduct.	Adduct.
Stylohyoid	(+)							
Digast. (ant.)	(+)							
Digast. (post.)	(+)							
Mylohyoid	+		+					
Geniohyoid	+		+			+		
Thyrohyoid	+		+		+			
Sternohyoid		+		+				
Sternothyroid		+	+		+			+
Hyopharyng.	+						+	
Thyropharyng.						+	+	
Cricopharyng.						+		

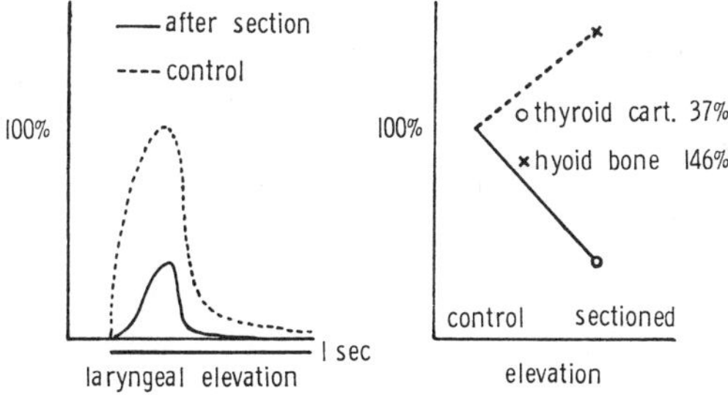

Fig.1. Changes in elevation of the thyroid cartilage and hyoid bone after section of the thyrohyoid muscle. Solid curve in the left panel shows up and down movements of the larynx. The laryngeal movement is apparently inhibited. Solid line on the right side shows the elevation of the thyroid cartilage. Dotted line shows the elevation of the hyoid bone. The elevation of the hyoid bone is increased relative to that of the control.

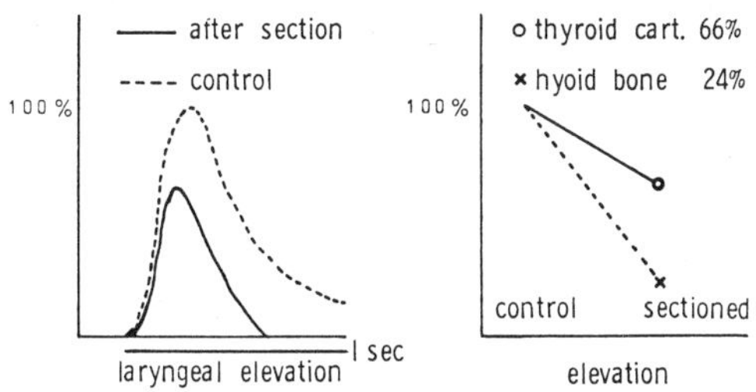

Fig.2. Changes in elevation of the thyroid cartilage and hyoid bone after section of the suprahyoid muscles. The elevation of both thyroid cartilate and hyoid bone are inhibited. The laryngeal elevation, however, remains relatively more active than that for the previous condition shown in Fig.1.

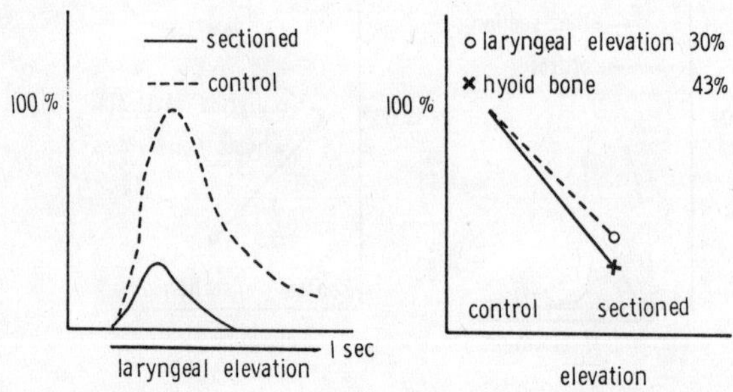

Fig.3. Changes in elevation of the thyroid cartilage and hyoid bone after section of the suprahyoid and thyrohyoid muscles. The laryngeal elevation is markedly disturbed, compared with Fig.1 and Fig.2.

Table 3. Effects of deletion of extrinsic laryngeal muscles on elevation of hyoid bone and thyroid cartilage during deglutition.

Muscle deleted	Hyoid bone	Thyroid cart.
Tongue muscles*	-2	-1
Stylohyoid	-1	0
Digastric	0	0
Mylohyoid	-1	0
Geniohyoid	-3	-2
Thyrohyoid	+2	-3
Sternohyoid	+1	+1
Sternothyroid	+1	+1
Hypopharyng.	+1	0
Thyropharyng.	0	0
Cricopharyng.	0	0

Degree of elevation compared with control is presented in the following ways.

+1: Slightly increased.
+2: Moderately increased.
+3: Greatly increased.
0: No significant change.
-1: Slightly decreased.
-2: Moderately decreased.
-3: Greatly decreased.

*Hypoglossal nerve dissected.

1) The geniohyoid and thyrohyoid muscles play the most important role in elevating the larynx.
2) The mylohyoid, stylohyoid, and tongue muscles participate in elevation of the larynx to some extent.
3) The sternohyoid and sternothyroid muscles may have an antagonistic action to laryngeal elevation.

2. Effects of Deletion of Extrinsic Laryngeal Muscles on Closure of the Larynx during Deglutition

Closure of the larynx during reflex swallowing was photographed with a 16 mm movie system under a suspension laryngoscope. The movements were analyzed using frame-by-frame analysis. The results from this series of experiments are shown in Figs. 4, 5, 6, 7, and 8. Figure 4 shows the inward movements of the laryngeal structures during swallowing. An inward movement is represented by a downward excursion of the curves. In the normal dogs, the arytenoids and vocal folds closed completely with a consistent time program during swallowing. It has generally been accepted that laryngeal closure is controlled by the contraction of the intrinsic laryngeal muscles which are innervated by the recurrent laryngeal nerves. After the recurrent laryngeal nerves were sectioned bilaterally, the closure of the larynx was markedly weakened. It is, however, important to note that, even in this situation, a complete closure of the larynx still takes place, even though the closure duration is shortened substantially (Fig.5).

After section of the bilateral inferior constrictor muscles, the laryngeal movements are still similar to that of the control shown previously; no significant disturbance in the laryngeal closure was observed during the reflex swallowing, as shown in Fig.6.

Figure 7 shows the movements of the laryngeal structures during reflex swallowing with both recurrent laryngeal nerves and inferior pharyngeal muscles sectioned. Compared with the previous two experimental conditions, the closure of the larynx was even weaker. Surprisingly, however, in this third condition, some closing movements of the laryngeal aperture still remained.

After section of the recurrent laryngeal nerves, inferior constrictors, and suprahyoid muscles, the closure of the larynx is affected markedly and there is no glottic closure at all.

From the results of this series of the experiments, the following conclusions appear to be justified:

(1) The intrinsic laryngeal muscles play the most important role in the laryngeal closure mechanism.
(2) The closure of the larynx is caused not only by the intrinsic laryngeal muscles but also by other muscles in some conditions.

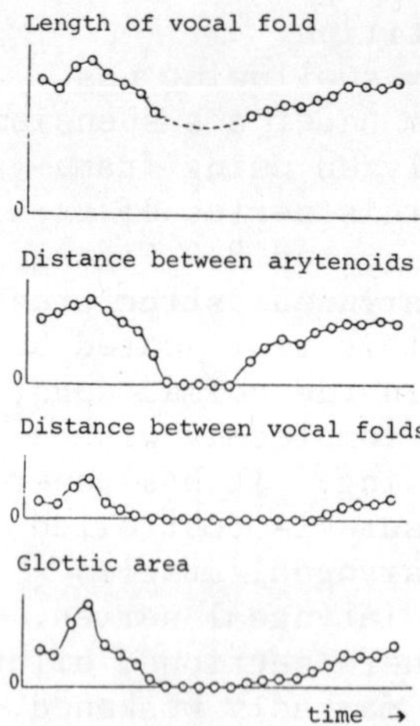

Fig.4. Laryngeal closure during deglutition observed through a suspension laryngoscope. Control condition.

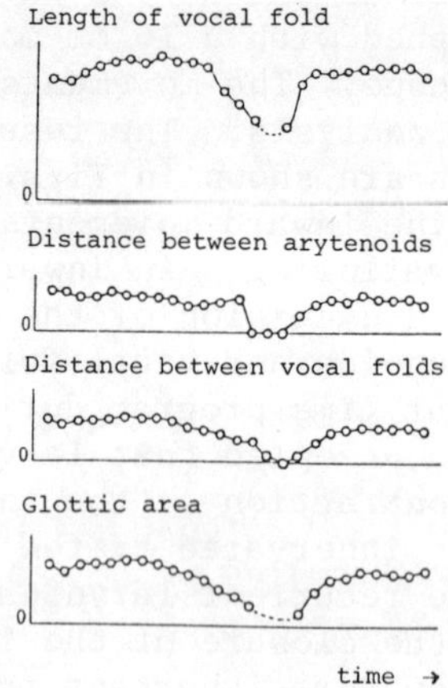

Fig.5. Laryngeal closure during deglutition observed through a suspension laryngoscope. Bilateral recurrent laryngeal nerves sectioned.

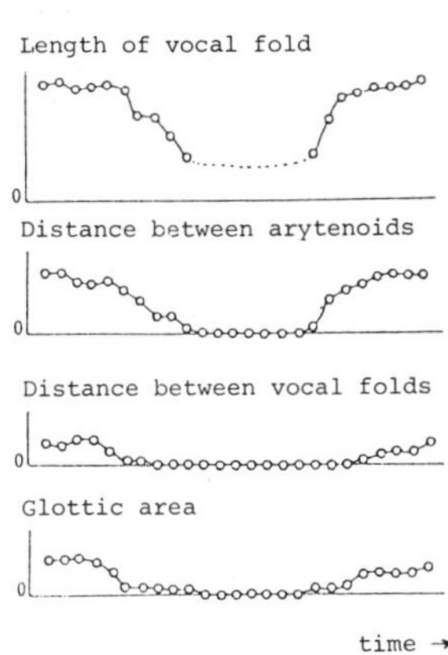

Fig.6. Laryngeal closure during deglutition observed through a suspension laryngoscope. Bilateral inferior pharyngeal constrictors sectioned.

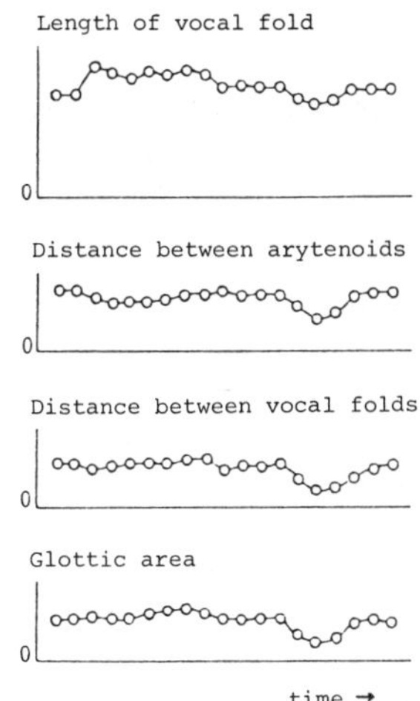

Fig.7. Laryngeal closure during deglutition observed through a suspension laryngoscope. Bilateral recurrent laryngeal nerves and inferior pharyngeal constrictors sectioned.

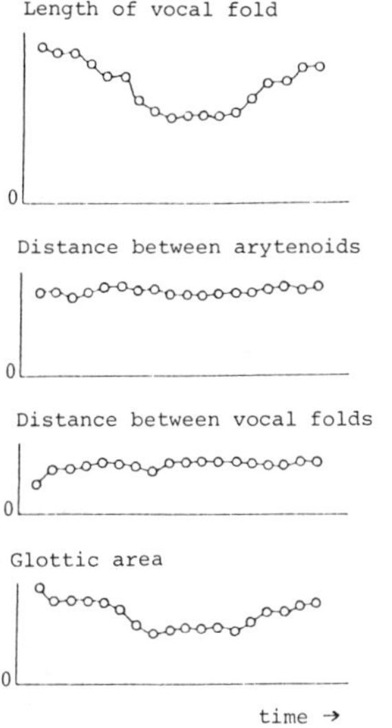

Fig.8. Laryngeal closure during degulutition observed through a suspension laryngoscope. Bilateral recurrent laryngeal nerves, middle and inferior pharyngeal constrictors, and suprahyoid muscles sectioned.

ACKNOWLEDGMENTS

This investigation was supported in part by a Grant-in-Aid for Scientific Research (No. 337040, 557402), the Ministry of Education, Science and Culture.

REFERENCES

Hirano, M., et al. (1967) The sternohyoid muscle during phonation: Electromyographic studies. Acta Oto-Laryng. 64; 500-507.

Hirano, M. (1975) Phonosurgery: Basic and clinical investigations. Otologia (Fukuoka). 21; 239-440.

Kunitake, H. (1971) Electromyographic studies of the extrinsic laryngeal muscles. Jap. Jour. Otol. Tokyo 74; 57-90.

Maeyama, T. (1975) Experimental investigation of the function of the intrinsic and extrinsic laryngeal muscles during deglutition, especially for elevation of the larynx. Otologia (Fukuoka) 21; 787-807.

Nozoe, I. (1975) The closure of the larynx during deglutition. Otologia (Fukuoka) 21; 762-786.

Shin, T. (1975) Closure of the larynx during swallowing. J. Jpn. Bronchoesophagl. 26; 131-142.

Sonninen, A.A. (1956) The role of the extrinsic laryngeal muscles in length-adjustment of the vocal cords in singing. Acta Oto-laryng. Supple. 130; 10-102.

CHAPTER 14
SUB- AND SUPRAGLOTTAL PRESSURE VARIATION DURING PHONATION

Yasuo Koike

Department of Otolaryngology,
Kinki University School of Medicine,
Osaka, Japan

The air-pressure variation in the vocal mechanism is one of the most important physiological variables related to phonation. The subglottal pressure behavior, for example, is known to be essential in controlling some basic speech features such as fundamental frequency and intensity. Articulations rely heavily upon the management of supraglottal air pressure. There are certain types of speech disorders attributable to defective adjustments of these pressures. Numerous studies, therefore, have been conducted on this topic from several disciplinary perspectives.

Information regarding air-pressure phenomena within the vocal mechanism is, however, still limited at this time, despite the widespread need and interest just noted. The paucity of this information seems to be based upon the technical difficulty of obtaining empirical data. Although the larynx and the trachea lie immediately under the skin in the anterior neck, and the direct distance from the skin surface to the subglottal space is quite small, this does not necessarily imply that the subglottal space is easily accessible from the outside world. If injury to the skin is to be avoided, the sub- and supraglottal spaces are in fact rather inaccessible for study. The subglottal portion of the trachea is particularly isolated during phonation, since it becomes a closed space while the glottis is closed for vocing.

Many methods have thus been devised to obtain records of subglottal or supraglottal pressure. These methods include some indirect techniques as well as certain direct procedures of recording.

Fry et al. (1952) showed that intraesophageal pressure changes are reflections of intrathoracic pressure changes. Van den Berg (1956), and Draper et al. (1959) tried to employ esophageal pressure as an estimate of subglottal pressure. A balloon was inserted into the esophagus by means of a connecting tube with a pressure transducer attached to its exterior end.

The validity of such indirect methods has been investigated (cf. McGlone (1967), Kunze (1964), and Lieberman (1968)) by comparing the esophageal pressure data directly with the subglottal pressure signal derived from a tracheal puncture. Although these authors are not in complete agreement, it seems that an esophageal balloon system can yield a reasonable estimate of subglottal pressure under certain limited conditions. If properly interpreted, these indirect methods may be useful in some types of research such as the analysis of prosodic features. The frequency bandwidth of such measurement systems is considerably limited because of the intervening tissues and structures between the subglottal space and the pressure sensing device. It is apparent that this limitation makes the study of the rapid pressure variations that occur during the vibratory cycle of the vocal folds less meaningful, even though Anthony and Maclachlan (1969) somewhat improved the frequency response of an indirect measurement system by placing a miniaturized transducer in the baloon.

The most commonly adopted approach to reaching the subglottal space has been the use of a puncture needle. Although this method can provide a direct means of measuring air pressure in the subglottal space, there exist some problems which require serious consideration. In addition to the pain and permanent scar formation at the neck, there are considerable medical risks involved. For example, the isthmus of the thyroid gland, including the anterior branch of the superior thyroid artery, occupies a considerable space in front of the trachea. Injury to this artery may develop a large hemorrhage. Subcutaneous emphysema may occur after the puncture. It seems apparent also, that this type of study should not be often repeated on the same subject. This consideration implies that the ability to test intra-subject reliability with such a procedure is rather limited. An alternative method for direct measurement of subglottal pressure wad developed by van den Berg (1956), who inserted a thin polyethylene catheter through the glottis.

Although this was a remarkable improvement, the frequency bandwidth of the measurement system was seriously limited because of the low pass filter effect of the long catheter between the transducer and the point of measurement in the trachea. A similar frequency response limitation holds true with the various methods of measuring supraglottal pressure. Most of the supraglottal pressure data has been obtained by inserting a tube into the pharynx either through the oral cavity or through the nasal cavity and the nasopharynx. Here again, the frequency bandwidth of the system is considerably limited.

The problem of frequency bandwidth with respect to both sub- and supraglottal pressure measurement was minimized by Koike and Perkins (1968, 1969) by introducing a miniaturized pressure transducer directly into the sub- or supraglottal space. Since the sensor is placed directly at a desired location in the speech mechanism, the problem of time lag and attenuation of higher frequencies has been minimized. The wide frequency bandwidth of the miniaturized transducers has made possible the analysis of a rapid wave, such as the vibratory pressure variation in the subglottal space or in the supraglottal area. This type of transducer is, however, fairly sensitive to temperature variations. It is possible to avoid the artifact due to temperature shift by selecting an appropriate frequency band for the analysis, since the response of the transducer to temperature variations in the vocal mechanism is much slower than the vibratory air-pressure variations.

Because of the apparent paucity of this type of empirical data, the author has attempted to study the vibratory air-pressure variations in the subglottal space, and in the supraglottal area, with this newly developed procedure.

METHOD

The vibratory air-pressure variation in the trachea was sensed by a miniaturized pressure transducer (Whittaker 1015C) placed in the trachea approximately 4 cm below the glottis. A detailed description of this type of transducer and of the technique of placement is provided elsewhere (Koike and Perkins, 1968; Koike, 1978). The supraglottal air-pressure variation was simultaneously picked up by a second identical transducer. The cables of the two transducers were bundled together so that the distance between the two transducers was fixed at 8 cm.

The output of each transducer was amplified and recorded respectively on a separate channel of an FM tape recorder (Hewlett Packard 3917B). The -3dB bandwidth of each transducer system was from DC to 5 kHz. Because the focus of the present study was upon the rapid pressure changes associated with vibratory behavior, a high-pass filter (50 Hz) was applied to the data prior to the analysis. The acoustic speech signal was recorded, via a microphone (Electrovoice 642) and an amplifier (Knight 966), on the third channel of the FM recorder.

The subject was a Japanese adult male (Y.K.) with a normal larynx. Surface anesthesia with 4% Xylocaine was applied, and the transducer bundle was introduced through the nasal cavity and the nasopharynx. The positions of the transducers were monitored with a laryngeal mirror. The subject sustained different vowels for various phonatory conditions, and produced limited speech utterances, including several different consonants.

The recorded signals were reproduced, digitized and stored on a magnetic disk controlled by a PDP-11/20 computer. The sampling rate was 10,000/sec. per channel. The tape speed of the FM recorder was reduced by a factor of four during the digitization in order to increase the relative sampling rate. The waveforms of the data were then graphically displayed on a CRT screen (Tektronix 4010) with the aid of a software system (SCRL ILS).

RESULTS

A typical pair of pressure waveforms is shown in Fig.1. The upper tracing gives the supraglottal pressure variation for the vowel [u], and the lower tracing denotes the corresponding subglottal pressure waveform as a function of time. From this waveform, it can be seen that the dominant negative peaks in the supraglottal pressure wave closely coincide with the dominant positive peaks in the subglottal pressure wave. This relationship between the supraglottal and the subglottal waveforms was consistently observed, regardless of the type of vowel or other phonatory conditions, as will be discussed.

The supraglottal pressure waveform was seen to vary greatly depending upon the type of vowel. The negative peaks corresponding to the fundamental vibratory cycle, nevertheless, were rather clear and easy to identify.

Figure 2, for example, demonstrates the pressure waveform for the vowel [a]. It is apparent that the supraglottal pressure waveform is different from that in Fig.1, though the negative dominant peaks are obviously identifiable.

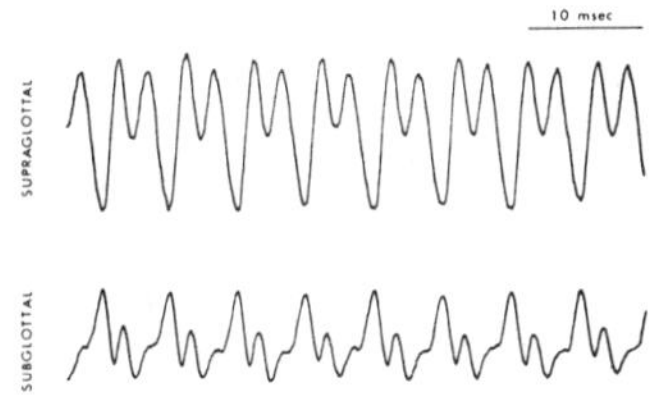

Fig.1. The sub- and supraglottal pressure waveforms for the vowel /u/.

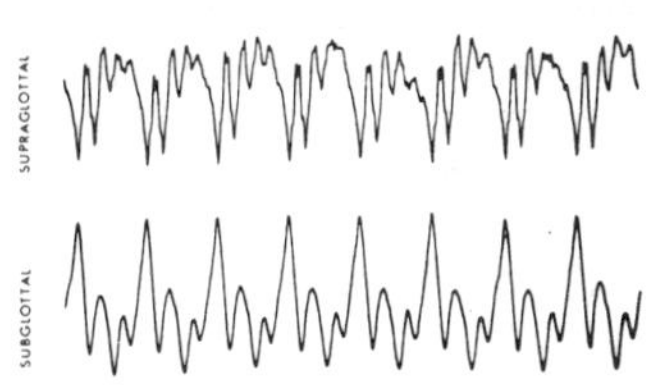

Fig.2. The sub- and supraglottal pressure waveforms for the vowel /a/.

Contrary to the supraglottal pressure wave, the waveform of the subglottal pressure variation was found to be quite stable. As seen in Fig.2, the major features of the subglottal pressure wave are quite similar to those shown in Fig.1. Apparentaly, the behavior of the supraglottal vocal tract does not remarkably affect the subglottal waveform, due probably to the high glottal impedance during phonation. The effect of changing the intensity of voice on the subglottal waveform is illustrated in Fig.3. The tracings represent, from the top to the bottom, a soft, a moderate, and a loud voice. The timing of the minor peaks, indicative of subglottal resonance, are rather invariant despite the change in the overall amplitude.

As shown in Fig.4, obvious similarity was found between the supraglottal pressure waveshape and the acoustic waveform observed simultaneously. The acoustic signal lags the supraglottal waveform slightly, probably because of the distance from the glottis to the microphone. In some instances the negative dominant peaks in the acoustic wave were less clear than those in the supraglottal pressure wave.

The coincidence of the dominant negative peaks in the supraglottal pressure wave and the dominant positive peaks in the subglottal pressure variation was not affected by changes in the fundamental frequency (F_0). Figure 5 shows this coincidence at four different fundamental frequencies. The upper four tracings denote the supraglottal pressure waveforms at four different values of F_0, and the lower four tracings reveal the subglottal pressure waveshape at each corresponding value of F_0. As indicated by the vertical lines in this figure, the dominant negative peaks in the supraglottal pressure wave correspond closely to the dominant positive peaks in the subglottal pressure signal, in spite of the shift in the fundamental frequency.

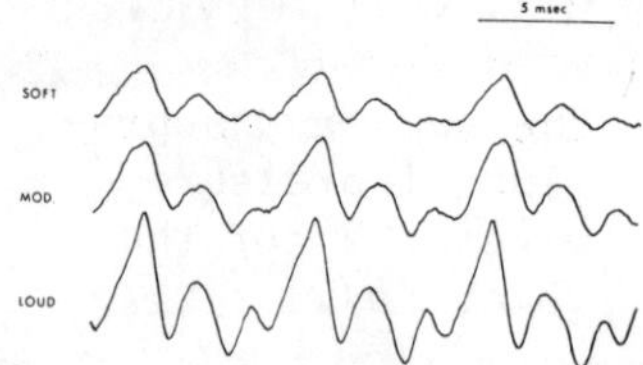

Fig.3. The effect of changing intensity upon subglottal pressure wave. Tracings denote, from top to bottom, a soft, a moderate, and a loud voice. The vowel is /a/.

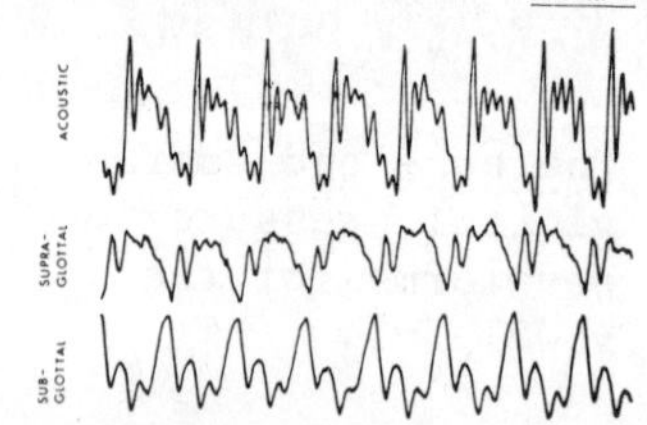

Fig.4. The acoustic speech wave (top tracing) and the air-pressure variations in the supra- and subglottal regions for the vowel /a/.

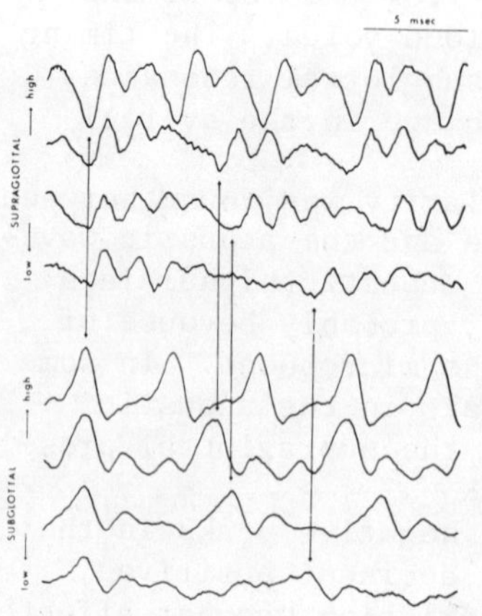

Fig.5. The effect of changing fundamental frequency upon the supraglottal pressure wave (upper four tracings) and the subglottal pressure variation (lower four tracings). Each vertical line connects a set of signals at a corresponding value of fundamental frequency.

The same relationship held true with falsetto voicing (Fig.6), and with phonations at various intensity levels. This coincidence was also confirmed for limited speech syllables with some consonants, as seen in Fig.7 which reveals the supra- and subglottal pressure waveforms for the utterance [aha]. While the glottis is open, an apparent noise, indicative of glottal eddies, is observed in the upper tracing as well.

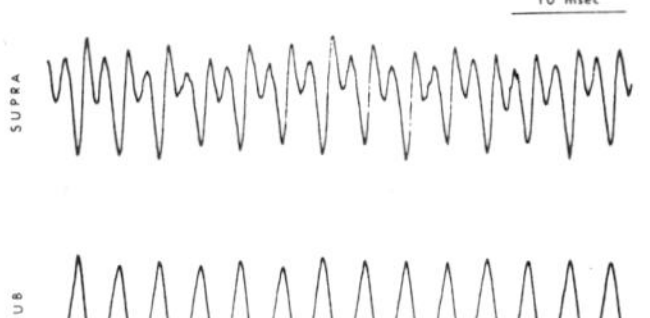

Fig.6. The sub- and supraglottal pressure waveforms for falsetto voicing.

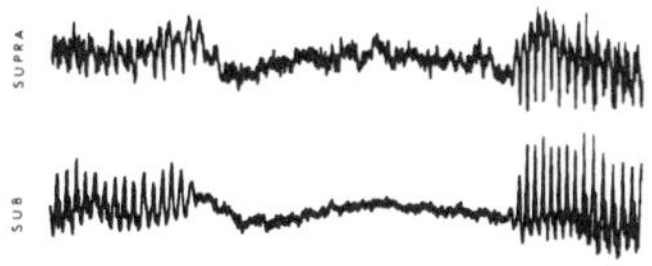

Fig.7. The sub- and supraglottal pressure waveforms during the utterance /aha/.

DISCUSSION

On the basis of the results presented above, it seems justifiable to suggest that there exists a close coincidence between the negative dominant peaks in the supraglottal pressure wave and the dominant positive peaks in the subglottal pressure variation. This coincidence is interesting because the supraglottal vocal tract is relatively independent of the subglottal air space during phonation, and the shape and the size of the vocal tract varies greatly depending upon the articulatory conditions. The supraglottal pressure could in principle behave more independently from the subglottal pressure variation.

The coincident of the peaks mentioned above, therefore, may indicate a rather strong and invariant relationship between the vocal tract and the subglottal air system. If both peaks may result from the same cause there has to be an underlying physical condition that assures this precise coincidence of the peaks regardless of the articulatory movements. The relationship between the sub- and supraglottal pressure waves may prove helpful, then, in elucidating certain aspects of the physiological mechanism of phonation. It is quite conceivable that the negative dominant peaks in the supraglottal pressure wave represent the moments of vocal tract excitation, judging from the apparently large amount of energy at this point. If this is the case, it would be feasible to predict the moment of vocal tract excitation from either pressure wave.

This moment of excitation may be related, furthermore, to the physiological glottal behavior, since it is known that the positive dominant peaks in the subglottal pressure wave coincide with the glottal minima (Koike and Hirano, 1973). It seems apparent that the relationship between the glottal motion and the acoustic events above and below the glottis needs to be further explicated. This type of knowledge should provide, in turn, a solid basis for certain technical areas such as linear prediction.

SUMMARY

The vibratory air-pressure variation in the subglottal space was recorded simultaneously with the vibratory pressure change in the supraglottal area and the acoustic speech wave on one male subject. A pair of identical miniaturized pressure transducers was employed to sense the pressures directly inside the vocal mechanism. It was shown that the positive dominant peaks in the subglottal pressure wave coincide closely with the negative dominant peaks in the supraglottal pressure variation. It was observed that the behavior of the supraglottal vocal tract does not remarkably affect the waveform of the subglottal pressure variation. The need for study of the relationship between the physiological motion of the glottis and the acoustic events in the larynx was emphasized.

ACKNOWLEDGMENTS

The author is indebted to Dr. David Broad for valuable suggestions and assistance. This study was supported, in part, by a Grant-in-Aid for Co-operative Research (No. 337040) from the Ministry of Education, Science and Culture of Japan.

REFERENCES

Anthony, J.K.F. and Maclachlan, D. (1969) A small transducer for sub-glottal pressure measurement. Work in Progress No. 3, 56-59, Dept. Phonetics and Linguistics, Edinburgh Univ.

Draper, M.H. et al. (1959) Respiratory muscles in speech. J. Speech Hearing Res. 2, 16-27.

Fry, D.L. et al. (1952) The measurement of intra-esophageal pressure and its relationship to intra-thoracic pressure. J. Lab. Clin. Med. 40, 664-673.

Koike, Y. (1978) A method for direct determination of subglottal pressure and its applications (Japanese text). Japan J. Logoped. Phoniat. 19, 212-216.

Koike, Y. and Hirano, M. (1973) Glottal-area time function and subglottal-pressure variation. J. Acoust. Soc. Am. 54, 1618-1627.

Koike, Y. and Perkins, W. (1968) Application of a miniaturized pressure tranducer for experimental speech research. Folia Phoniatrica 20, 360-368.

Kunze, L.H. (1964) Evaluation of methods of estimating subglottal air pressure. J. Speech Hearing Res. 7, 151-164.

Lieberman, P. (1968) Direct comparison of subglottal and esophageal pressure during speech. J. Acoust. Soc. Am. 43, 1157-1164.

McGlone, R.E. (1967) Intraesophageal pressure during syllable repetition. J. Acoust. Soc. Am. 42, 1208(A).

Perkins, W. and Koike, Y. (1969) Patterns of subglottal pressure variations during phonation. Folia Phoniatrica 21, 1-8.

Van den Berg, J.W. (1956) Direct and indirect determination of the mean subglottic pressure. Folia Phoniatrica 8, 1-24.

DISCUSSION

Rothenberg: How close to the glottis can the upper transducer be placed? If it can be placed very close, the pressure recorded can be very useful in measuring the effect of source-tract acoustic interaction. The strong negative peaks in the supraglottal pressure are apparently due to the inertive supraglottal impedance, and act to sustain the glottal flow as the vocal folds close, until the sealing of the vocal folds forces the flow to zero. This cause the skew in the flow waveform discussed in my paper at this conference (Chapter 21).

Koike: Because of the anatomical conditions such as the existence of the false vocal folds, the closest distance one can reach with the above mentioned procedure would be approximately 1 cm from the glottis.

Stevens: The sound-pressure waves of opposite polarities above and below the glottis would be expected since the acoustic excitation of the supra- and subglottal cavities is the same volume-velocity waveform but of opposite sign. The lowest natural frequencies of the supra- and subglottal regions dominate the sound-pressure response, and these two frequencies are roughly equal for a neutral supraglottal configuration — roughly 500 Hz.

Titze: The point of closure is the point where the supraglottal pressure is minimum. The maximum radiated acoustic pressure seems to be delayed by no more than 1 - 2 milliseconds in Dr. Koike's diagram, based on the indicated time scale. This seems to be a reasonable acoustic delay.

Fujimura: You are probably too modest in drawing conclusions concerning implications of your data. Not only are the positive and negative peaks in sub- and supraglottal pressure related to each other, but also the waveforms during the closure period seem to be well related to each other. This is good material to be discussed quantitatively in the light of models---two-mass or multi-element like Titze's. That is, we can interprete your data with these models and at the same time evaluate the validity of the models in light of the observed data.

I also wonder if it is too much to ask to place another transducer at a different depth in the trachea, so that we can learn more about the subglottal system. Even though I appreciate the study of Ishizaka et al. [K. Ishizaka, M. Matsudaira, and T. Kaneko, Input acoustic-impedance measurement of the subglottal system. J. Acoust. Soc. Am. 60, 190-197 (1976)] on the acoustic characteristics of the subglottal system, we need more data in this area.

Titze: To follow up on Dr. Fujimura's and Dr. Stevens' comments, the glottal volume flow is the link between the subglottal and supraglottal pressures. As the volume flow decreases prior to closure, the supraglottal pressure, which is roughly proportional to the volume flow, decreases. On the other hand, the subglottal pressure increases because there is less pressure drop in the subglottal region as the volume flow decreases. The inverse phase relationship is therefore inevitable.

CHAPTER 15
VOCAL EFFICIENCY INDEX

Nobuhiko Isshiki

Kyoto University, Kyoto, Japan

In patients with a hoarse voice, we usually find that imperfect closure of the glottal gap during phonation naturally causes a continuous leakage of air, thus increasing the mean flow rate. Conversely, too tight a closure of the glottis, such as in spastic dysphonia, decreases the mean flow rate, say below 100 cc/sec or even 80 cc/sec. The airflow rate during phonation can be a good indicator of the glottal condition, assuming the expiratory force is fairly constant. Actually, measurement of airflow during phonation has been well established as a useful diagnostic gauge of laryngeal diseases. It is especially informative in assessing the effectiveness of a treatment, e.g., before and after surgery. Numerous data have already been reported on the measurement of flow rate during phonation.

This paper is concerned with the development of an index of vocal efficiency, which provides a measure of how effectively the airflow is converted into sound at the glottis. Assessment of vocal efficiency really involves many technical problems, such as the characteristics of the flowmeter, and the effect of resonance on the vocal output.

MEASUREMENT OF AIRFLOW

We consider first the characteristics of the flowmeter. Various types of flowmeters are now available for studying airflow rate during phonation. To date, the pneumotachograph is the most popular device for this purpose.

The working principle of a pneumotachograph is based on the fact that the air-pressure drop across a resistance (a screen or numerous parallel tubes) is proportional to the airflow passing through the resistance.

A spirometer also is quite useful and accurate enough, if the information we want is only the mean flow rate during phonation. On the other hand, a hot-wire flowmeter has been regarded by many as inadequate for studying the quick transient phenomena of speech, because the response is too slow. In particular, a hot wire, once cooled by air flow, takes a long time to return to the previous high temperature level.

Recently, a new system has been developed to overcome this drawback of hot-wire systems (as shown in Fig.1). A heated wire is maintained at a constant temperature by a feedback of electric current. That is, cooling of the wire by airflow is instantaneously compensated back to

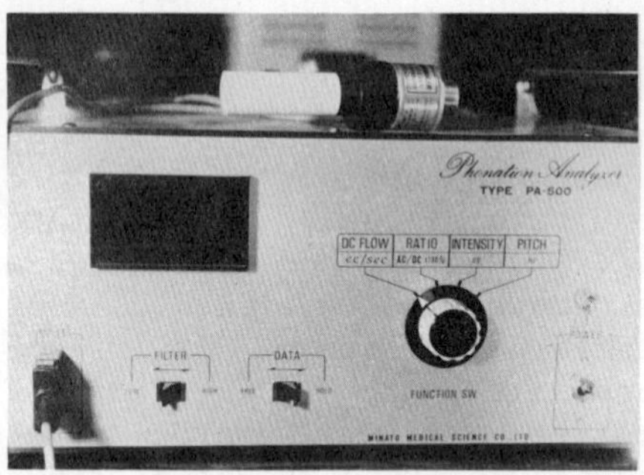

Fig.1. Phonation analyzer consisting of a hot-wire flowmeter and digital displays of the mean airflow rate during phonation, AC/DC, fundamental frequency, and intensity of voice.

the previous temperature level by regulated increase of the electric current to heat the wire. By using a very fine wire, the frequency response can (theoretically) be made nearly flat up to 5 kHz. This finer wire is, however, fragile, and is easily broken. Figure 2 shows the frequency response of a hot-wire flowmeter that we used, which is fairly flat up to about 0.7 kHz. The difference in the electric potential of a heated wire is proportional to the root of the 4th power of velocity of airflow, and this response curve is linearized by an electronic circuit. The final relationship between flow rate and

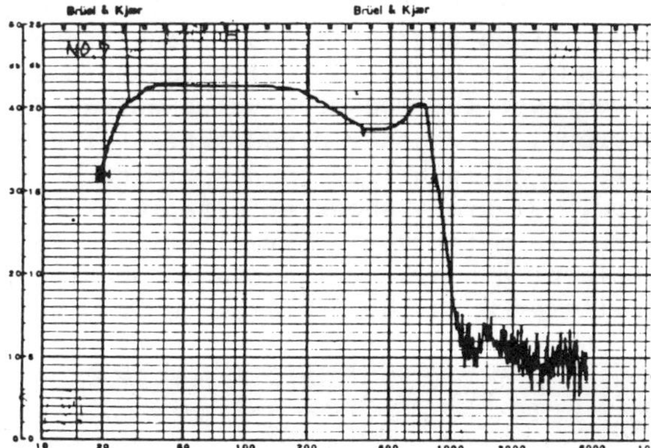

Fig.2. The frequency response of a hot-wire flowmeter used for the study.

the output voltage of the meter is shown in Fig.3. The measured value is also affected by the temperature, moisture, and composition of the gas.

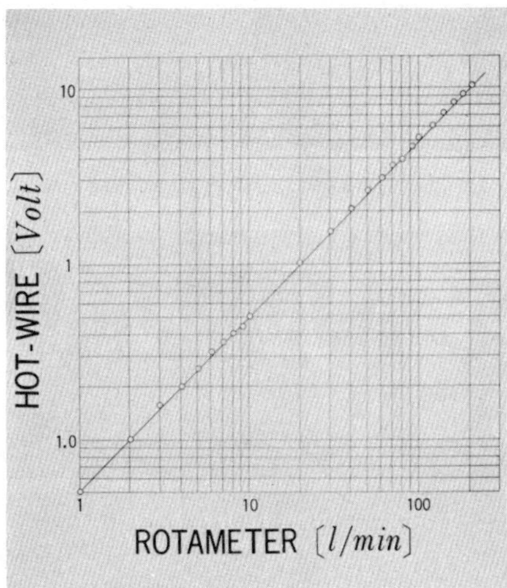

Fig.3. The relationship between the flow rate and output voltage of the hot-wire system.

At a constant temperature, a 10% increase of moisture results in an increase of the measured value by 0.5%, while a one centigrade degree rise of temperature decreases the measure by 0.5%. For clinical purposes, there is no need to correct the measured value unless the environment is extreme. The other disadvantage of the hot-wire flowmeters is an inability to discriminate the direction of airflow. Figure 4 shows an example of the output of the hot-wire flowmeter for a normal voice. Figure 5 shows an example of a hoarse voice due to vocal cord paralysis. The difference in the patterns between a normal

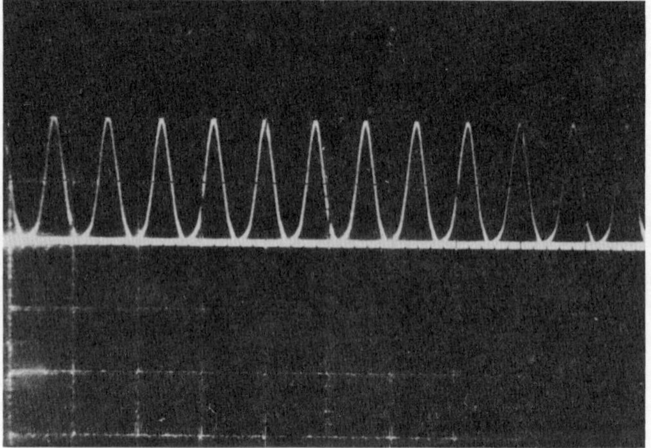

Fig.4. The airflow wave for a normal voice.

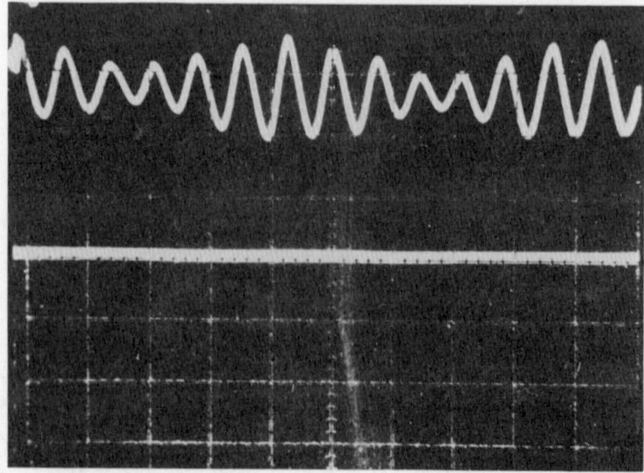

Fig.5. The airflow wave for a hoarse voice (vocal cord paralysis).

and a hoarse voice is that, in the abnormal voice, there is a higher mean flow rate or DC (direct current) component and a lower AC (alternating current) component. This general finding led to the idea that objective measurement of the ratio of the AC component to the DC component may be more meaningful than a simple measurement of the DC component.

DEFINITION OF VOCAL EFFICIENCY

Vocal efficiency may be defined differently from different viewpoints. From a physiological perspective, this index may be defined as the ratio of vocal intensity to the energy consumed by the body for phonation per unit time. The measurement of vocal efficiency in this sense can only be approached roughly by analysis of the expired gas. This type of measurement is apparently impractical as a routine vocal function test.

From the engineering viewpoint, the vocal efficiency may be defined as the ratio of vocal intensity to the glottal power, viz., subglottal air pressure times glottal airflow. Difficulty of measuring subglottal air pressure makes this mechanical vocal efficiency index impractical as a clinical test.

The third item related to vocal efficiency is ratio of AC to DC flow. The glottis functions as a converter of airflow from direct current to alternating current, producing a primary laryngeal tone. In many laryngeal diseases, this glottal converter does not work efficiently. In this sense, the AC/DC ratio (i.e., the effective value of the AC component divided by the mean flow rate) seems meaningful in assessing the glottal function. The AC/DC ratio is not a vocal efficiency measure *per se*, although it reflects how efficiently the larynx is working. Therefore, an AC/DC ratio may better be defined as a vocal efficiency *index* so that confusion with the true vocal efficiency is avoided.

On the supposition that the glottal volume velocity wave can be approximated by triangular waves, we can obtain a rough idea of how the AC/DC ratio changes with variation of the glottal waveform. The four curves in Fig.6 are drawn so that the mean flow rates or DC components are the same for each curve. The abscissa indicates time, and the ordinate volume velocity. The parameter *a* signifies a duty cycle and *T* the period of one cycle.

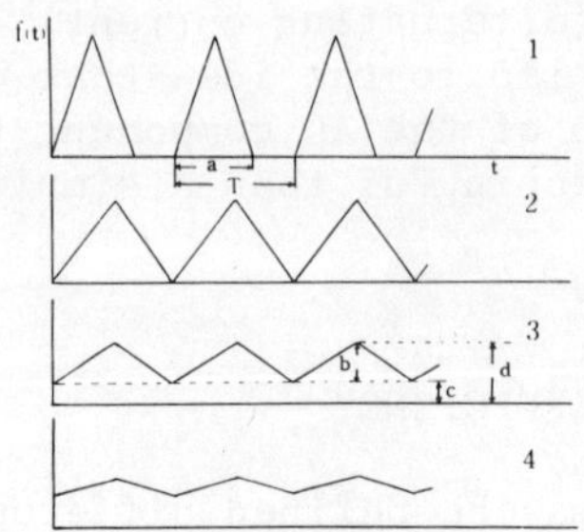

Fig.6. The glottal volume velocity wave can be approximated by triangular waves. It is demonstrated how the AC/DC ratio changes with or without the glottal gap. The four waves are drawn so that the mean flow rates are the same for each of them.

The opening quotient is therefore defined as a/T. If the glottis is closed longer or has a small opening quotient, the glottal wave will become sharp and high in amplitude, producing a more intense voice, which is rich in harmonic components in higher frequency regions. In this case, the larynx can be said to be working very efficiently. With a constant leakage of air, as in the hoarse voice example, the AC component decreases (as shown by the bottom line in Fig.6). If the effective value (root mean square value) of the AC component is calculated, we can determine the vocal efficiency index as a function of the opening quotient and further as a function of the ratio of the minimum to maximum value (c/d in Fig.6). Figure 7 shows the result of calculations from waveforms of this kind. The right side of the middle vertical line represents the rms of AC over DC as a function of the opening quotient, which was already calculated by Flanagan (1972).

The quasi-central vertical line represents the case where the glottis is closed just momentarily, like the second wave in Fig.6. The region to the left of this line represents imperfect closure of the glottis. As shown in Fig.7, the vocal efficiency index is always below 0.5 for the imperfect closure of the glottis. It is clinically important to note that a vocal efficiency index below 0.5 implies a theoretically imperfect closure of the glottis.

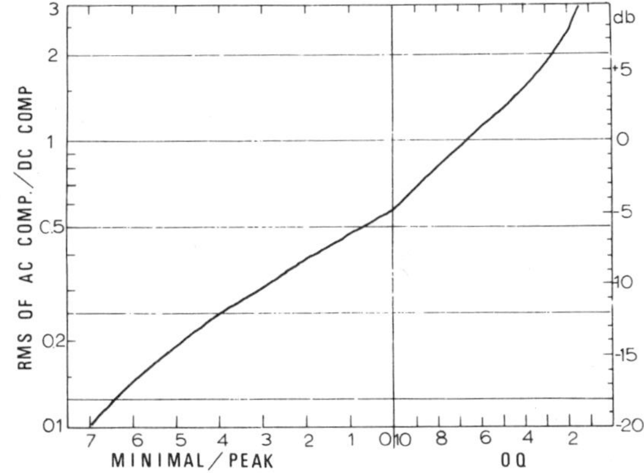

Fig.7. The ratio of the rms value of the AC component to the DC component is plotted for different opening quotients (section of curve to right of vertical line) and for different degrees of imperfect closure of the glottis as specified by the ratio c/d in Fig.6 (section of curve to left of vertical line).

SOME PRELIMINARY RESULTS

We have made a special instrument which permits automatic calculation of the AC/DC ratio as well as digital display of DC flow, fundamental frequency, and amplitude. Figure 8 shows the AC/DC ratio for normals and for patients with various laryngeal diseases. Patients with a large glottal gap showed a very low AC/DC ratio; for instance, the ratio for vocal cord paralysis (with a large gap) always falls below 0.5. Roughly speaking, 0.5 is the critical index value which separates the normal from the imperfect closure of the glottis for the hoarse voice. However, it does not mean that the greater the index, the better the glottal function in a physiologic sense. Hyperfunctional voice such as ventricular phonation shows a very high value, over 0.8.

EFFECTS OF VOCAL-TRACT RESONANCES: THE SONDHI TUBE

We turn now to a discussion of the problems associated

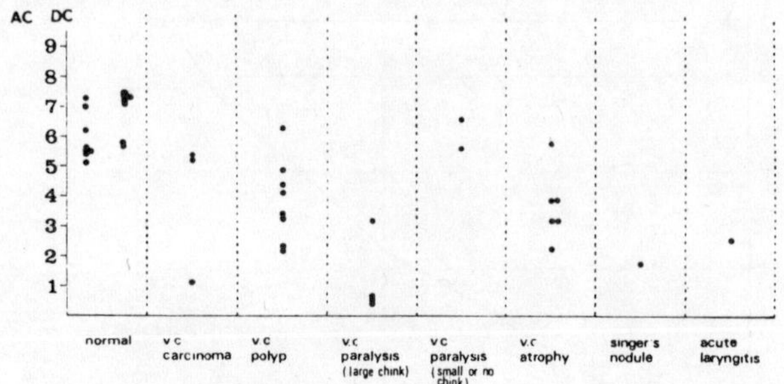

Fig.8. The AC/DC ratio (vocal efficiency index) for normal subjects and patients with various laryngeal diseases.

with the use of hot-wire flowmeters and calculation of the AC/DC ratio. First, it should be emphasized that the output curve of the flowmeter is not the glottal wave per se, but is influenced by the resonance cavity which consists of the vocal tract and the flowmeter tube.

As is well known, if one of the harmonics of the glottal wave occurs at a resonant frequency, then the output amplitude will be greater than when one of the harmonics occurs away from a resonance peak. The difference in amplitude caused by the resonance effect has nothing to do with the actual glottal efficiency and ideally should be eliminated when we attempt to derive a measure of the glottal efficiency.

There may be multiple ways to reduce or eliminate the resonance effect of the vocal tract. The use of an inverse filter is probably the best one in terms of accuracy, but is impractical for a daily clinical test.

Sondhi (1975) has invented a very ingenious as well as simple gadget which greatly suppresses reflection of sound. It consists of a metal tube, two meters long, with a long glass-wool cone lining (Fig.9). A narrow tunnel inside the cone is made as an outlet for the exhaled air phonation. The voice is recorded by a microphone which is attached to the wall of the tube. Acoustic analysis of the tube indicates that the amplitude of the reflected wave is 23dB below that of the incident wave. In an attempt to obtain an approximation to the glottal sound, the outer end of the hot-wire tube was connected to the Sondhi tube. Without the Sondhi tube, significant spectral peaks are observed in the output of the flowmeter when this signal is analyzed by the sonagraph (as shown by the spectral section in Fig.10). In contrast, when the Sondhi tube is used, the resonance effect is fairly well suppressed, as shown by Fig.11. The frequency spectrum of the flowmeter output seems quite similar to the spectrum expected for the glottal source.

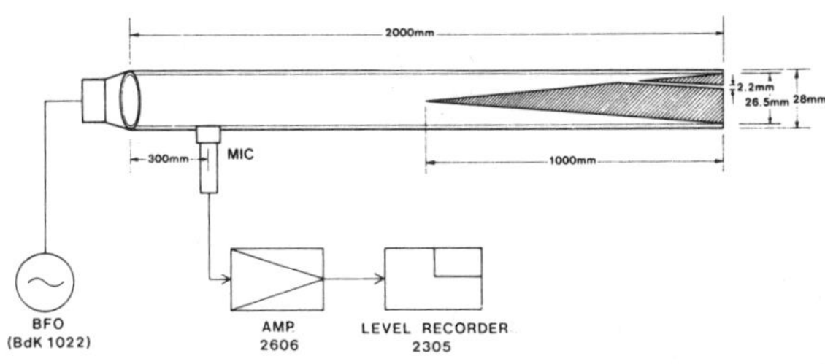

Fig.9. Schematic demonstration of the Sondhi tube. This arrangement is used for calibration of the tube. In actual use, the speaker's lips are placed around the left end of the tube.

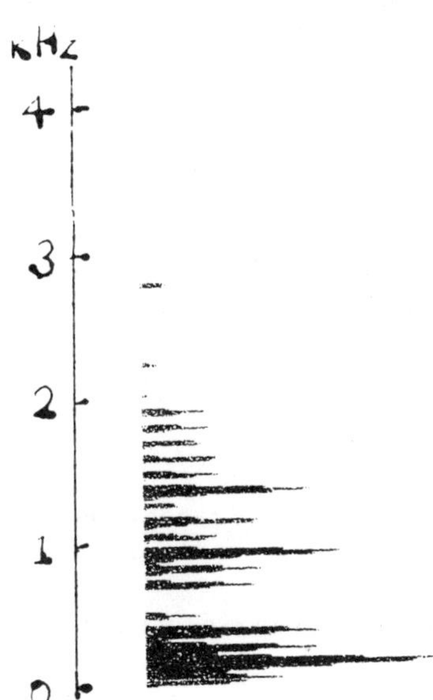

Fig.10. The output of the flowmeter during phonation as analyzed by sound spectrography.

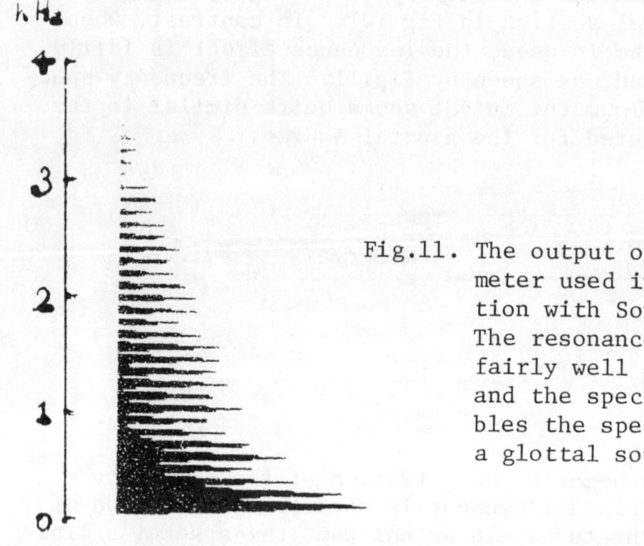

Fig.11. The output of the flowmeter used in combination with Sondhi tube. The resonance effect is fairly well suppressed, and the spectrum resembles the spectrum of a glottal source.

The drawback in the use of the Sondhi tube is that a patient with a large glottal gap feels difficulty in producing sound because of the narrow outlet for airflow in the tube. The presence of the tube may thus have an influence on the functioning of the larynx, but this influence is presumably not as great as the expected difference in the value of the AC/DC ratio for normal and pathologic voices. Furthermore, use of the tube minimizes variation due to the influences of vocal tract resonances.

In summary, the vocal efficiency index as measured in the way proposed in this paper appears to be clinically significant for judging the glottal function.

REFERENCES

Flanagan, J.L. (1972) Analysis, Synthesis and Preception of Speech 2nd edition. Berlin: Springer-Verlag.

Isshiki, N., and Von Leden, H. (1964) Aerodynamic studies. Arch. Otolaryng. 80, 206-213.

Isshiki, N., Yanagihara, N., and Morimoto, M. (1966) Approach to the objective diagnosis of hoarseness.

Folia Phoniatrica 18, 393-400.

Isshiki, N., Okamura, H., and Morimoto, M. (1967) Maximum phonation time and air flow rate during phonation. *Ann. Otol. Rhinol. Laryng.* 76, 998-1008.

Sondhi, M.M. (1975) Measurement of the glottal waveform. *J. Acoust. Soc. Am.* 57, 228-232.

DISCUSSION

Rothenberg: It appears that many different types of efficiency measures are possible. As you point out, your measure is not a true efficiency. Perhaps it is more of a breathiness measure. We have been experimenting with measures that are closer to aerodynamic efficiency, and that relate output power (radiated acoustic energy) to input power (subglottal pressure times glottal airflow). But then one must decide whether to use the unmodified radiated acoustic power as the output measure, or to weight the frequencies according to the response of the ear, as in the standard "A" weighting used for sound pressure measurements. At this point, I do not think that we can show that any one measure is universally better than any other. Perhaps a breathiness measure would be informative in one situation, and an "A-weighted" efficiency measure would better in another situation.

I believe that the frequency response of a hot-wire anemometer is a function of the flow level. At low levels the response may not be as good as your measurements indicate. However, the measurement you make of the rms value of the AC portion of the waveform probably does not require a broad frequency response, since the rms value of a glottal pulse is mostly determined by the fundamental frequency component and the lowest harmonics.

I have one other caution to pass on that might be of some help to you. The "Sondhi" tube should probably be thought of as a "low-reflection" termination, rather than as a reflection-free termination. The major resonances that result from this tube, though they will be very damped, will have been moved down to near the fundamental frequency where they can cause a great deal of phase error. A phase error of only 10 or 20 degrees near the fundamental frequency can cause a significant distortion of the waveform. Though the waveform from a Sondhi tube may be good enough to test breathiness (as in your application) I think that some independent verification is needed before the details of the waveshape can be trusted.

Isshiki: As to the frequency response of the hot-wire flowmeter, we have measured it under the condition of a constant flow of oxygen gas from 100-200 cm^3/sec. Consequently the frequency characteristic curve that I have shown is probably applicable to the voice production conditions. We have not yet measured the frequency response under extreme conditions of airflow.

We disagree with you as to the effect of resonance on the AC component of the air flow. I think that even with the use of a pneumotachograph and a mask we cannot be free from the problem of the resonance effect by the vocal tract.

Whether we should weight the vocal intensity according to the auditory characteristics or not depends upon what we want to know. If we are interested in the amount of information delivered by phonation, weighting the vocal output, that is transformation from intensity to loudness, is meaningful. Rather, we are interested in the pure function of the glottis, and therefore we do not think that kind of weighting is necessary for our purpose.

Titze: Something has been bothering me for some time. Vocal efficiency, as measured by the ratio of radiated acoustic power to pulmonary power, can change by 20 dB in changing vocal effort from conversational speech to shouting or singing. Let me elaborate. A sound pressure of about 95dB re 0.0002 μbar (as measured in an anechoic chamber at 1 m from the mouth) corresponds to maximum effort, whereas conversational speech is at about 65dB. The pulmonary input power (determined by the product of subglottal pressure and average flow rate) does not change much more than about 10 dB. Thus, a 20 dB difference in the resulting vocal efficiency would, according to your graph, predict an extremely small opening quotient, much less than 0.1. Is that realistic?

Isshiki: As you pointed out, the variation in sound pressure level at 1 m is from about 95 dB for shouting to 65 dB for soft speech. This great range of intensity variation (30 dB) is possible only when the mouth opening is free to change. If the size of the mouth opening is kept constant, the vocal intensity variation is within a much narrower range, usually around 15 dB. The subglottal power variation will account for roughly 10 dB as you suggested, and the remaining 5 dB may be controlled by glottal efficiency or opening quotient at a certain pitch. Naturally, how much the subglottal power and glottal efficiency contribute to the intensity of glottal sound respectively varies greatly with the individual and with the vocal pitch.

Fujimura: Isn't the assumption of symmetric triangular waveforms too strong?

Isshiki: Since we are interested in the effective value of the glottal wave, and not in the frequency components of the wave, simplification of the wave into a symmetric triangular shape seems to be justified. It is certainly an over-simplification if we want to speak about the frequency components of the waves.

Stevens: When the Sondhi tube is used, the impedance seen by the vocal folds may be quite different from the impedance seen when the vocal tract is in a normal vowel configuration. It is possible that this different impedance, which is primarily resistive for the Sondhi tube, might have an influence on the vocal fold vibration pattern. Thus, the volume-flow waveform using the Sondhi tube must be interpreted with care, keeping in mind the possible effect of the different loading characteristics.

Ishizaka: To evaluate the loading effect, let us first compare the resistive impedance or the characteristic impedance of the Sondhi tube with the glottal resistance R_g, although it is recognized that R_g is essentially a flow-dependent resistance. The characteristic impedance Z_0 of a tube of area A is $Z_0=\rho c/A$, and hence the value of Z_0 for $A=5 cm^2$ is about 8 acoustic ohms. On the other hand, the average glottal resistance around the peak opening, at which the volume velocity is typically 600-700 cm^3/sec, will be of the order of 12 acoustic ohms, which is almost comparable to Z_0. Therefore, it is probable that the loading effect might have some influence upon the glottal flow especially around the peak opening, but only a little influence upon the cord behavior.

I have once made a computer simulation of phonation with and without the Sondhi tube by means of the dynamic vocal cord/vocal tract with yielding walls. There is no apparent difference in the A_g waveform and in the fundamental frequency for the two cases; that is, the Sondhi tube has little influence upon cord vibration.

The Sondhi tube or the reflectionless termination _does_ have an effect on the U_g waveform. The ripple on the U_g waveform reflecting the acoustic interaction between the glottal flow and the tract resonances does not exist for the Sondhi tube, but the U_g waveform near its peak tends to be slightly flat when the tube is used. This fact indicates an aspect of the essential features of cord vibrations--namely that the vibration pattern with the vertical phase difference is resistant to changes in the external acoustic loading.

However, this computer simulation was made for normal phonation in the chest register. For some types of weak vibration in pathological cases the Sondhi tube might have a notable influence upon cord vibration itself. Thus, generally speaking, in the application of the Sondhi tube to pathological larynges the loading effect must be kept in mind, as Prof. Stevens has pointed out.

CHAPTER 16
SOME SYSTEMS PHYSIOLOGY CONSIDERATIONS FOR VOCAL CONTROL

Eric M. Müller, James H. Abbs, and
Jesse G. Kennedy, III

Speech Motor Control Laboratories,
University of Wisconsin-Madison,
Madison, Wisconsin, USA

INTRODUCTION

In the last 15 years there has been a new level of sophistication in the study of nervous system control of "intended" motor behavior. Perhaps the best examples of this are seen in neurophysiological analyses which have been extended from in-vitro preparations to waking animals and man; and those in which quantitative data on system sub-components have been synthesized into formal models for testing and refining hypotheses on human motor control (cf. Evarts and Fromm, 1978; Hatze and Buys, 1977; Crago, Houk, and Hasan, 1976; Stein and Oğuztöreli, 1976). These endeavors have focused on the spinal motor system with emphasis on limb movement control. As detailed by Abbs and Müller (1980), the knowledge gained from these advances may not provide direct parallels to the brain stem or higher neural mechanisms utilized in the control of the biomechanically more complex midline structures involved in speech. Nevertheless, this extensive work provides basic directions through which to advance and shape our perspectives regarding speech motor control. In this context, our research emphasis over the last ten years has been an attempt to exploit these advances in neurophysiology and systems analysis and to combine them with more traditional approaches from phonetics and communications engineering (Abbs and Eilenberg, 1976; Müller, et al., 1977; Abbs, et al., 1977). In the course of this work we have become increasingly aware of the importance of basic information on the neuromuscular substrate of the speech system. Without such information, it is very difficult to determine (via conventional analyses of speech physiology "observables") the extent to which crucial aspects of motor performance reflect contributions of: 1) peripheral biomechanical properties, 2) brain stem or spinal cord "reflexive" actions, 3) central nervous system control, or most probably, 4) critical system interactions between these subcomponents.

While our efforts utilizing this combined approach have focused primarily upon the speech motor physiology of the lips and jaw, there appear to be some useful insights for the parallel study of vocal control. Figure 1 is an attempt to illustrate the relation between existing formal models of the larynx, which deal primarily with the mechanics, aerodynamics, and acoustics of the vocal fold vibration itself, and the domain of our focus; viz., the neuromuscular mechanisms which actively control the biomechanics of the soft tissues, the overall conformation of the laryngeal structures, and thus, the fundamental frequency and other aspects of vocal fold vibration.

Based upon the components of neuromuscular control shown in Fig.1, we should like to review some of our thoughts and experimental results on speech system neural control and biomechanics with an emphasis of those mechanisms having apparent implications for the laryngeal motor system.

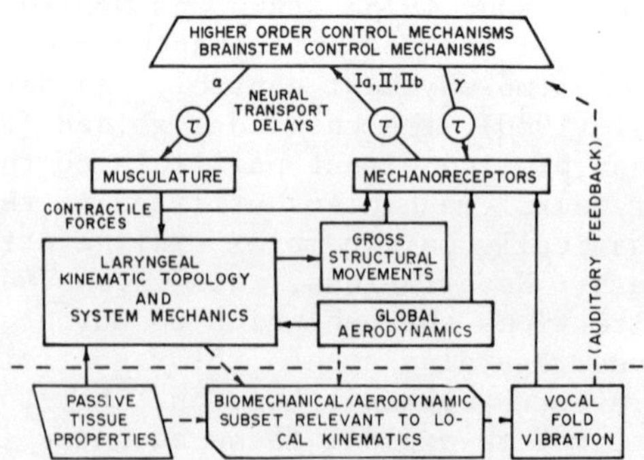

Fig.1. A schematic representation of the major subcomponents involved in the control of gross structural movements of the larynx. Typical models of vocal fold vibration restrict themselves to consideration of the components below the dotted line.

MOTOR CONTROL SYSTEM BIOMECHANICS

As is shown in Fig.1, the system biomechanical variables under consideration are more comprehensive than those considered in most work on vocal fold vibration. From the standpoint of neuromuscular control, this particular emphasis is based upon the premise that knowledge concerning the system's overall biomechanics is crucial in attempting to determine what (in a biophysical sense) the nervous system is trying to control. Indeed, one's lack of knowledge or assumptions regarding a motor system's biomechanics may have a strong influence on hypotheses concerning its underlying nervous system control. For example:

1) If one overestimates the significance of the tissue biomechanics (e.g., visualizes the inert tissue at the periphery as a large inertio-viscoelastic system driven by the contractile force of the muscles) and ignores the dynamics of the contractile process (e.g., assumes that the contractile force, myoelectic activity and descending motor program are somehow equivalent), then aspects of the observed movement such as overshoot, undershoot, damped oscillations, and tremor may be viewed as indicating the way that these biomechanical properties constrain the "intended motor gesture". Indeed from some early speech production papers one gets the impression that the vocal tract would reconfigure from one phonetic element to the next in a quantal manner were it not for such 'inertioviscoelastic' constraints. On the other hand, if the tissue mechanics are viewed as being relatively simple (e.g., a system of springs--in such a system the contractile force and movement are equivalent) the same response patterns are explained (depending upon one's persuasion) as either an aspect of the descending central motor program, or a response pattern related to the characteristics of the peripheral feedback pathways (i.e., loop gains, neural transport delays, receptor transfer characteristics, etc.)
2) In a similar vein, if one reflects upon the potential nonlinearities due to muscle mechanics, geometric variations in force translation, and the rheology of the antagonistic load, one is either: (a) bewildered by the utter complexity of a motor

control program that is able to "contend" with such nonlinearities, (b) prompted to view the nonlinearities as an optimal means by which the central controller's task is simplified, or (c) persuaded that the burden on the central controller is eliminated by the linearizing effects of the peripheral feedback mechanisms.

3) Finally, if one does not attend to the biophysics of the motor event there is the possibility of ascribing direct neural control to aspects of movement that, in fact, are the consequence of a complex interaction between the contractile forces produced by the musculature and other forces originating, for example, in the dynamic characteristics of the tissues and aerodynamic environment with which the motor system communicates. That is, the actual manifestation of neural control may be the "tuning" of biomechanical characteristics (e.g., muscle stiffness) rather than the moment-to-moment generation of the movement itself (e.g., as in the control of muscle length). A relevant example of this latter misinterpretation is the neurochronaxic theory of vocal fold vibration.

Figure 2 illustrates a conceptualization we have found useful in our analysis of labial/mandibular system biomechanics. It schematically summarizes some of the major variables which must be considered when analyzing the neuromuscular control of even the most basic motor system. This flow diagram depicts the generation of unidimensional movement via a single muscle coupled to its _in vivo_ physiological load. We will assume for this example that the load is simply passive tissue with a single degree of freedom; thus, movement of the load and the change in muscle length are equivalent.

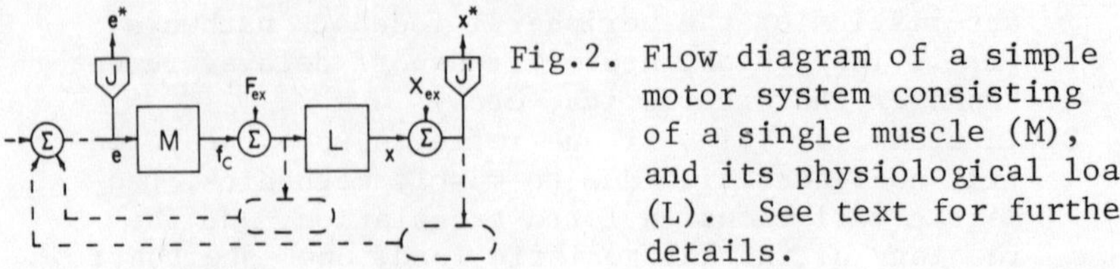

Fig.2. Flow diagram of a simple motor system consisting of a single muscle (M), and its physiological load (L). See text for further details.

In relation to Fig.2, let us assume that our research objective is to empirically delineate: 1) the muscle mechanics transfer function (M) relating contractile force (f_c) to the motoneuron activation level (e), and 2) the transfer function of the _in vivo_ load (L) against which f_c acts in order to create movement (x). In most real _in vivo_ systems there are, for all practical purposes, only two system observables: some indirect estimate of the activation level of the motoneuron population observed via EMG ($e^*=e\cdot J$) (DeLuca, 1979) and some aspect, albeit remote, of the muscle length related to the observed movement ($x^*=x\cdot J'$). The actual _in vivo_ forces in the system are seldom amenable to direct measurement, although they can be estimated from the EMG or movement (i.e., e^* or x^*) with knowledge of the transfer functions M/J and $\frac{1}{LJ'}$, respectively. Similarly, muscle length (x) and its derivative ($\dot{x}$), which figure prominently in the transfer characteristics of muscle, are also difficult to measure directly and must be estimated ($x^*=x\cdot J'$).

In a typical experiment, as indicated in Fig.2, externally supplied tensile forces (F_{ex}) and/or displacements (X_{ex}) are applied, for example, to the soft tissue of the lips to derive its transfer characteristics; here we are visualizing the perioral tissue acting as the load (L) against which another muscle (M), e.g., buccinator, must pull. In order for these experiments to yield tractable results, the excitable portion of the tissue (i.e., muscle) must either be quiescent or at a known constant level of contraction. A potential problem with a simple signal analysis approach to determining L is the possibility that F_{ex} or X_{ex} may, via afferent feedback pathways (shown as dashed lines in Fig.2), reflexively activate the muscle and thus confound the _in vivo_ observations. In addition to the potential artifact due to neural feedback, one also must be wary of the characteristically nonlinear nature of all biological systems and design experiments accordingly (e.g., use a small signal analysis approach). A further experimental consideration is that the range of F_{ex} and X_{ex} must correspond to the contractile forces and movements that are utilized normally during speech production. Thus, it is necessary to precede such experiments with an analysis of the physiological range of at least the movements (x^*) and the EMG levels (e^*) used during speech. In this respect the laryngeal system is quite unlike the lips and jaw with which we are more familiar. We have found the bandwidth of the lip/jaw movements during speech to be less than 15 Hz. Those aspects of laryngeal kinematics under direct neural control (i.e., the contractile forces and the concomitant changes in muscle stiffness) probably have a bandwidth that is roughly the same order of magnitude as lip/jaw movements. However, the vibratory movements of the vocal folds are obviously much higher in frequency. The contractile machinery, as the effector organ of the nervous system, is not capable of such speed; by contrast, some sensory organs (e.g., mechanoreceptors) are quite sensitive to these high frequencies and thus may figure prominently in the control of F_o.

Within the 15 Hz physiological range of the lips, the passive tissue of the face (i.e., one aspect of the load against which the facial muscles contract) has the dynamic stiffness characteristics shown in Fig.3. A mechanical analog of the dynamic response of the passive tissue derived from the sinusoidal analysis as well as stress relaxation and creep data is also shown in the figure. Conspicuously absent from this model is a mass component, especially in contrast to most models of vocal fold vibration. Within the frequency/amplitude range of lip movements for speech the inertial term is relatively insignificant. Similarly, the effective mass of the vocal folds may be negligible in a neuromuscular model of laryngeal articulation (as contrasted to specific models of the relatively high frequency local kinematics of the folds, *per se*).

The general nonlinear properties of muscle contraction have been well documented by both classical and more recent invasive experiments. Figure 4 is a mathematical model of the contractile properties of striated muscle based upon the work of Carlson (1957). On the basis of data obtained in our laboratory, the coefficients in the equations have been scaled in order to approximate roughly the contractile characteristics of the buccinator muscle. As shown in the figure, the contractile force (f_c) is dependent not only upon the level of activation (e), but also upon the length of the muscle (x) and its rate of shortening ($\dot{x}$). Note that the three-dimensional plot shown here only depicts the isopleth for a single activation level; the displayed contour, of course, varies as a function of e.

Determining the specific nature of these characteristics for a particular muscle, *in vivo*, is extremely difficult in humans. This is due not only to methological/

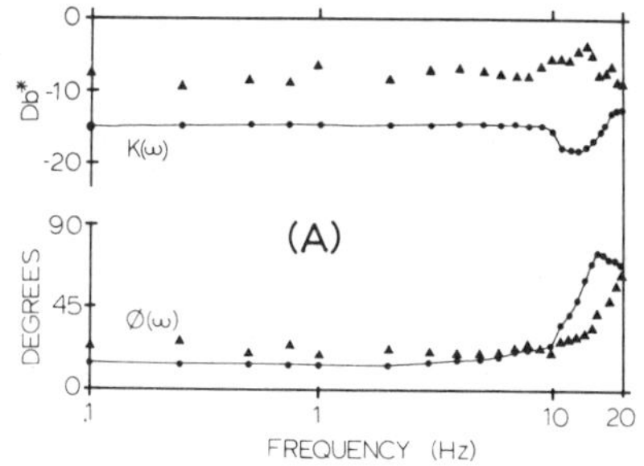

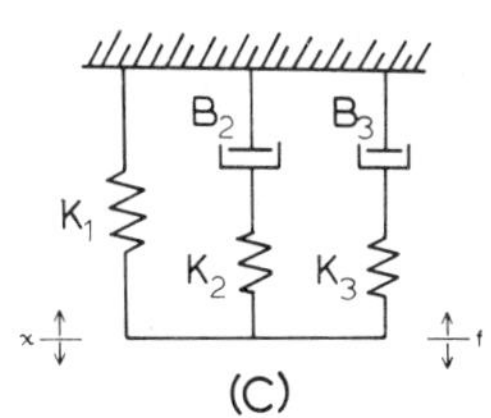

K1 =64.0 K2 =8.4 K3 =22.6 GM-WT/CM

B2 =129.0 B3 =1.1 GM-WT/CM/SEC

B2/K2 =15.36 SEC

B3/K3 =0.05 SEC

FORCE
Fp(O)=70 GM-WT
Fa=48 GM-WT
-0
(B)
0 60 120 180
time (sec)
0.75 cm step
DISPL.
-0

Fig.3. Mechanical characteristics of the soft tissue response of the face to anterior-medial/posterior-lateral displacements of the oral angle.

(a) Dynamic stiffness ($K(\omega)$ calculated in dB re: 1 kgm/cm) and phase angle ($\phi(\omega)$ calculated force re: displacement). Circles denote the response of the tissue when it is passive, and triangles represent response when obicularis oris is maintaining a constant level of contraction.

(b) Stress relaxation in response to a step change in displacement. F_p is the initial peak force and F_a is the asymptotic level approached by the relaxing force.

(c) A model of the mechanical characteristics of the perioral tissue. Typical coefficient values are K_1=46.0, K_2=8.4, K_3=22.6 gm-wt/cm; B_2=129.0, B_3=1.1 gm-wt sec/cm; B_2/K_2=15.36 sec; B_3/K_3=0.05 sec. More details concerning the dynamic characteristics of the soft tissue of the face as well as the contractile mechanics of the facial muscles may be found in Müller and Abbs (1980).

observational limitations, but also because generally it is not possible to mechanically 'uncouple' the muscle from its *in vivo* physiological load. In some cases it is possible to analytically subtract the intervening effects of the load (e.g., the viscoelastic properties of the tendon and soft tissues, the inertia of bone and cartilage, and the forces contributed by concomitantly active antagonistic muscles) provided data on these subsystems are available. We have had some success in attempting to devrive the transfer function (M) (from Fig.2) for the orbicularis oris muscle. By virture of the rather unique anatomical position of this muscle, we are able to directly measure f_c and x via transducers attached to the oral angle. Moreover, with a special servo-controlled mechanical signal generator, we also are able to constrain orbicularis oris to contract isometrically (x=constant, f_c and e* vary) or isotonically (f_c=a constant value, x and e* vary). The data from these experiments are somewhat similar to those summarized in Fig.4.

It is reasonable to assume that the laryngeal musculature is characterized by nonlinearities comparable to those described for the limb and perioral musculature. As such, one important aspect of these data for laryngeal control is the nonlinear relationship between f_c (analogous to longitudinal tension of the folds), e (roughly analogous to EMG in the vocalis muscle), x (vocal fold length), and $\dot{x}$ (rate of change in vocal fold length). For example, changes in vocalis length resulting from the contraction of the cricothyroid muscles will create corresponding and perhaps undesirable changes in the longitudinal tension of vocalis if there are not appropriate compensatory adjustments in the activation level of the vocalis. The complex nature of the combined transfer function of muscle and its antagonistic load demonstrates the need to excercise extreme caution in the interpretation of EMG in relation to muscle force and movement. While experiments yielding specific biomechanical data from the laryngeal musculature undoubtedly will require the use of animal models or special treatment of excised larynges, such information should be of value in developing more formal models of vocal neuromuscular control as well as a basis for refined interpretation of laryngeal EMG data.

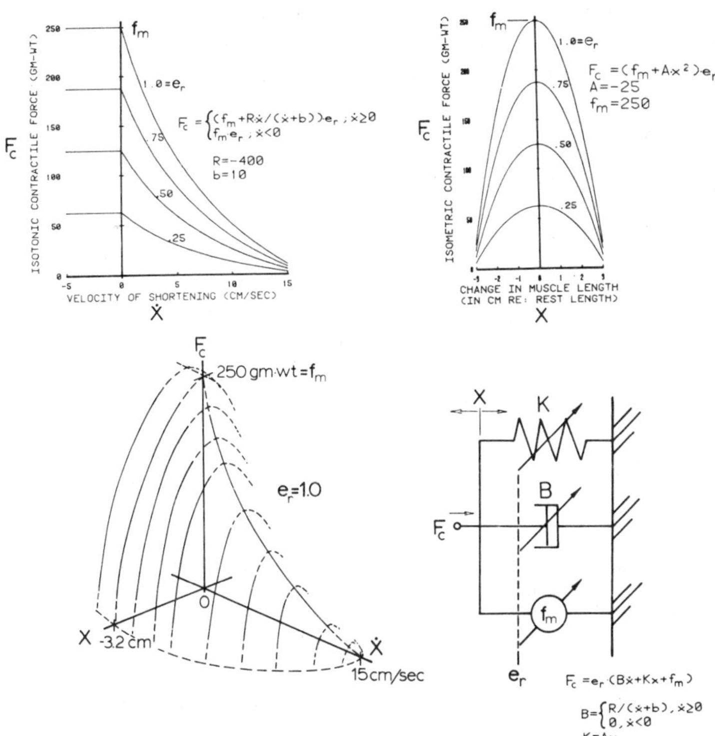

Fig.4. A model of striated muscle contractile mechanics based on the work of Carlson (1957). f_m represents maximum contractile force, e_r represents the level of muscle activation relative to maximum contraction, and R, b, and A are constants. All coefficients have been scaled in order to roughly depict the contractile characteristics of the buccinator muscle. The graphs from left to right across the top of the figure depict: Isotonic force versus velocity of shortening, relative level of activation is the parameter; isometric force versus muscle length, the parameter again is relative activation level; and a composite force versus length versus velocity isopleth at a constant activation level. In the analog of the contractile mechanics shown in the lower left plot, the elements are parametrically forced as a function of e_r.

POSSIBLE LARYNGEAL NEURAL CONTROL MECHANISMS

As detailed earlier, consideration of system biomechanics provides some rather specific directions for considering the nature of underlying neural control. While some of our previous research has dealt with the influence of auditory feedback upon laryngeal control and the possibility of certain upper airway-laryngeal-respiratory interactions (Müller and Brown, 1980; Folkins and Abbs, 1976; Barlow and Abbs, 1978), perhaps the most relevant neural control considerations for the present paper are those which relate to the nonlinearities of the contractile process as discussed above.

The larynx apparently is well-endowed with mechanoreceptors to provide ongoing afferent information for control of many parameters including muscle length, muscle tension, laryngeal cartilage joint positions and muscosal tissue deformation (Martenson, 1968; Seto, 1963). As part of this rich afferent innervation, both muscle spindles and some functional equivalent of muscle tension receptors similar to Colgi tendon organs appear to be present in primates (Baken, 1971; Larson, Sutton, and Lindeman, 1974; Lucas Keene, 1961). As Sears (1968) commented over a decade ago, the question of the muscle spindle seems to me absolutely fundamental... this receptor plays a specific role in a reflex mechanism which automatically stabilizes the demanded movements against the load. The question of whether or not the laryngeal muscles can be controlled in this way seems to me to be of vital significance. (p. 111) While a number of investigators have considered the potential contributions of laryngeal mechanoreceptors to the control of vocal behavior, no formal models of these afferent control mechanisms have emerged. The hypothesis we would like to offer concentrates on the possible contribution of muscle spindles <u>and</u> tendon receptors, or their functional equivalents, to the direct control of longitudinal <u>stiffness</u> (or its inverse, compliance) of the vocalis muscle. By virtue of the complex relationship between longitudinal stiffness, its transverse component, and their significant influence on vocal fold vibration, we are proposing that there may be a "neurocybernetic" aspect in the control of vocal fundamental frequency as well as in the control of gross structural movements in the larynx.

As documented by extensive neurophysiological observations, spindle receptors, due to their anatomical connections, apparently are sensitive to muscle length and its derivative (Matthews, 1964). Because afferent feedback from spindles is excitatory to the motoneurons innervating the same muscle, many neurophysiologists have suggested that this afferent system contributes to the regulation of muscle length, i.e., is a length control system. Such a proposed system would be unsatisfactory for the control of vocal pitch because vocal fold stiffness rather than length is the most relevant and non-redundant variable related to the vocal fundamental vibratory cycle. From these considerations, and contrary to some claims in the laryngeal physiology literature (Baken, 1971), it would appear that the muscle spindle-based control system would not be the most appropriate feedback mechanism for controlling vocal fold stiffness.

If this interpretation is correct, what then might be the role of muscle spindles in vocalis? A possible explanation is available from the recent work of Houk and his colleagues (Houk, 1974; Houk, 1978; Nichols and Houk, 1973; Nichols and Houk, 1976). They have shown that the stiffness of the spindle-based feedback mechanism is not substantial enough to support the operation of a functional length control system regulating position, and that the muscle tension afferents from tendon receptors (inhibitory to autogenic motoneurons) actually act to reduce the stiffness of the muscle. In this context, length and tension feedback loops would appear to oppose one another, yielding an impossible situation in which a motor system attempts to regulate both muscle length and tension. In response to this apparent inconsistency, Houk proposed that neither muscle length nor muscle force is the regulated variable of this dual receptor feedback system, but rather, that it is the "stiffness" of the muscle that is regulated. Stiffness is defined by Houk as the ratio of the contractile force to muscle length--i.e., the "derivative" of the force-length curve shown in Fig.4. Note that this is the stiffness of the force-actuating mechanism based on isometric data and not the biorheological stiffness (in the Houkean sense) of the muscle tissue *per se*; other factors, such as the 'short range stiffness' of muscle, also need to be considered.

In attempting to apply Houk's notions concerning stiffness control in motor systems to the larynx we will consider the stiffness (Φ) of the vocal folds to have three components: the stiffness due to the passive tissue, Φ_p; the additional stiffness added when the accompanying muscle is active, Φ_d; and an additional stiffness contributed by the neural control mechanism, $\Delta\Phi$. Since Φ_p is a constant and presumed to be linear it needn't be considered in the control process. However, because Φ_d is quite nonlinear (cf. the force-length curve in Fig.4, where $\Phi_d = \partial f_c/\partial x$ at any given e level) the stiffness of the muscle will vary nonlinearly as a function of its length and excitation level. In the analysis which follows we will show that as a result of the apparent neuromotor architecture of the system an additional stiffness ($\Delta\Phi$) is added which automatically compensates for nonlinearity of Φ_d such that Φ is linearized. Furthermore, we will show that by virtue of the feedback mechanism, muscle stiffness may be controlled by three independent neural control parameters which may be "manipulated" by a speaker, and that this mechanism may either regulate the stiffness (i.e., keep it constant) or control changes in stiffness in order to help affect a change in the fundamental frequency of the voice. The mathematical analysis which follows is based on the owrk of Houk and his colleagues.

As schematically illustrated in Fig.5, the elements of this control concept include: i, the descending nervous system drive; f_c, the muscle contractile force; x, muscle length; e, the muscle activation signal (roughly equivalent to EMG); M, the muscle transfer function; L, the antagonistic load; S, the gain of the spindle afferent feedback, and T, the loop gain of the tendon receptor afferent feedback.

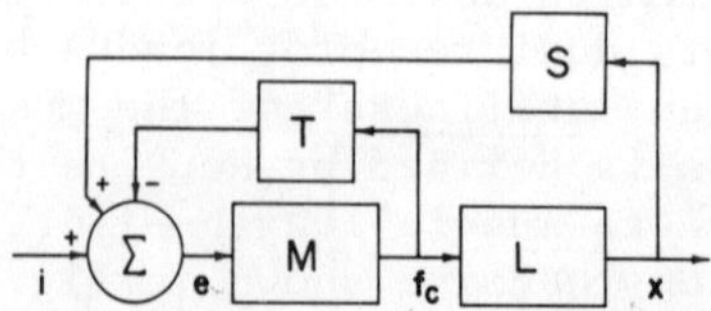

Fig.5. Flow diagram of a hypothetical motor system in which muscle stiffness is servoregulated. See text for further details.

The loop gains, S and T, are variables that may be controlled independently via the gamma efferent system, or at the synaptic or interneuronal level. We will assume for the purpose of this example that the contraction is primarily isometric; thus, the nonlinear relationship between f_c and $\dot{x}$ (cf. Fig.4) need not be considered, because $\dot{x}=0$. Moreover, for purposes of this illustration, time delays due to neural and myoelectric transport, and excitation contraction coupling are excluded. By utilizing a small signal analysis approach and Taylor's theorem we can approximate the nonlinear relationship between f_c, x, and e at an arbitrary operating point on the force-length curve as

$$f_c = F(x,e) = x \cdot \frac{\partial f_c}{\partial x} + e \cdot \frac{\partial f_c}{\partial e} = K \cdot x + A \cdot e \tag{1}$$

where $K = \partial f_c / \partial x$ (the force-length gradient) and $A = \partial f_c / \partial e$ (the force-excitation gradient) and the values of K and A vary with the operating point. By rearranging terms we may solve for the isometric stiffness of the deafferentated muscle (Φ_d):

$$\Phi_d = f_c/x = K + Ae/x = K + Ai/x \tag{2}$$

where e = i in the deafferentated condition. Note that in this condition the stiffness is dynamically controlled by the descending control signal, i. This control scheme is quite complex due to the nonlinear relationship between i and Φ_d (i.e., K is a function of x, and A is a function of e which in this case equals i). Given the system configuration represented in Fig.5, the total muscle stiffness as a result of the inclusion of the feedback pathways may be calculated:

$$e = i + f_c \cdot T - x \cdot S, \tag{3}$$

and from equation (1) above

$$e = (f_c - k \cdot x)/A. \tag{4}$$

Thus,

$$(f_c - K \cdot x)/A = i + f_c \cdot T - x \cdot S, \tag{5}$$

from which we may solve for the muscle stiffness (Φ) when in the feedback configuration:

$$\Phi = f_c/x = \frac{(K + Ai/x) - SA}{1 - TA} \tag{6}$$

which by virture of equation (2) reduces to

$$\Phi = \frac{\Phi_d - SA}{1 - TA} = \frac{S - \Phi_d/A}{T - 1/A} \tag{7}$$

In addition, it may be shown that the increased stiffness ($\Delta\Phi$) due to the feedback is

$$\Delta\Phi = \Phi - \Phi_d = \frac{\frac{S}{T} - \Phi_d}{1 - \frac{1}{TA}} \tag{8}$$

Next consider the situation in which the loop gains are relatively low (i.e., $S \to 0$ and $T \to 0$) by virtue of an 'intended' reduction in the loop gains or due to a disease state,

$$\Phi \to \Phi_d = K + (A/x)i. \tag{9}$$

Conversely, if the descending command signal is relatively small (i.e., $i \to 0$, and thus $\Phi_d \to K$) and the loop gains are relatively high (i.e., $T >> 1/A$ and $S >> K/A$) equation (7) reduces to

$$\Phi \to S/T \tag{10}$$

Note that the stiffness is linearly related to the ratio of the feedback gains and independent of the contractile nonlinearities K and A. That is, as the feedback gains increase, the effective stiffness of the muscle is progressively less influenced by the force-length nonlinearity of the contractile process (contrast equations (9) and (10))

Of what value might the servoregulation of muscle stiffness be in the control of the vocalis muscle? Assuming that the stiffness of vocalis is a primary variable in the control of vocal fundamental frequency, its servoregulation through short-latency peripheral feedbak offers a means by which: 1) the nonlinear contractile properties of this muscle (or any other laryngeal muscle) might be compensated for "automatically" and with minimal CNS control complexity, and 2) the stiffness (and thus to a great extent, the pitch of the voice) may be automatically maintained independent of changes in vocal fold length. For example, it is apparent that the vocal folds, including the vocalis muscle, undergo rather substantial changes in length. Such length changes would, in a deafferentiated muscle, lead to corresponding nonlinear variations in the stiffness of the vocalis unless its level of activation was programmed concurrently to compensate. By contrast, given the feedback configuration shown in Fig.5, stiffness itself (rather than muscle length or force) could be directly controlled by a central motor program which regulates the relative gain of the feedback loops. Thic control could be accomplished both at the suprasegmental level via the gamma efferent system as well as at the synaptic and interneuronal levels. To the extent to which muscle "stiffness" (as defined by force-length curve), and longitudinal and transverse "stiffness" (in the biorheological sense) are related, this capability may be an important aspect of the neuromotor control of fundamental frequency as well as the gross movements of the laryngeal structures. That is, by simply maintaining relatively high and constant loop gains (i.e., S/T), the stiffness of the folds will be maintained constant (see equation (10)). Moreover, because both the descending neural control signal (i) and the stiffness are linearly related for small changes in i (see equations (2) and (6)), the baseline stiffness (due to S/T) may be modulated via i in order to effect small corrections in pitch or create tremolo.

One specific example of the value of stiffness control is the situation that occurs when a deafferentated muscle is stretched while it is contracting. Initially, the muscle force rises sharply in response to stretch. However, when the stretch exceeds a fraction of a millimeter, the force yields abruptly, resulting in a corresponding abrupt change in stiffness (Joyce, et al., 1969; Nichols and Houk, 1976). This yielding behavior has been suggested to be related to an internal property of the contractile process. Parallel observations made with intact dorsal roots indicate that the feedback response to such stretch effectively allows the muscle to be lengthened while maintaining its stiffness. When the cricothyroid stretches the vocal folds (and the vocalis muscle), why is it that this yielding behavior is not manifested either as a "break" in fundamental frequency, or as a "slackening" of the vocal folds, or both? One might suggest that the stiffness regulation, such as described here, plays a role in the control of vocalis stiffness, comparable to that hypothesized in the control of the limb muscles. One issue of concern with regard to the operation of these possible regulatory mechanisms is the potential influence of afferent and efferent neural transport delays. However, neural time delays may be minimized in their influence due to the natural mechanical properties of contracting muscle. For example, contracting muscle, when stretched, does not immediately yield; there is a finite period before induced length changes are manifest. As noted by Joyce, et al. (1969), this "short-term stiffness" may reduce the otherwise potentially detrimental influence of neural transport delays on the stability of motor regulations.

In addition to the changes in vocal fold length that occur as a function of the normal motor program controlling the laryngeal musculature, perturbatios in length may occur as a result of external forces (cf. external frame function, Sonninen, 1968) and thus affect the stiffness of the vibrating folds. A stiffness regulatory control mechanism would, for example, enable a trained singer to precisely maintain or manipulate vocal fold vibration frequency in face of continuous changes in upper airway and respiratory mechanical influences or performance-related movements of the torso, limbs, and head; all of which could be expected to influence vocal fold stiffness. Aerodynamic variations, particularly transglottal pressure changes, occurring naturally as a part of vocal intensity control or variations in upper airway occlusion would also appear to be of some significance as mechanical influences upon the vocal folds.

It might be also hypothesized that a <u>differential</u> stiffness control mechanism exists in the larynx which allows for the independent regulation of the stiffness of the vocal fold cover (via cricothyroid contraction) and the vocal fold body (via vocalis contraction). Given the apparent importance of the relative stiffness of these two components of the vibrating vocal folds, such an independently interacting mechanism has considerable appeal (cf. Fujimura, Chapter 19 , and Titze, Chapter 26 of this book).

While the hypothesis presented here is almost certain to be too simple an explanation of the manner in which the stiffness of the vocal folds is controlled, we hope it stimulates the development of additional models that likewise would attempt to incorporate the numerous afferent mechanisms which are potentially available for the control of phonation. As such models become more refined they will require additional biomechanical, neurophysiological and histological information acquired through further exploration of the laryngeal mechanism of both animal and human material.

In this brief overview we have attempted to address some issues in the general area of neuromuscular control that seemed, from our perspective, to be applicable to the control of the larynx during speech production. The danger of such an undertaking, given our relative naiveté concerning the phonatory processes, is one of oversimplifying the complex laryngeal control process in order to fit our level of understanding. We apologize if this has occurred and look forward to more sophisticated quantitative analyses of the laryngeal control process that address the issues raised in this paper.

REFERENCES

Abbs, J.H. and Eilenberg, G.R. (1976) Peripheral mechanisms of speech motor control. In Contemporary Issues in Experimental Phonetics, Norman J. Lass (ed.), New York: Academic Press, Chapter 5.

Abbs, J.H. and Müller, E.M. (1980) Speech motor physiology I: Operation of neural control processes among disparate motor systems. In The Production of Speech, P. MacNeilage (ed.), in press.

Abbs, J.H., Müller, E.M., Hassul, M., and Netsell, R. (1977) A systems analysis of possible afferent contributions to lip movement. Paper presented at the American Speech and Hearing Association Convention, Chicago (November).

Baken, R.J. (1971) Neuromuscular spindles in the intrinsic muscles of a human larynx. Folia Phoniat., 23, 204-210.

Barlow, S.M. and Abbs, J.H. (1978) Some evidence of auditory feedback contribution to the ongoing control of speech production. Paper presented at the American Speech and Hearing Association, San Francisco (November).

Carlson, F.D. (1957) Kinematic studies on mechanical properties of muscle. In Tissue Elasticity, J.W. Remington (ed.), Washington, D.C.: American Physiological Society; 55-72.

Crago, P.E., Houk, J.C., and Hasan, Z. (1976) Regulatory actions of the human stretch reflex. Journal of Neurophysiology 39; 925-935.

DeLuca, C.J. (1979) Physiology and mathematics of myoelectric signals. IEEE Trans. Biomed. Eng. BME-26; 313-325.

Evarts, E.V. and Fromm, C. (1978) The pyramidal tract neuron as summing in a closed-loop control system in the monkey. In New Developments in Electromyography and Clinical Neurology, J.E. Desmedt (ed.), Vol. 4, Basel: Karger.

Folkins, J. and Abbs, J.H. (1976) Additional observations on responses to resistive loading of the jaw. Journal of speech and Hearing Research 19, 820-821.

Hatze, H. and Buys, J.D. (1977) Energy-optimal controls in the mammalian neuromuscular system. Biol. Cybernetics 27, 9-20.

Houk, J.C. (1974) Neural control of movement and posture. In Medical Physiology, V. Mountcastle (ed.), St Louis: Mosby.

Houk, J.C. (1978) Participation of reflex mechanisms and reaction time processes in the compensatory adjustments to mechanical disturbances. In New Developments in Electromyography and Clinical Neurology, J.E. Desmedt (ed.), Vol. 4, Basel: Karger.

Joyce, G.C., Rack, P.M.H., and Westbury, D.R. (1969) The mechanical properties of cat soleus muscle during controlled lengthening and shortening movements. Journal of Physiology, London, 204, 461-474.

Larson, C., Sutton, D., and Lindeman, R.C. (1974) Muscle spindles in non-human primate laryngeal muscles. Folia Primatologia 22, 315-323.

Lucas Keene, M.F. (1961) Muscle spindles in human laryngeal muscles. Journal of Anatomy 95, 25-29.

Martensson, A. (1968) The functional organization of the intrinsic laryngeal muscles. In Sound Production in Man, Annals of the New York Academy of Sciences, 91-97.

Matthews, P.B.C. (1964) Muscle spindles and their motor control. Physiol. Review 44, 219.

Müller, E.M., Abbs, J.H. Kennedy, J.G., and Larson, C. (1977) Significance of biomechanical variables in lip movements for speech. Paper presented to the American Speech and Hearing Association, Chicago.

Müller, E.M. and Brown, W.S., Jr. (1980) Variations in the supraglottal air pressure waveform and their articulatory interpretation. In Speech and Language N. Lass (ed.), Vol. 4, New York: Academic Press. (In press.)

Nichols, T.R. and Houk, J.C. (1973) Reflex compensation for variations in the mechanical properties of a muscle. Science, 181, 182-184.

Nichols, T.R. and Houk, J.C. (1976) The improvement in linearity and the regulation of stiffness that results from the actions of the stretch reflex. Journal of Neurophysiology 39, 119-142.

Sears, T.A. (1968) Discussion in Sound Production in Man, Annals of the New York Academy of Sciences, P. 111.

Sears, T.A. and Newsom Davis, J. (1968) The control of respiratory muscles during voluntary breathing. Annals of the New York Academy of Sciences (Sound Production in Man), 183-190.

Seto, H. (1963) Sensibility of the digestive organs. In Studies on Sensory Innervation (Human Sensibility), Chas. C. Thomas (ed.), Springfield.

Sonninen, A, (1968) The external frame function in the control of pitch in the human voice. Annals of the New York Academy of Sciences (Sound Production in Man), 68-90.

Stein, R.B. and Oğuztörelli, M.N. (1976) Tremor and other oscillations in neuromuscular systems. Biol. Cybernetics 22, 147-157.

IV. MODELS OF VOCAL FOLD VIBRATION

Section Editor: Ingo R. Titze

Department of Speech Pathology and Audiology, University of Iowa, Iowa City, Iowa, USA

SECTION EDITOR'S INTRODUCTORY REMARKS

Twenty or thirty years ago a session on models of vocal fold vibration would probably have consisted of displays and demonstrations of a number of mechanical analogs, such as Svend Smith's Munyo. The general topic of modelling would also have included experimentation on excised larynxes. It must be remembered that excised larynxes, whether animal or human, are also models of the real system *in vivo*.

Today, mechanical analogs have been replaced, to a large extent, by computational (mathematical) models. These models consist of statements of physical laws in some sort of computer language. When executed in the proper sequence, these laws are used to predict air and tissue movement in speech production. Often the only thing one can physically observe is the final output, displayed on some oscillographic screen, or perhaps played over a digital-to-analog converter. This makes careful scrutiny of the models difficult for all but a few highly skilled mathematicians. Some of you may find yourselves becoming a bit impatient with the mathematical detail. Unfortunately, rigorous modelling cannot be appreciated very well in terms of highlights. Its essence lies in the step-by-step sequence of logical statements. Thus, to fully appreciate mathematical modelling, one needs to be at the nuts and bolts level. Realizing that it is a tedious task, and realizing *a priori* that certain assumptions render the models too restrictive, many of us elect not to become critics, but perhaps to gaze at them in some combination of admiration and disgust.

Generally speaking, models are very valuable in that they allow us to make predictions beyond what can or has been measured. Where measurements tell us what is, models tell us what can be, and what ought to be, in yet unexplored situations. They help us to decide which measurements should definitely be made and which measurements should never be made. Finally, models are always based upon assumptions and simplifications. If all the simplifications were removed, the model would become the real system, the prototype. The crucial step is to decide what simplifications are appropriate and defensible on the basis of key measurements. If the measurements are not available, we sometimes regretfully default to intuition.

CHAPTER 17
EQUIVALENT LUMPED-MASS MODELS OF VOCAL FOLD VIBRATION

K. Ishizaka

University of Electro-Communications,
Chofu, Tokyo, Japan

EQUIVALENT NETWORK AND EQUATIONS OF MOTION

The vocal cords are an aeromechanical oscillator in which vibration can be self-sustained through the interaction of tissue with air flow through the glottis. The vibratory behavior of the cord oscillator is different from that of a linear combination of free vibrations of the vocal cords with no air flow, because of the aerodynamic reaction. The difference and the oscillation mechanism can conveniently be elucidated analytically by means of an equivalent lumped-constant model with two degrees of freedom - a so-called two-mass model fo the vocal cords, as shown in Fig.1 (Ishizaka and Matsudaira, 1968; Ishizaka and Flanagan, 1972). In the two-mass model, the vocal cord is represented by two mechanical resonators, each consisting of a mass, spring and resistance (m, s and r), which are coupled by a spring s_3. This modeling of the vocal cords can represent the first two natural frequencies and hence the normal modes corresponding to these frequencies. Although the masses m_1 and m_2 are assumed to undergo lateral motion only, vertical motion can be involved in the model by considering an additional degree of freedom (Ishizaka and Flanagan, 1977). The vertical motion, however, has little effect on the glottal impedance and hence on glottal flow and intraglottal pressure, which in turn reacts on the vocal cords. Therefore, for simplicity the vertical motion will not be considered further in this paper.

When the acoustic loading effects of the subglottal system and the vocal tract are ignored, the equivalent network representation for the cord oscillator can be assumed, as a first approximation, to be that shown in Fig.2.

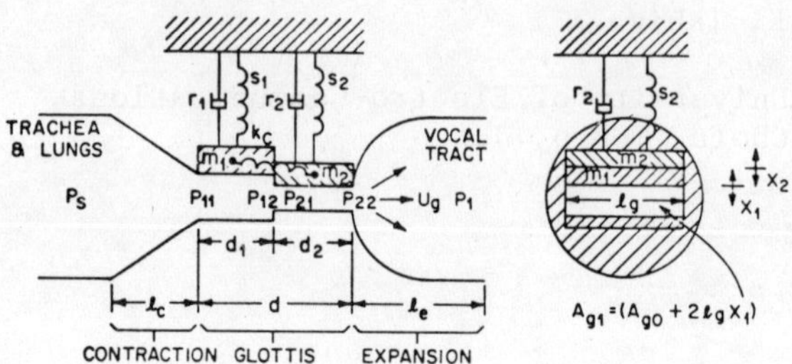

Fig.1. Schematic diagram of the two-mass approximation of the vocal cords.

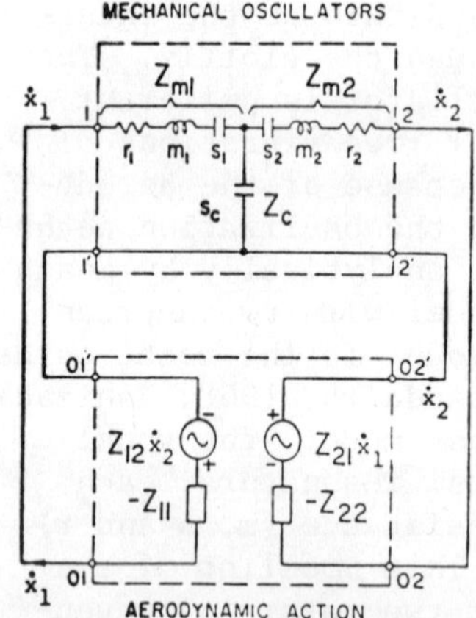

Fig.2. Equivalent network for the mechanical system of the two-mass model.

In the figure, the upper half represents the mechanical system of the vocal cords approximated by the two-mass model. Zm_1 and Zm_2 are the mechanical impedances of the lower and upper mechanical resonators, respectively, and $\dot{x}_1$ and $\dot{x}_2$ are the velocities of m_1 and m_2, respectively. The lower half of the equivalent network represents the aerodynamic reaction upon the mechanical system through the intraglottal pressure. The dependent generators, $Z_{12}\dot{x}_1$ and $Z_{12}\dot{x}_2$, represent the forces acting on the masses m_2 and m_1 respectively, which are caused by $\dot{x}_1$ and $\dot{x}_2$, respectively. Z_{11} and Z_{22} are the equivalent impedances pertaining to the self-reactions of $\dot{x}_1$ and $\dot{x}_2$ upon m_1 and m_2, respectively. For bilaterally symmetric vibrations of the vocal cords, twice the values for the aerodynamic reactions due to $\dot{x}_1$ and $\dot{x}_2$ should be taken. During the collision of the bilateral vocal cords, an additional boundary condition will be taken into account. Bilaterally asymmetric cord vibrations have been studied by physiological experiments and computer simulation but will not be involved in this paper (Isshiki, et al. 1977; Ishizaka and Isshiki, 1976). The two-mass model also can include a so-called one-mass model of the vocal cords as a special case for the coupling stiffness $s_3 = \infty$, whose vibratory mode corresponds to cord vibration with no vertical phase difference in the lower and upper margins of the vocal cords.

The motion of the two masses can be described as

$$\left[r_1 + pm_1 + \frac{s_1+s_3-\phi}{p}\right]\dot{x}_1 - \frac{s_3}{p}\dot{x}_2 = F_1 \doteq \frac{-\phi}{p}\dot{x}_2$$

$$-\frac{s_3}{p}\dot{x}_1 + \left[r_2 + pm_2 + \frac{s_2+s_3}{p}\right]\dot{x}_2 = F_2 \doteq 0 \qquad (1)$$

with

$$\phi = l_g \cdot d_1 \rho \ \nu^2/(2h),$$

where p is the complex frequency,
F_1 and F_2 are the forces acting on m_1 and m_2, respectively,
l_g is the effective length of the vocal cords,
ν is the average particle velocity of air flow across the glottal area,
ρ is the air density,
d_1 and d_2 are the thicknesses of m_1 and m_2, respectively,
and h is the glottal width.

Note that in this first approximation the aerodynamic reactions are represented through the factor ϕ only, so that $Z_{12} \doteq -\phi/p$, $Z_{11} \doteq \phi/p$ and $Z_{21} \doteq Z_{22} \doteq 0$. Therefore, for $\phi = 0$ equation (1) describes the motion of m_1 and m_2 with no air flow.

NATURAL FREQUENCIES AND NORMAL MODES

The natural frequencies and the normal modes can be obtained by setting $\phi = 0$, $F_1 = F_2 = 0$ and also $r_1 = r_2 = 0$ for simplicity. The natural angular frequencies are given by

$$\begin{matrix}\omega_{n1}\\ \omega_{n2}\end{matrix} = \sqrt{\left[\frac{\Omega_{10}^2+\Omega_{20}^2}{2}\right] \mp \sqrt{\left[\frac{\Omega_{10}^2-\Omega_{20}^2}{2}\right]^2 + (k_0\Omega_{10}\Omega_{20})^2}} \quad (2)$$

where $\Omega_{10} = \sqrt{(s_1+s_3)/m_1}$ = the resonance angular frequency when m_2 is clamped,

$\Omega_{20} = \sqrt{(s_2 + s_3)/m_2}$ = the resonance angular frequency when m_1 is clamped,

$$k_0 = s_3/\sqrt{(s_1+s_3)(s_2+s_3)}$$

and $\omega_{n1} < \omega_{n2}$.

From Equation (2) we have

$$\omega_{n2}^2 - \Omega_{20}^2 = \Omega_{10}^2 - \omega_{n1}^2 = \nu^2 \text{ for } \Omega_{10} < \Omega_{20}$$

$$\text{or } \omega_{n2}^2 - \Omega_{10}^2 = \Omega_{20}^2 - \omega_{n1}^2 = \nu^2 \text{ for } \Omega_{10} > \Omega_{20}, \quad (3)$$

$$\text{where } \nu^2 = \sqrt{\left[\frac{\Omega_{10}^2 - \Omega_{20}^2}{2}\right]^2 + (k_0\Omega_{10}\Omega_{20})^2} - \left|\frac{\Omega_{10}^2 - \Omega_{20}^2}{2}\right|$$

$$= \sqrt{a^2+\Gamma^2} - |a|, \quad \Gamma = k_0\Omega_{10}\Omega_{20} = s_3/\sqrt{m_1 m_2},$$

$$a = \frac{\Omega_{10}^2 - \Omega_{20}^2}{2}$$

This relation between the natural frequencies and the clamped frequencies is shown in Fig.3. The spacing between the two natural frequencies is greater than the spacing between the clamped resonance frequencies.

Inserting equation (2) into equation (1) gives the normal modes, that is,

$$\frac{\dot{x}_2}{\dot{x}_1}\Big|\omega_{n1} = \frac{1}{M} \cdot \frac{\Gamma}{\nu} > 0 \text{ and } \frac{\dot{x}_2}{\dot{x}_1}\Big|\omega_{n2} = -\frac{1}{M}\frac{\Gamma}{\nu} < 0 \quad (4)$$

where $M = \sqrt{m_2/m_1}$.

Equation (4) indicates that the masses m_1 and m_2 move in the same direction with the relative amplitudes given by equation (4) when vibrating at the lower natural frequency f_{n1}, and the masses move in opposite directions with the relative amplitudes specified by equation (4) at the higher natural frequency f_{n2}.

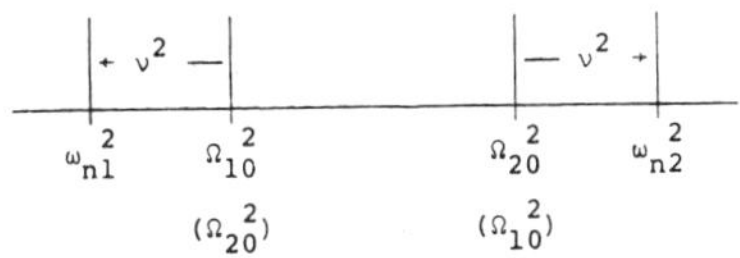

Fig.3. Relationship between the clamped frequencies Ω_{10} and Ω_{20} and the natural frequencies ω_{n1} and ω_{n2}.

CONDITIONS FOR OSCILLATION

We now consider the condition for a buildup of harmonic oscillation. The eigenvalues of equation (1) are approxmated as

$$s_1,\ \overline{s}_1 = \left[-\frac{\beta_1+\beta_2}{2}+\sigma\right] \pm j\omega_0 = \alpha_1 \pm j\omega_0$$

$$s_2,\ \overline{s}_2 = \left[-\frac{\beta_1+\beta_2}{2}-\sigma\right] \pm j\omega_0 = \alpha_2 \pm j\omega_0 \tag{5}$$

$$\text{where } \sigma^2 = \Omega_1\Omega_{20}\frac{k^2}{2(1+\sqrt{1+k^2})} - \left[\frac{\Omega_1-\Omega_{20}}{2}\right]^2$$

$$\omega_0^2 = \Omega_1\Omega_{20}(1+\sqrt{1+k^2})/2 + \left[\frac{\Omega_1-\Omega_{20}}{2}\right]^2$$

$$k^2 = \frac{(\phi-s_3)s_3}{(s_1+s_3-\phi)(s_2+s_3)}$$

$$\Omega_1^2 = (s_1+s_2-\phi)/m_1 \tag{6}$$

For the buildup of harmonic oscillation,

$$\alpha_1 > 0$$

$$\text{or } \sigma > (\beta_1 + \beta_2)/2 > 0, \tag{7}$$

and the oscillation frequency is given by $f_0 = \omega_0/2\pi$. To satisfy the inequality (7), it requires at least that

$$\Omega_1\Omega_{20}\,\frac{k^2}{2(1+\sqrt{1+k^2})} \gg \left[\frac{\Omega_1 - \Omega_{20}}{2}\right]^2 \tag{8}$$

and

$$s_1 + s_3 > \phi > s_3.$$

Notice that Ω_1 and k^2 are functions not only of the cord tissue but also of ϕ, which is dependent on the subglottal pressure and the glottal area. A numerical example of ϕ as a function of the glottal width h is shown in Fig.4 for subglottal pressures of 5, 10 and 15 cm H_2O, where d_1 and $d_2 = d/2$. The value for k is less than unity, normally, and increases with an increase in ϕ.

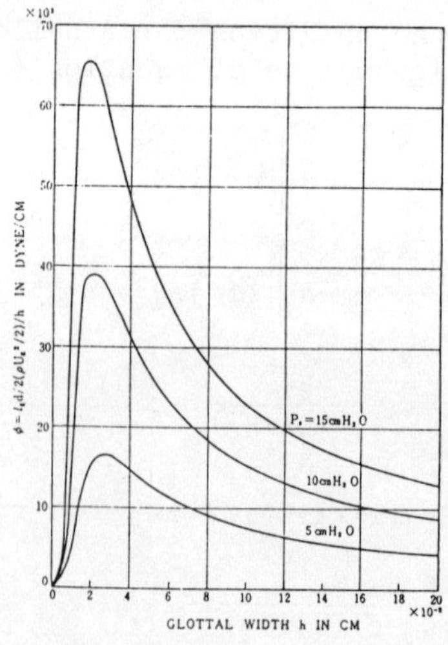

Fig.4. Numerical example of ϕ as a function of the glottal width.

It is apparent that the oscillation condition (7) can be satisfied favorably when $\Omega_1 \doteq \Omega_{20}$, although this condition is not necessary. Let us consider the oscillation condition when $\Omega_1 = \Omega_{20}$. In this case σ and ω_0 are further approximated as

$$\sigma \doteq \frac{k}{2}\sqrt{\Omega_1\Omega_{20}} = \frac{k}{2}\Omega_{20}$$

$$\omega_0 \doteq \sqrt{\Omega_1\Omega_{20}\{1+(k/2)^2\}} = \Omega_{20}\sqrt{1+(k/2)^2} \tag{9}$$

If we define the damping ratio approximately as

$$\zeta_1 = \beta_1/\Omega_{20} \text{ and } \zeta_2 = \beta_2/\Omega_{20}$$

then the oscillation condition can conveniently be expressed as

$$\alpha_1 = \sigma - \left[\frac{\beta_1+\beta_2}{2}\right] = \Omega_{20}\left\{\frac{k}{2} - \left[\frac{\zeta_1+\zeta_2}{2}\right]\right\} > 0. \tag{10}$$

This expression is instructive because we know the gross damping ratio of the vocal cords to be of the order of 0.2 according to the separate measurements by T. Kaneko (1976) and N. Isshiki (1977). The oscillation frequency in this case is approximately given by equation (9).

Notice that the two natural frequencies f_{n1} and f_{n2} in free vibration are now degenerated, by virtue of the aerodynamic reaction, into the single oscillation frequency $f_0 = \omega_0/2\pi$, when the oscillation condition is satisfied. The two separate natural frequencies no longer exist when the vocal cords commence a buildup of harmonic oscillation. However, the two normal modes exist at the oscillation frequency. This is the principal mechanism of the cord oscillator in the chest register, where the lower and upper margins of cord tissue vibrate with a phase difference, as will be shown below. This situation is numerically exemplified in Fig.5, in which the damping factors and the eigenfrequencies (real part and imaginary part of the characteristic equation) are shown as a function of the average flow velocity across the glottal slit. For $\alpha_1 > 0$ the cord oscillator can selfvibrate.

The oscillation mode is given by

$$\frac{\dot{x}_1}{\dot{x}_2} \doteq j(1+s_2/s_3)k\sqrt{1+(k/2)^2} \tag{11}$$

which indicates that x_1 leads x_2 in phase by about 90°. (The mechanical damping of the vocal cords acts to reduce the phase difference).

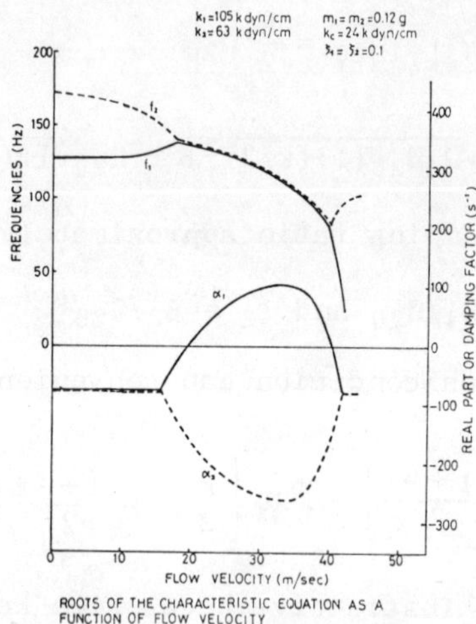

Fig.5. Eigenfrequencies f_1 and f_2 and damping factors α_1 and α_2 as a function of flow velocity. Calculations are based on parameter values shown at the top of the figure.

NONLINEAR FACTORS

The self-excited oscillator in general must contain nonlinear factors that will lead to a limitation in the steady-state amplitude of the vibration. In the cord oscillator such nonlinear factors are the nonlinear relation between the intraglottal pressure and glottal area, the collision at glottal closure, and nonlinear visco-elastic properties of the cord tissue. Study of the vibratory behavior of the vocal cords with these nonlinear characteristics is greatly facilitated by means of digital simulation. (See, for example, Titze and Talkin, 1979.)

We will show here only one example by computer simulation to indicate how the nonlinear elasticity during collision will affect the fundamental frequency of cord vibration. We model the nonlinear restoring force due to the deformation of the cord tissue during collision in terms of a hard spring characteristic, i.e.,

$$f(x) = k_c x \cdot (1+\eta_K x^2)$$

where x is the deformation of the cord tissue due to collision, k_c is a linear stiffness, and η_K is a coefficient representing the nonlinearity. This nonlinear relation has been incorporated in our computer model of the vocal cord/vocal tract.

Figure 6 shows the fundamental frequency as a function of the subglottal pressure obtained by the computer simulation (Ishizaka and Flanagan, 1972). The parameter in the figure is η_K. Note that for a subglottal pressure greater than several cm H_2O the fundamental frequency no longer varies with the subglottal pressure for $\eta_K = 0$, i.e. for a linear stiffness, whereas for $\eta_K = 100$ the fundamental frequency variation with the subglottal pressure is about 2 Hz/cm H_2O. This variation compares well with data measured on human subjects. The figure $\eta_K = 100$ also corresponds to that obtained from static measurements of elasticity on a fresh, excised human larynx by T. Kaneko et al. (1971).

One of the most difficult problems is the analytical treatment and formulation of air motion and the intraglottal pressure in relation to cord motion. The difficulty arises from the Navier-Stokes nonlinear equation. In earlier work, we neglected the compressibility of air in the glottis and the heat conduction loss at the surface of the vocal cords for simplicity, because the flow velocity in the glottis is much less than the sound velocity of air. Also, the velocity of cord motion is much slower than the glottal flow velocity. In our recent work (Ishizaka and Flanagan, 1977), we included in our computer model of the vocal cords air volume displaced by the vibrating vocal cords (displacement flow) together with the air compressibility and the heat conduction loss. Results of the computer simulation indicate that the effects of these factors on cord vibration and the quality of speech sounds are not significant for normal cord vibration in the chest register. These factors, however, might be considered for higher frequency modes of vibration, or for pathological cord vibration, where detailed, local deformation of the cord tissue is significant.

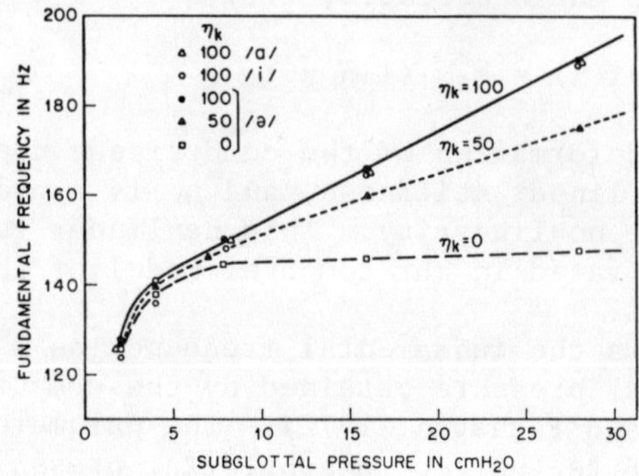

Fig.6. Variation of fundamental frequency with subglottal pressure for various values of the parameter η_K.

SUMMARY

By means of the two-mass model fo the vocal cords, it has been shown that the oscillatory mode with vertical phase differences is essential for vocal fold vibration. These vertical phase differences, with the motion of the lower mass preceding that of the upper mass, are consistent with the observation of a traveling wave along the mucosa. The importance of the wavy motion of the cord mucosa in the vocal mechanism was first proposed by I. Hiroto (1966) in his mucoviscoelastic-aerodynamic theory some fifteen years ago, when van den Berg's aerodynamic-myoelastic theory, corresponding to the one-mass model, was generally accepted. As we have seen, one of the advantages of the equivalent lumped-constant models is to allow us analytical treatment, as well as computer simulation, of the system being considered. Another advantage in the computer simulation is its computational economy.

REFERENCES

Flanagan, J.L. and Ishizaka, K. (1978) Computer model to characterize the air volume displaced by the vibrating vocal cords. J. Acoust. Soc. Am. 63, 1559-1565.

Hiroto, I. (1966) The mechanism of phonation; its pathophysiological aspect. Pract. Otolaryngol. (Kyoto) 39, 229-291 (in Japanese).

Ishizaka, K. and Flanagan, J.L. (1972) Synthesis of voiced sounds from a two-mass model of the vocal cords. Bell Syst. Tech. J. 51, 1233-1268

Ishizaka, K. and Flanagan, J.L. (1977) Acoustic properties of longitudinal displacement in vocal cord vibration. Bell Syst. Tech. J. 56, 889-913.

Ishizaka, K. and Isshiki, N. (1976) Computer simulation of pathological vocal-cord vibration. J. Acoust. Soc. Am. 60, 1193-1198.

Ishizaka, K. and Matsudaira, M. (1968) What makes the vocal cords vibrate? Proceedings of the 6th Int. Congr. Acoust. Tokyo, vol. 2, B9-12.

Ishizaka, K. and Matsudaira, M. (1972) Fluid mechanical consideration of vocal cord vibrations. Speech Comm. Res. Lab. Monograph No. 8.

Isshiki, N. (1977) Functional surgery of the larynx (In Japanese).

Isshiki, N., Tanabe, M., Ishizaka, K. and Broad, D.J. (1977) Clinical significance of asymmetrical tension of the vocal cords. Ann Otol. Rhinol. and Laryngol. 86, 1-9.

Kaneko, T. Asano, H., Miura, H., and Ishizaka, K. (1971) Biomechanics of the vocal cords. Pract. Otolaryngol. (Kyoto) 64, 1229-1235 (in Japanese).

Kaneko, T. et al. (1976) Biomechanics of the human vocal cords. Pract. Otolaryngol. (Kyoto) 69, 1963-1969

Titze, I.R. and Talkin, D.T. (1979) A theoretical study of the effects of various laryngeal configuraitons on the acoustics of phonation. J. Acoust. Soc. Am. 66, 60-74.

DISCUSSION

Koike: A few years ago I saw a motion picture made by Paul Ward and Paul Moore of a girl who could sing a chorus, i.e., a duet, all by herself. How would your model account for this kind of diplophonia?

Ishizaka: We have not specifically attempted to model this phenomenon. Consequently, I am sorry to say that I cannot give you a satisfactory answer.

Hirano: Considering the fact that as physicians we are often more impressed by cosmetics than mechanics of the vocal folds, my question is, can you explain to some of us cosmetical doctors what kind of physical phenomena can be explained by your model? Can you give us some examples, so that we can have a better understanding of your model from a medical standpoint? That would be very helpful to us.

Ishizaka: Some time ago I came to an understanding of the oscillation mechanics of the vocal cords. The vocal cords self-oscillate as a result of interaction with the air flow. Traditionally, one reads that the vocal cords close through the action of Bernoulli pressure, and when the vocal cords are closed, they begin to be forced apart by subglottal pressure. Then the vibration continues through periodic variation of these forces. But, is this explanation good enough for understanding the physical processes of vocal fold vibration? I could never quite understand from this statement whether the vocal cords should self-oscillate or not. So I tried to restate why the vocal cords cannot self-oscillate with a reduction of air flow. But it is very difficult to explain concisely the oscillation mechanics without an equation. Dr. Titze, can you formulate a brief explanation of the vocal mechanics?

Titze: If I understand Dr. Hirano's question, I think he is looking a little bit more for applications of your model, and I think you've done some excellent simulation on the bilateral asymmetrics. Maybe you can address that point a little bit.

Ishizaka: The two-mass model of the vocal cords can be used as a speech synthesizer when combined with a computer model of the vocal tract. In order to synthesize speech with a computer, it is desirable to compute in real time, if possible. So it is better if the model can be simple. If the model cannot represent the fundamental nature of the mechanism of oscillation, it cannot produce non-sharp, non-synthetic-sounding speech.

Also, the model can be modified to include an asymmetrical configuration, as we have demonstrated with Dr. Isshiki by simulating vocal fold paralysis. In that case the local deformation of the vocal cord along the length direction may not be important. Perhaps it will not be necessary to add additional mass, i.e., more than two masses. So, in that particular case, the two-mass model can represent some of the pathological behavior of the vocal cord. More detailed study to demonstrate the need to increase the number of masses to more than two is called for.

Stevens: I would like to try to state, in non-mathematical terms, what seems to be the important contribution that Dr. Ishizaka's two-mass model has made to an understanding of the mechanism of vocal-fold vibration. What Dr. Ishizaka has shown is that a significant transfer of energy from the air flow to the mechanical vibratory system can be achieved if the upper and lower edges of the folds undergo in-and-out motions that are out of phase. The phase lag of the upper edge with respect to the lower edge permits energy to be fed to the mechanical system due to the subglottal pressure when the lower edges are approximated, and due to a negative pulse of Bernoulli force when the upper edges are farther apart than the lower edges. The wavelike motion on the surface of the vocal folds (which can be represented very roughly by two masses vibrating, with the displacement of the lower mass preceding that of the upper mass) provides the necessary conditions for creating the forces due to fluctuating pressures on the vocal folds, so that vibration can be maintained. While it is possible to maintain vibration under some conditions when each vocal fold is represented as a single mass executing lateral motions, this is a tenuous kind of vibration, since not much energy is available from the aerodynamic forces to maintain vibration.

Titze: I agree. We experimented with one-mass models a fair amount and concluded that the only asymmetry condition in the driving forces (i.e., different forces during opening and closing phases of the vibratory cycle) that one can get from a one-mass model comes from glottal or vocal tract inertance. Aerodynamic or acoustic inertance creates an asymmetry in the driving forces with respect to opening and closing because the glottal impedance is not the same. This asymmetry in the forces can sustain oscillation. If one eliminates glottal air inertance and vocal tract loading from the simulation, oscillation stops altogether. But I agree that it is an inefficient mechanism for sustaining oscillation.

Ishizaka: I am not sure about the oscillation mechanics of the vocal cord in the falsetto register. The two-mass model, I think, does not necessarily explain the oscillation mechanics for falsetto.

CHAPTER 18
BIOMECHANICS AND DISTRIBUTED-MASS MODELS OF VOCAL FOLD VIBRATION

Ingo R. Titze

Department of Speech Pathology and Audiology,
University of Iowa, Iowa City, Iowa, USA

INTRODUCTION

As a link between neurophysiology and acoustics, the field of biomechanics offers theories of tissue and air movement that allow prediction of configurational states, modes of vibration, and magnitudes of displacement of laryngeal tissue resulting from forces developed within the speech musculature. Causal relationships between muscle contraction and precise configurational states of the larynx could be established if the theories, or portions thereof, were deemed applicable and supported by certain key measurements. Kinematic description of articulatory and phonatory movement, relatively abundant in the literature, can aid in establishing causality in a statistical sense, but more complete kinetic descriptions are needed to relate force and displacement and to predict the acoustic output for a single event. The basic elements of such descriptions are presented in this report.

FUNDAMENTAL OF SOFT TISSUE MECHANICS

The human vocal folds consist of a variety of soft tissues, including the epithelium (mucous membrane), the superficial (mucosal) layer, the vocal ligament, and the vocalis muscle (Hirano, 1975). The viscoelastic properties of these tissue layers have not been investigated extensively. Some data are available from steady-state force-elongation curves (Hast, 1966; van den Berg, 1958; Hirano, 1975), but variability resulting from the age and type of the cadavers, from sample preparation and specification, and from inconsistency in the physical quantities measured is sufficiently large to render the contributions incomplete and difficult to compare. Dr. Kakita will describe some of the viscoelastic quantities later in this conference (Chapter 25 of this book). Measurements on tissues other than the vocal folds are abundant in the literature, but there seems to be sufficient variability among organs of the body to allow only qualitative comparisons. Prediction of material properties on a microscopic (molecular) level is even more restrictive (Fung, 1968).

Since the major portions of the vocal folds are composed of muscle, we begin our discussion with a traditional description of muscle mechanics. On an empirical level, this usually involves static force-elongation relationships (Fig.1). If the relationships are to be independent of the size or shape of the muscle, some normalization with respect to cross-sectional area and length of the muscle is usually possible. Force is then replaced by force per unit area, or stress, and elongation is replaced by elongation per unit length, or strain. The force-elongation relationship then becomes a stress-strain relationship. If it is possible to express this relationship mathematically, it is termed the constitutive equation.

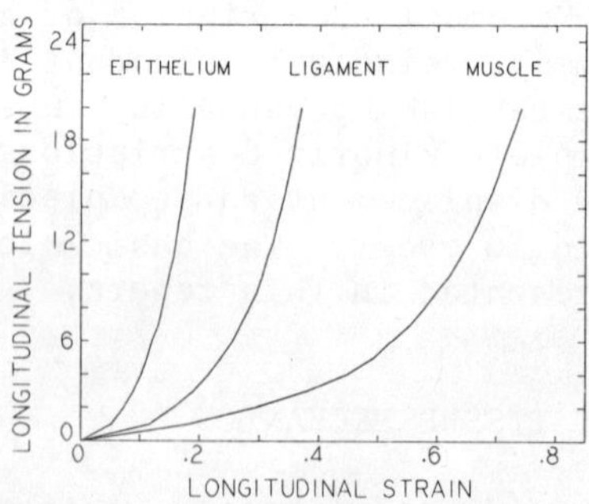

Fig.1. Average force-elongation curves for three tissues of the vocal fold measured in the direction of the fibers (after Kakita, Chapter 25 of this book, and Hirano, unpublished).

For an elastic material, the constitutive equation reduces to Hooke's Law, stating that stress and strain are proportional. Thus, if the stress (or stresses) acting on an elastic material are known, the deformation is totally predictable from Hooke's Law. Furthermore, the response is immediate for a perfectly elastic medium. No consideration of time delay or history of previous deformation is needed.

Unfortunately, muscle (or any human tissue) does not obey Hooke's Law. It is well known that a muscle subjected to a sudden step-change in strain will develop a smaller steady-state stress than the initial value at the time the strain occurred. This phenomenon is called stress relaxation and is a direct consequence of the viscous nature of the tissue. There is a strong resistance to the rate at which the deformation takes place. A related phenomenon is strain creep. When a sudden stress is imposed upon a muscle, the tissue tends to creep to its final strain at a rate solely determined by the material properties. A simple one-dimensional lumped-element model that incorporates relaxation and creep, as well as the internal contractile nature of muscle, is shown in Fig.2a. This classical model was described nearly half a century ago by Hill (1938). Originally the lumped constants k_p (parallel spring) and k_s (series spring) were assumed to be linear in the sense that they obeyed Hooke's Law. More recent treatments have incorporated "exponential" springs (Glantz, 1974), but the basic model is still appropriate. A viscous element b (dashpot) is included to model the energy loss and response delay.

As a first attempt in obtaining a constitutive equation relating stress and strain (or force and displacement) in a muscle along the direction of its fibers, it is important to analyze this simple model. Let $\Psi(t)$ be the displacement (from equilibrium) of the free end of a muscle that is rigidly attached to a boundary at the other end. (We might think of the vocalis fixed anteriorly at the thyroid cartilage and freed at the arytenoid cartilage.) The force applied at the free end is f(t), the internal contractile force is $f_c(t)$, and the internal displacement (action in relation to myosin) is $\Psi_i(t)$. A simplified schematic representation of this internal displacement is shown in Fig.2b.

Assuming that the deformation is slowly-varying, i.e., the inertial forces are negligible, the forces must balance at the two nodes indicated in Fig.2a.

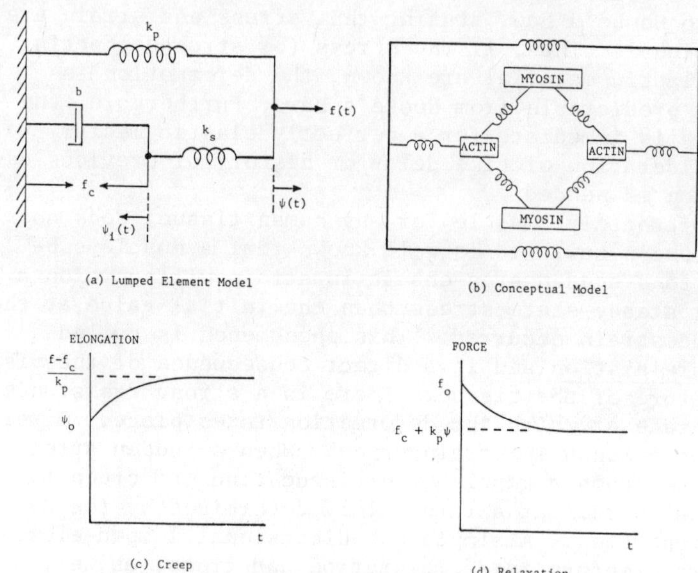

Fig.2. Classical muscle model ((a) and (b)) and its response to sudden changes in stress (d) and strain (c).

$$k_p\psi + k_s(\psi + \psi_i) = f \tag{1}$$

$$b\,\frac{d\psi_i}{dt} + k_s(\psi + \psi_i) = f_c \tag{2}$$

These equations can be combined into one equation by solving (1) for ψ_i and its derivative, and substituting the expressions into (2). The result is

$$b\,\frac{k_p + k_s}{k_s}\,\frac{d\psi}{dt} + k_p\psi = f - f_c + \frac{b}{k_s}\,\frac{df}{dt}\,. \tag{3}$$

This first order differential equation has a certain symmetry with respect to the variables ψ and f. It does not matter which of these we designate as the input variable (driving function) and the output variable (response). If f is the driving function, then

$$\psi = (1/\tau k_p)e^{-t/\tau}[\int(f-f_c + \frac{b}{k_s}\frac{df}{dt})e^{t/\tau}dt + C] \qquad (4)$$

is a general solution of (3), where C is an integration constant and τ is a time constant, defined as

$$\tau = \frac{b(k_s + k_p)}{k_s k_p} \qquad (5)$$

A similar solution can be written for f in terms of ψ, but with b/k_s as the time constant.

Note that the internal contractile force f_c is in direct opposition to the externally applied force f. A good example of such a force combination in speech physiology is the vocalis contractile force and the cricothyroid contractile force, the latter being effectively an external force applied to the ends of the vocalis muscle. Thus, in establishing the steady-state elongation of the muscle, one needs to consider the difference between the two forces. (See Fujimura, Chapter 19 of this book.)

The time-independent solution is immediately obvious from (3). Since, by definition, the derivatives vanish in the steady state,

$$\psi = (f-f_c)/k_p \qquad (6)$$

or

$$f = f_c + k_p\psi \qquad (7)$$

An isometric condition can be predicted from equation (6) By definition, muscle elongation is zero for an isometric contraction, and the internal force f_c balances the external force f. (ψ_i is, of course, non-zero, indicating that relative displacement of actin and myosin within the muscle can occur.) For non-isometric contractions, the total external force is the sum of the active internal force of contraction and a passive force of elongation, as demonstrated in equation (7). It is clear that Hooke's Law is not obeyed by the muscle if active contraction occurs. Even though a linear relationship exists between f and ψ (if k_p is a constant), force and elongation are not proportional.

The general time-dependent response to a step function is simply exponential drift from an initial state to a steady state. Examples of creep and relaxation are shown in Figs.2(c) and (d). Note the difference in polarity of the drift. Creep is an increase in elongation, whereas relaxation is a decrease in force. Precise quantitative solutions can be obtained with equation (4) and its inverse.

In the description of vocal fold vibration, one is concerned primarily with passive tissue deformations resulting from aerodynamic and acoustic stresses. It is assumed that the complete biomechanical response of laryngeal tissue can be approximated by superposition of two responses. The first is a slowly-varying response to active muscular forces that generate a quasi-stationary laryngeal configuration. The second response is then assumed to be a passive variation around this configuration, where zero displacement represents the lowest energy state, i.e., a stable mechanical equilibrium. It is more meaningful, therefore, to derive a <u>differential constitutive equation</u>, relating small changes of force and elongation around a specified bias condition. In particular, if we assume sinusoidal time variations of the form $e^{i\omega t}$, a differential force to elongation ratio can be derived from (3).

$$\frac{\Delta f}{\Delta\psi} = \frac{k_p + i\omega b\,(k_p + k_s)/k_s}{1 + i\omega b/k_s} = \frac{k_p + \omega^2 b^2 (k_p + k_s)/k_s^2 + i\omega b}{1 + \omega^2 b^2/k_s^2}\,, \qquad (8),\ (9)$$

For moderate to low losses, such that

$$(\omega b)^2 << k_s^2\,, \qquad (10)$$

the differential force-elongation relationship becomes <u>linearly viscoelastic</u>,

$$\frac{\Delta f}{\Delta\psi} = k_p + i\omega b = \overline{k}_p\,, \qquad (11)$$

where $\overline{k}_p$ is a complex number. It appears that not only is the force-elongation curve linearized, but Hooke's Law is obeyed if we think of the spring constant as having a real and an imaginary part, in direct analogy with the extension of resistance to impedance.

In much of our analysis of phonation we will consider equations of the form of (11) as constitutive equations for tissue vibrations about an equilibrium configuration, whereas equations of the form (3) or (7) may be necessary to analyze gross tissue displacement. It is clear, however, that equation (11) must be extended to include elongation in several dimensions. Furthermore, it will be necessary to describe the response of an entire distributed system of viscoelastic tissue. This leads us into the area of continuum mechanics and its rather specialized nomenclature.

DESCRIPTION OF VOCAL FOLD TISSUE AS A VISCOELASTIC CONTINUOUS MEDIUM

We have discussed one-dimensional deformation of a muscle as a whole. Such an approach would be appropriate if deformation were indeed uniform throughout the given tissue member. Often, however, movement is constrained at several "rigid" boundaries, such as bones or cartilages, making uniform displacement unlikely. In fact, only excised portions of tissue can be strained uniformly. It is therefore imperative that one find a way of expressing stress and strain as a function of position within the tissue. In addition, the elastic, viscous, and inertial properties may vary continuously in several dimensions. Definitions and notation need to be expanded to incorporate these generalities.

A. Stress and Strain in Three Dimensions

Biological continua are subject to the same physical laws of motions as any other material. Newton's law and conservation of mass and momentum, as well as balance of energy and entropy, are frequently called upon to establish basic cause-effect relationships in the dynamics of tissue movement. For any continuous substance, whether it be a gas, a liquid, or a solid, we can generally identify *internal forces*, *surface forces*, and *body forces*. Internal forces are those which represent the microscopic interactions between molecules within the material. These are often the most difficult to describe on a macroscopic level, especially in biological materials, because the molecular structure is very complex. The constitutive equations are attempts at such macroscopic representations of internal molecular forces.

Since the extent of the material is generally finite, surface forces can exist at the boundaries. These forces are often responsible for setting the entire system into motion, but they may also serve to constrain the system. The descriptions of the forces and motion at the surfaces are termed the *boundary conditions*.

Additional forces, such as gravitational forces or electromagnetic forces, may be imposed on any portion of tissue. These are the so-called body forces. They are proportional to the mass of a given tissue *element*. (An element is a small, but macroscopic, portion of the continuum within which all properties may be considered constant.) The inertial force, i.e., the product of mass and acceleration of a tissue element, may be thought of as a body force.

The proper balance of the collection of all forces is a statement of Newton's laws of motion, or simply, the *equations of motion*. Often more than one equation of motion is necessary to describe the dynamics of even a single tissue element. In particular, if displacement at some point within the tissue occurs in three dimensions, one can define a *displacement vector* $\vec{u}$ as follows:

$$\vec{u} = \xi\hat{i} + \psi\hat{j} + \;\hat{k} \qquad (12)$$

where $\hat{i}$, $\hat{j}$, and $\hat{k}$ are unit vectors in the x, y, and z directions, and ξ, ψ, and ζ, are the respective *components of displacement*. (The displacement is measured from an equilibrium position of each element rather than a common origin.) Thus, the cartesian coordinates x, y, and z are used to describe the equilibrium position of a tissue element, whereas the Greek symbols describe additional nonequilibrium displacement.

The number of *degrees of freedom* of the system corresponds to the number of independent displacements which are possible for the entire system. For a finite number of elements, this can be up to six degrees (three translational and three rotational) for each element. A continuum, however, has an infinite number of elements, and hence an infinite number of degrees of freedom. When disturbed by an impulse, the system will respond in any number of its *natural modes*, each mode being a unique combination of displacements of all the tissue elements. Thus, a continuum generally has an infinite number of modes. Unless the system is *degenerate*, the number of modes equals the number of degrees of freedom. A more complete discussion of tissue modes in the vocal fold structure can be found in Titze and Strong (1975).

If the displacements are smoothly-varying functions with existing higher-order derivatives, the following component strains can be defined (see, for example, Sokolnikoff, 1956; Timoshenko and Goodier, 1951 or Saada, 1974):

$$e_{xx} = \frac{\partial \xi}{\partial x} \tag{13}$$

$$e_{yy} = \frac{\partial \psi}{\partial y} \tag{14}$$

$$e_{zz} = \frac{\partial \zeta}{\partial z} \tag{15}$$

$$e_{zy} = e_{yz} = \frac{\partial \zeta}{\partial y} + \frac{\partial \psi}{\partial z} \tag{16}$$

$$e_{yx} = e_{xy} = \frac{\partial \psi}{\partial x} + \frac{\partial \xi}{\partial y} \tag{17}$$

$$e_{xz} = e_{zx} = \frac{\partial \xi}{\partial z} + \frac{\partial \zeta}{\partial x} \tag{18}$$

The double subscript is needed on each component strain to specify the directionality of the strain and the plane on which it is defined. Several types of strain are suggested in the above equations. In simple extension (elongation), the displacement increases in a direction (first subscript) normal to the plane (second subscript), whereas in simple shear the displacement increases in a direction parallel to the plane. Figure 3 illustrates these two cases. The strain in Fig.3a would be identified as $e_{xx} = \partial\xi/\partial x$, and the strain in Fig.3b would be identified as $e_{xz} = \partial\xi/\partial z$ (with $\partial\zeta/\partial x = 0$). Various combinations of simple strains can result in compression or dilation [Fig. 3c], rotations, or other types of compound deformations.

In order to relate strain and stress of an element to its material properties, it is necessary to describe the effects of all the nearest-neighbor elements. As stated earlier, stress is a force distributed over a finite area, but it can be defined at a specific point if the area is allowed to shrink to zero. Thus, in precise notation, $\sigma_{xz}(x, y, z, t)$ is a stress in the x-direction acting on a surface in the z-plane that has shrunk to zero at the point x, y, z. The stress can also vary according to time t. There are six independent stresses, corresponding to

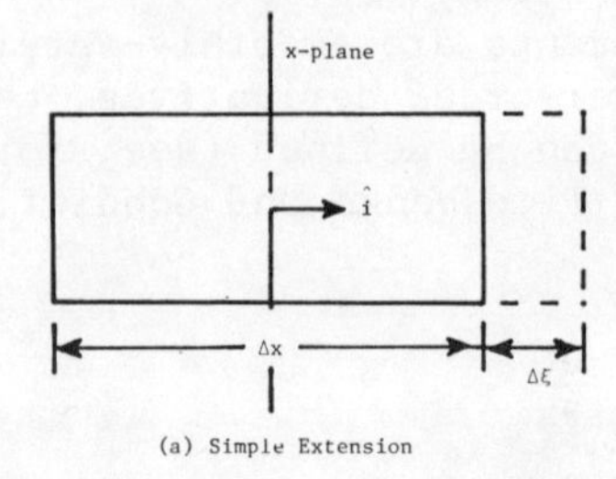

(a) Simple Extension

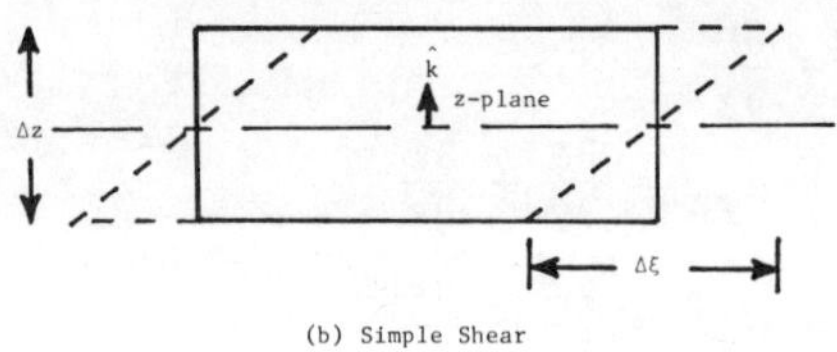

(b) Simple Shear

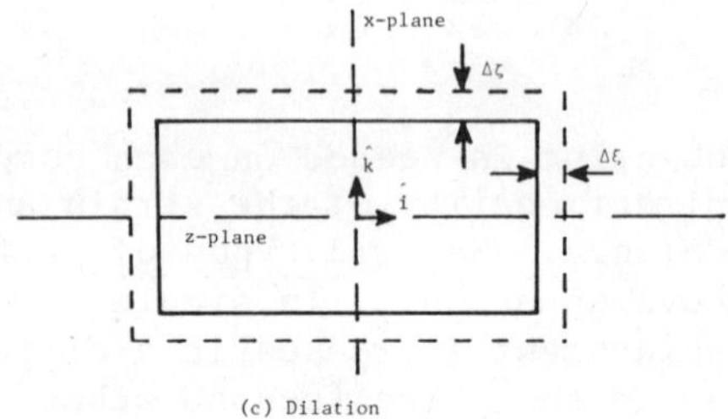

(c) Dilation

Fig.3. Illustrations of several simple deformations of a tissue element.

the six independent strains in equations (13) through (18), for each tissue element. The relationship between all of these stresses and strains depends, of course, on the viscoelastic properties of the specific tissue in question.

B. Viscoelastic Properties of Vocal Fold Tissue

Most material properties are best described by a strain-stress-history diagram. Perfectly elastic materials have no strain or stress history, as mentioned previously. When all stress is removed, all strain vanishes. Hence, one does not need to keep track of previous deformations. A liquid obviously does not fall into this category, since it generally does not return to an equilibrium configuration. Neither does a plastic material such as clay. Human tissues are composed of elastic fibers surrounded by liquid. One would expect them to be neither purely elastic nor purely viscous, but rather viscoelastic. Therefore, because of the viscous nature of laryngeal tissue, stress and strain histories may play an important role in laryngeal biomechanics. Although little imphasis has been placed on this in the past, one might wonder what short-term history effects are involved in prolonged phonation, or what roles they play in vocal fatigue and development of vocal fold pathology. As stress relaxes or creep occurs, what strategy is involved to maintain the desired phonatory conditions?

A material is called homogeneous if the properties are evenly distributed within a given element. Any real substance becomes inhomogenous on an atomic or molecular level. On a microscopic level many substances, including human tissues, are reasonably homogeneous. It is quite possible for human tissues to be nonuniform, however, indicating that the properties may be varying from element to element, i.e., spatially. The properties of the vocal fold as a whole are quite nonuniform, as demonstrated by the layered configuration of the body and cover.

If the material properties are dependent upon the direction in which they are measured, e.g., if shear in one plane results in a different stress than the identical shear in another plane, the material is said to be nonisotropic. Most organic substances tend to be nonisotropic, primarily because of the presence of tissue fibers. These fibers usually respond differently longitudinally (in a plane parallel to the fiber direction) than transversely (in a plane perpendicular to the fiber direction). As a first approximation, fibrous substances may be classified as transversally-isotropic, or orthotropic.

A substance is compressible if the density changes under the application of stresses. Strictly speaking, all substances are compressible, but if the deformations of interest are such that the volume of the substance is not changed appreciably, we may regard them as incompressible. At ultrasonic frequencies, the deformations are of the same order as the volumetric changes. The tissues must therefore be considered compressible at ultrasonic frequencies. Tissue vibration at audio frequencies, on the other hand, such as vocal fold vibration, occur near a surface and always involve deformation in more than one dimension. A strain in one direction is accompanied by a corresponding opposite strain in another direction, leaving the volume and density unaffected. The strains are also much larger than those at ultrasonic frequencies. Hence, for our purposes, biological tissues are incompressible.

In summary, the viscoelastic properties of the system of layers of vocal fold tissue may be assumed to be incompressible, orthotropic, homogeneous, and nonuniform. In addition, linearity can be assumed if vibration about a static strain is not excessive in amplitude. We will now attempt to quantify these viscoelastic properties by postulating a three-dimensional constitutive equation relating stress and strain in vocal fold tissues.

C. Constitutive Equations for Vocal Fold Tissue in Vibration

As stated in equation (11), a muscle in a constant state of contraction under uniform one-dimensional oscillatory strain obeys Hooke's Law for small amplitudes. The oscillatory behavior around an equilibrium configuration approaches that of a system of masses, springs, and dashpots. One can rewrite equation (11) slightly on a per unit area and per unit length basis, such that

$$\Delta f/\Delta s = (k + i\omega b)\,\frac{\ell}{\Delta s}\,\frac{\Delta\psi}{\ell} \tag{19}$$

where Δs is the surface over which f is distributed, and ℓ is the length of the muscle. According to our previous definitions, $\Delta f/\Delta s$ is a stress and $\Delta\psi/\ell$ is a strain. The equation assumes a somewhat new appearance under replacement of absolute (lumped) quantities with per unit (distributed) quantities

$$\sigma_n = \bar{c}\, e_n \tag{20}$$

where $\bar{c}$ is a complex elastic constant, σ_n is the one-dimensional normal stress, and e_n is the corresponding strain. Only one subscript is needed here because interpretation of the plane on which the stress acts in not ambiguous and a specific cartesian orientation need not be chosen.

Since e_n is dimensionless, the units of $\bar{c}$ and σ_n are identical, usually expressed in dyn/cm^2. Note that a lumped-element elastic constant can be converted to a distributed-element elastic constant by multiplying by the length of the tissue sample and dividing by its cross-section.

For nonuniform strains in three dimensions, equation (20) needs to be expanded to include all possible stresses and strains on all six surfaces of a small tissue element. Each surface has one normal stress and two shear stresses, but it can be shown that not all of them are independent (Saada, 1974). A complete set of constitutive equations may be written in matrix form as follows:

$$\begin{pmatrix} \sigma_{xx} \\ \sigma_{yy} \\ \sigma_{zz} \\ \sigma_{zy} \\ \sigma_{yx} \\ \sigma_{xz} \end{pmatrix} = \begin{pmatrix} \lambda+2\mu & \lambda' & \lambda & & & \\ \lambda' & c' & \lambda' & & & \\ \lambda & \lambda' & \lambda+2\mu & & & \\ & & & \mu' & & \\ & & & & \mu' & \\ & & & & & \mu \end{pmatrix} \begin{pmatrix} e_{xx} \\ e_{yy} \\ e_{zz} \\ e_{zy} \\ e_{yx} \\ e_{xz} \end{pmatrix} \qquad (21)$$

There are five independent viscoelastic constants, namely λ, λ', c', μ and μ'. The notation and specific choice of these constants come from the theory of elasticity, where they are more specifically referred to as Lamé constants (Sokolnikoff, 1956; Timoshenko and Goodier, 1969; Saada, 1974).

An equivalent representation in terms of Young's moduli, Poisson's ratios, and shear moduli is equally common. It expresses equation (21) in inverse form, such that unknown strains are computed from known stresses. Experimentalists sometimes prefer this alternate description because it fits the usual laboratory procedure of applying known stresses and measuring the resulting deformations. Theorists, on the other hand, prefer the description given here because it allows for symmetry and economy in the mathematical formation. Transformations between the constants can be found in most textbooks on elasticity.

All of the viscoelastic constants may be complex if losses are present. Orthotropy is specified by the prime-unprime distinction as a superscript, incompressibility is specified by making the bulk incompressibility constants λ and λ' large in relation to the shear elastic constants μ and μ'. Nonuniformity of the tissue properties, i.e., the layered structure, is specified by making any or all of the elastic constants position-dependent.

If isotropy is assumed rather than orthotropy, the number of independent elastic constants is reduced to two, since by symmetry, $\lambda' = \lambda$, $\mu' = \mu$, and $c' = \lambda + 2\mu$. This is a significant simplification. Some experimental work is needed to determine under which conditions such a simplification is justifiable. The measurements conducted by Kakita (Chapter 25 of this book) shed some light on the transverse-longitudinal distinction.

For the purpose of modelling vocal fold vibration, we consider equation (21) as the three-dimensional constitutive equation. Together with Newton's second law of motion and the boundary conditions, this equation is the core of the mathematical formulation of vocal fold tissue mechanics. More detail can be found in Titze (1976), and Talkin (1979). We will now show, on a purely descriptive level, how the formulation can be used in distributed mass models of the vocal folds.

DISTRIBUTED-MASS MODELS OF VOCAL FOLD VIBRATION

The complexity of the viscoelastic properties makes it impractical to attempt an exact analytical solution to determine the nature of vocal fold vibration under self-oscillating conditions. The difficulty is magnified by the fact that the boundary conditions at the glottis are strongly influenced by airflow and vocal fold collision, two rather complex dynamic processes in and of themselves. A computer simulation is therefore the only viable means for obtaining a solution to this complex problem. Details of such a simulation are beyond the scope of this paper. The following steps outline the basic approach.

1) Assume an equilibrium configuration. This involves the selection of initial positions and zero velocities of a three-dimensional array of tissue elements (Fig.4), the initial surface contours, and the elastic constants within each tissue element.
2) For the given configuraiton, the airflow is calculated according to the pressure-flow relationships developed by van den Berg, et al. (1958) and Ishizaka and Matsudaira (1972).
3) From the calculated pressure profile, the normal and tangential stresses on the free surfaces of the vocal folds are computed. They form a portion of the boundary conditions.
4) The stresses of constraint on surfaces that are

normally attached to other structures, such as cartilages and other non-vibrating tissue, are claculated by an image technique. These are additional boundary conditions.

5) From the given positions and velocities, the internal stresses are calculated via the constitutive equation for each tissue element.
6) New positions and velocities are now computed from the equations of motion and the combined boundary conditions.
7) The procedure is repeated from step 2.

In the process of the simulation, a large number of physiological quantities can be monitored. These include three-dimensional vibratory movement, tissue stresses, airflow, glottal pressure profiles, vocal tract pressures (if a vocal tract is included in the simulation), and any number of so-called glottographic signals. The latter may include glottal area function and medial surface contact area. Potentially, therefore, biomechanical modelling of the phonatory process has the advantage of producing and accepting data at many levels. We hope to make use of this capability in future refinements of the model.

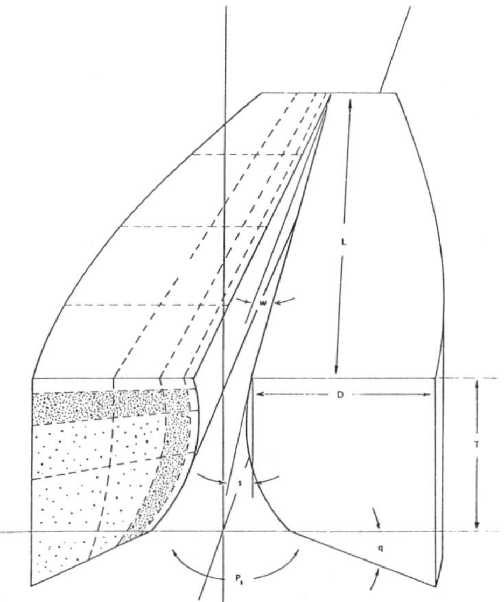

Fig.4. Schematic representation of a computational model of the vocal folds, showing tissue layers and geometric parameters.

Examples of some of the outputs of the simulation are shown in Figs.5 and 6. In Fig.5 we show top and frontal sectional views of simulated vocal fold motions for several adjustments that deviate slightly from a nominal configuration (Fig.5a). Seven frames, representing approximately one cycle, are shown for this nominal configuration, and corresponding frames for each additional adjustment are shown in Figs.5(b) through (g). In part (b) the vocal folds have been adducted more tightly than in the nominal case. This increased adduction limits both the maximum glottal width and the extent of vertical movement (frontal section). In part (c) the opposite adjustment is demonstrated. The pre-phonatory glottal width has been increased slightly to allow a small, but constant, opening at the posterior end. This opening produces airflow leakage during the "closed" portion of the cycle.

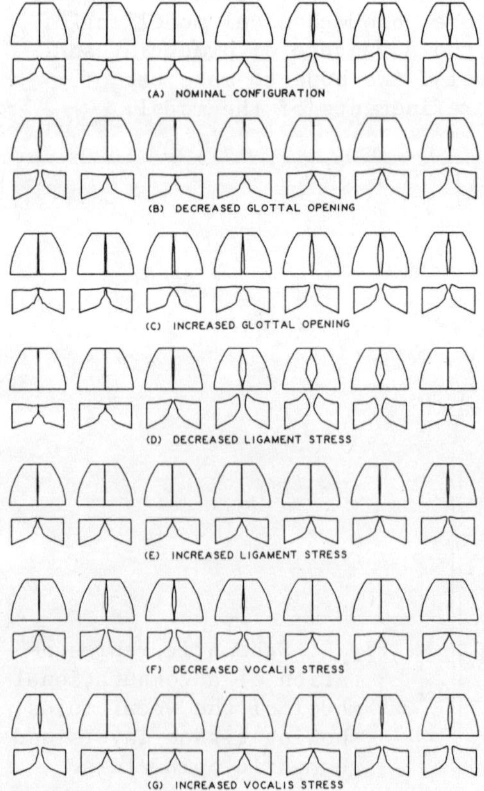

Fig.5. Top and frontal views of simulated vocal fold motions for several different pre-phonatory adjustments.

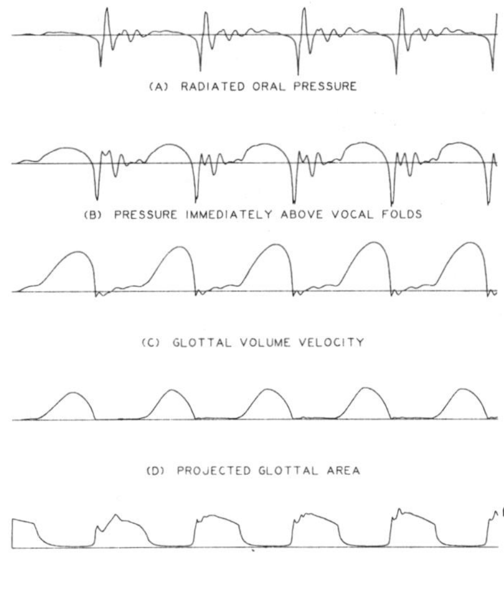

Fig.6. Simulated waveforms that constitute a portion of the output of the computational model.

In parts (d) and (e) the stiffness in the ligament has been decreased and increased, respectively. Note that decreased stiffness (or stress) in the ligament allows for considerable increase in mobility of the tissue, as seen by the large vibrational amplitude in part (d). Increased stiffness (or stress) in the ligament, on the other hand, restricts tissue motion much like increased adduction. Some variations in vocalis stress conditions are shown in parts (f) and (g). Specific detail about the parameters involved in each of these adjustments can be found in Titze and Talkin (1979).

Figure 6 shows some of the acoustic outputs, beginning with the oral radiated pressure and proceeding backwards toward quantities measurable at the larynx, such as supraglottal pressure, volume flow, area function, and medial surface contact area. Note that the supraglottal pressure (Fig.6b) appears as a hybrid between the oral radiated pressure and the glottal volume flow. During vocal fold closure it resembles the oral pressure in that a large amount of formant ripple is present immediately after closure. The incident and reflected pressures from the vocal tract determine the net supraglottal pressure. During glottal opening, however, when subglottal damping is introduced, the formant structure is rapidly attenuated and the supraglottal pressure follows more nearly the shape of the volume flow.

A second point of interest is the difference between glottal volume velocity and glottal area function (parts c and d). Whereas the volume flow is skewed to the right (speed quotient greater than one), the area function is nearly symmetric. In fact, the speed quotient is slightly less than one in this particular case. Note also that the glottal area has less formant ripple than the volume flow. This comparison indicates that actual tissue disturbances resulting from vocal tract interactions with the source are not as large as the flow disturbances. Tissue inertia serves as a low-pass filter.

Finally, comparison of glottal area function with medial surface contact area reveals that these two signals complement one another. Significant changes in contact area occur during glottal closure (the flat portion in the glottal area waveform). Likewise, significant changes in the glottal area take place when there is basically a saturated (no contact), open situation. One might hypothesize, therefore, that a combination of these waveforms has the best chance of providing an accurate picture of movement of the medial surface of the vocal folds. Research is in progress to relate these measurable acoustic quantities to viscoelastic parameters in order to establish a closer tie between muscle physiology and phonatory acoustics. Further details of the model and its applications can be found in Titze and Talkin (1979; 1980).

FUTURE DIRECTIONS

The application of viscoelastic theories to the construction of functional models of the larynx in phonation has been reviewed. The distributed parameters approach provides the potential for studying a wide range of tissue properties, most of which have not been fully determined experimentally. This conference provides the stimulus, if not precise directives, for an enlarged thrust toward basic biomechanical research in voice production. The question is no longer, can we produce reasonably natural sounding simulated voice, but rather, can we use the simulations to understand and quantify the mechanical processes in order to distinguish them from higher level processes. One does not have to search deeply to find applications for such quantification in areas of normal, professional, and pathological voice.

REFERENCES

Fung, Y.B. (1968) Biomechanics: Its scope, history and some problems of continuum mechanics. In Physiology, Applied Mechanics Reviews 21, No.1, 1-20.

Glantz, S.A. (1974) A constitutive equation for the passive properties of muscle. J. Biomechanics I, 137-145.

Hast, M.H. (1966) Physiological mechanisms of phonation: Tension of the vocal fold muscle. Acta Otolaryngologica (Stockholm) 62, 309-318.

Hill, A.V. (1938) The heat of shortening and the dynamic constants of muscle. Proc. Royal Soc. (Ser. B) 126, 136-195.

Hirano, M. (1975) Phonosurgery: Basic and clinical investigations. Otologia (Fukuoka) 21, 239-440.

Ishizaka, K. and Matsudaira, M. (1972) Fluid mechanical considerations of vocal cord vibration. SCRL Monograph No. 8, Speech Comm. Res. Lab., Santa Barbara.

Saada, A.S. (1974) Elasticity. New York: Pergamon.

Sokolnikoff, I.S. (1956) Mathematical Theory of Elasticity. Second edition. New York: McGraw-Hill.

Timoshenko, S.P. and Goodier, J.N. (1970) Theory of Elasticity. Third edition. New York: McGraw-Hill.

Titze, I.R. (1976) On the mechanics of vocal fold vibration. J. Acoust. Soc. Am. 60, 1366-1380.

Titze, I.R. and Strong, W.J. (1975) Normal modes in vocal cord tissues. J. Acoust. Soc. Am. 57, 736-744.

Titze, I.R. and Talkin, D.T. (1979) A theoretical study of the effects of various laryngeal configurations on the acoustics of phonation. J. Acoust. Soc. Am. 66, 60-74.

Titze, I.R. and Talkin, D.T. (1980) Simulation and interpretation of generalized glottographic waveforms. Annals of Otolaryngology. In Press.

Van den Berg, J.W. (1958) Myoelastic-aerodynamic theory of voice production. J. Speech Hearing Research 1, 227-244.

DISCUSSION

Titze: By way of introduction I would like to try to differentiate between the work that Professor Ishizaka has done and the work that we have done in recent years. Where he has concentrated heavily of the fluid flow and the interaction between the tissue and the fluid flow, our emphasis has been directed more towards the possible variations in tissue vibrations that one encounters on the basis of the various viscoelastic properties of the tissue. We have also investigated the boundary conditions and their effects.

Fujimura: I think it is very important that we can compare the predicted contact area with direct observation. When the model is complex enough, we always have to worry about the risk that we can adjust the system by manipulating many independent variables in such a way that the output is comparable to what is observed. By having different levels of observation that can be compared with computed predictions of independent quantities, we can gain more confidence about the validity of the model.

Abbs: Are you intending ultimately to drive your model with EMG signals? Those of us interested in neural control see that as an important step in validating a model.

Titze: That is one of the long-range goals we have, although we cannot say that these goals are going to be accomplished soon. Our experiments conducted with Tom Baer at Haskins Laboratories provide us with as many simultaneous measurements as one can currently get. We can measure contact area with the laryngograph, EMG, transillumination, and radiated sound pressure. Hopefully, if we can get all these data lined up properly to "tune" the model, we can try a kind of synthesis using actual EMG signals to drive the model. I don't expect much at first, but it is worth a try.

Abbs: Do you think the three-element ideal contractile element muscle model will serve your needs to drive your model with EMG signals from cricothyroid and vocalis muscles? Would you not rather use a parametrically forced* model, which provides force by virtue of changing the parallel elastic component of the model? The parametrically forced model has been demonstrated to provide a better representation of muscle performance than the ideal contractile element model and is also a more "isomorphic" representation of muscle physiology.

Titze: I used the basic muscle model only to establish a linear viscoelastic constitutive equation. Beyond that, we use a purely distributed approach, i.e., a continuum model. If the parametrically forced model you mentioned is a better representation of muscle and cannot, in the small amplitude sense, be made equivalent with a linearly viscoelastic continuum model, we may be in trouble. It is something that needs to be looked into further.

Recall that our present strategy involves two steps. The first is the static problem involving large strains and complex muscle contractions. The second is a more conventional vibration problem. Most of our effort so far has been directed toward the second step.

Baer: Your model that will actually be relating EMG to the vibration is still a functional model in terms of relating EMG to configuration first, and then relating configuration to vibration pattern. That is, you are not specifically modelling the joints and the movements around them. The movements of the cricoid and the thyroid cartilages, for example, are not modelled *per se*. That is a step that needs to be included, ultimately.

Titze: I agree.

Abbs: I'm concerned more specifically with the translation between EMG and muscle force, which is very complex. We found that the ideal contractile model doesn't work. The parametric force model is far better for both isometric and isotonic contractions.

Baer: Will you elaborate on what that model is?

Abbs: Essentially what you do is to use the activation signals to change the elasticity and the viscosity of the elements. The paper by Green (see footnote above) takes classical twitch-tension curves and other physiological data and compares the ideal contractile with the parametrically forced model. We did some simulation ourselves with some other data we have and found that the parametrically forced model represents the force-elongation relationship better than the ideal contractile model. With the ideal contractile model you can impose some longitudinal forces, but you are not changing the stiffness of the muscle, and that is obviously very important, specifically with regard to the vocalis muscle.

Titze: As I think about it, our treatment of the vocalis muscle is similar to what you have called the parametric approach. We do actually change the stiffness as we model muscle contraction. Again, I think that the question of which model to use is appropriate primarily for the static solution, rather than for small signal vibration around a quiescent strain.

Isshiki: You have mentioned that in your model the most important factor that governs the vocal pitch is the length of the vocal cord. I am interested in this finding from the surgical viewpoint. There are many people who want their pitch raised, especially transsexuals. One of the surgical possibilities is to shorten the vocal cord by making an adhesion at the anterior commissure. I actually hesitate to do this surgery, because it may hinder the normal vibration of the vocal cord. But for future information, I would like to know about how much the vocal pitch is expected to be increased in your model by shortening of the vocal cord length, by 1 mm for instance.

Titze: I think it can be estimated fairly well by assuming that fundamental frequency changes inversely with length. You can, to first order, apply the equation for vibrating strings. Thus, if you shorten the length by 10%, the frequency increases to 1/0.9, or 11%. If you shorten the vocal folds by 50%, the frequency increases to 1/0.5, or 100%. That is only an estimate, of course, but it seems to hold up fairly well in our model.

Ishizaka: My question is a technical one, and it is concerned with the accuracy of your computer simulation. The discretization in space and time is strictly limited in the finite difference method which you used, because the original partial differential equation is of the hyperbolic type. In your paper (Titze and Talkin, 1979), you use the sound velocity of air in the vocal tract instead of the velocity of the wave propagation in the tissue to determine the travelling wave.

Titze: No, not to determine it. We just expressed it in terms of the sound velocity in air.

Ishizaka: Did you use a sampling frequency above 40 kHz?

Titze: Yes. Generally, we have to sample the tissue displacements at 35 kHz or higher.

Ishizaka: But what if the tissue is considered to be incompressible? You describe in your paper how to assure computational accuracy. But those comments were made for the case of compressible tissues.

Titze: That is correct. We cannot assume 100% incompressibility because the wave velocities would be infinite, and the computer could not keep up with that, obviously. So we have to assume some compressibility. The criterion we used is that the incompressibility factor λ should be about an order of magnitude greater than the shear elasticity μ. That assumption will produce a reasonably high degree of incompressibility, but not 100%. These are indeed compressional waves propagated in the tissue. One has to be careful that the simulation can keep up with those waves. The sampling frequency must be high enough to allow the compressional waves to dampen out.

Ishizaka: But if the sampling frequency is much higher than the exact frequency related to the desired wave propagation, the accuracy is not good enough.

Titze: There is always the problem of stability versus accuracy in computer simulation. If you try to bring the stability into check by increasing the sampling frequency, then there is a greater chance for inaccuracy, and vice versa.

Ishizaka: If the accuracy of the computer simulation is not clear as we change parameters, such as mass and thickness, I'm not sure the results of the simulation are reliable. As Dr. Fujimura pointed out, we can manipulate parameters to get the desired result.

Titze: I will agree that, at this point, I could never guarantee something like 1 or 2% accuracy in the simulation. For one thing, the elastic parameters we put into the system are not accurately determined. We will find out from Dr. Kakita's presentation (Chapter 25 of this book) that measured values are of the "order of magnitude" type. When we get to the point that we know the tissue parameters to within 2%, for example, then we shall go back and make sure our simulations are at least that accurate. But at this point there is no need for that. I think I gave you a fairly good indication of what the accuracy is in the paper you referred to. We showed some diagrams where we compared simulation with analytical paper and pencil solutions. The accuracy decreased at high frequencies but was good enough at the low frequencies.

Ishizaka: Was that made for the incompressibility condition?

Titze: No, actually that comparison was not for the incompressibility condition. That is a good point. We still need to make the general comparison.

Baer: Maybe it will be useful if we could make a general comment on what kind of interactions there are between the aerodynamics system and the mechanical system? Do the aerodynamic boundary conditions affect the pattern of vibration in a significant way?

Titze: That is a topic that has intrigued me for a long time. As you know, we have looked to see how much the fundamental frequency, for example, is affected by aerodynamics. We have found that in almost all of our simulations the fundamental frequency is in fact matched with the natural frequency of the tissue. The aerodynamic factors seem to be distributed over a small region during the cycle. As Dr. Ishizaka has shown, the pressure on the bottom mass of the two-mass model becomes very large and negative over an apparently short region in the glottal cycle, prior to closure. In that region most of the aerodynamic coupling takes place. Outside that region we don't find nearly the same strength of interaction. In the overall picture, then, we find that fundamental frequency is primarily elastically controlled, with relatively little aerodynamic control.

Baer: If vibration frequency in the vocal fold model corresponds pretty much to a normal mode, a standing wave pattern, does the air flow affect the mechanics of wave propagation on the tissue surfaces?

Titze: The distribution of the aerodynamic forces governs which mode is going to be selected. But once a mode, or combination of modes, has been excited, the system will basically operate according to that mode. It's very much like a vibrating plate with various resonance modes. Depending on how you blow over it or strike it, i.e., at which point you apply the disturbance, you will select a certain combination of modes. But you are not going to change the vibration characteristics of the modes themselves with the forcing function.

Ishizaka: I don't agree with that. This is why I showed, in my paper, the relationship between the fundamental frequency of the system under self-oscillation and its relationship to the natural frequencies of the model.

Titze: I believe your results are correct, but I also believe that the strong coupling between airflow and tissue mechanics is restricted to a small range of glottal widths prior to closure.

* Green, D.G. (1969) A note on modelling muscle in physiological regulators. Medical and Biological Engineering 7 41-48; and Perkell, J.S. (1974) A physiologically-oriented model of tongue activity during speech production. Unpublished Ph.D. Thesis, Massachusetts Institute of Technology, Cambridge, Mass.

CHAPTER 19
BODY-COVER THEORY OF THE VOCAL FOLD AND ITS PHONETIC IMPLICATIONS

Osamu Fujimura

Bell Laboratories, Murray Hill,
New Jersey 07974, USA

A SIMPLE MODEL

Hirano (1977) has proposed that the human vocal folds can be decomposed into three anatomical structures - the body, the cover, and a transitional layer between the two. Based on this anatomical finding and some related physiological observations, he concludes that the vocal cord movement in vibration is characterized by the participation of loosely coupled substructures, i.e., the body that contains the thyroarytenoid muscles, and the cover, a totally passive component. Given this interpretation, the physical system of the vocal cord may be depicted as in Fig.1, with respect to its longitudinal expansion-contraction.

Fixed mechanical terminals (walls in Fig.1b) A and C are assumed, functionally representing the linkage of the vocal cord to the arytenoid cartilage, and the linkage of the cricothyroid muscle to the cricoid cartilage, respectively. A rigid (massive) element T represents a linkage between the thyroarytenoid and cricothyroid muscles via the theyroid cartilage. The three-dimensional anatomical system, which includes the muscles and cartilages mentioned above and involves rotational movements of the thyroid cartilage with respect to the cricoid cartilage (see Fig. 1a), is translated into a mechanical elastic model (Fig.1b). Assumed here is an appropriate geometric transformation from the anatomical to the functional elements. This transformation defines effective forces, displacements, and constants relating these quantities.

According to the classical interpretation of vocal cord

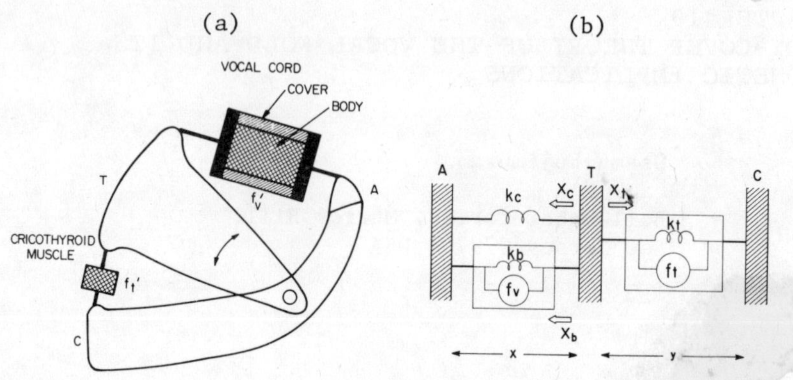

Fig.1.(a) Schematic representation of the vocal cords and the cartilages to which they are attached. The cricoid, arytenoid, and thyroid cartilages are depicted by C, A, and T, respectively.
(b) Transformation of the rocking movements and forces in (a) into equivalent translational movements and forces. See text.

length adjustment, we assume a solid structure of the thyroid cartilage linked to another solid structure consisting of the cricoid and arytenoid cartilages, as a basic mechanical model (Fig.1a). The linkage is formed by a fixed-point hinge that allows only relative rotation of the cartilages around the fixed axis. The complex of thyroarytenoid muscles, which we simply represent by a single "vocalis" muscle and further identify as the body for our present purpose, is paralleled by the passive cover. The length of this parallel structure, x in Fig.1b, is by definition common to both cover and body. The contraction of the vocalis muscle produces the motive force f_v' in Fig. 1a, or its transform f_v in Fig.1b. These two forces are monotonically related. They tend to shorten both body and cover, counteracting the passive elastic reaction represented by a spring with a constant k_t, as well as the motive force f_v' produced by muscle contraction. Both are pertinent to the cricothyroid muscle. If the vocalis contraction stays constant in terms of f_v', the cricothyroid contraction results in an elongation of the vocal cord. The elements with elastic constants k_t, k_c, k_b, represent passive (and lossy) springs. When we consider dynamic characteristics of the vocal cord adjustments, we need to consider mechanical resistances and the effective inertia of T, as well as internally distributed inertia, elasticity and friction for each muscle*.

EFFECTS OF MUSCLE CONTRACTIONS

The point of interest is the behavior of the vocal cord as a function of relevant muscle contractions, and their cortical control assisted by various pathways of feedback. The vocal cord length x is a function of f_t and f_v, if we consider the elastic constants as given parameters. The characteristics of the vocal cords with respect to their vibration, however, depends not only on their length, but also their elastic properties and mass distribution. Even though we are not going to discuss such vibration characteristics themselves (cf. Titze and Talkin (1979)), given the gross sketch of the overall system, we now need to evaluate the implications of the structure of the vocal cords as depicted above with respect to parametric adjustments of the larynx.

Anatomical structures that consist of muscles and tissues generally exhibit elastic properties that are characterized by nonlinear and direction-dependent, nonuniformly distributed elastic constants. One strong characteristic seems to be that the total unit, defined by boundaries that do not allow transfer of material, approximately conserves volume (mass of course is strictly conserved), whatever the detailed deformation may be. As the result of vocalis contraction, therefore, the cover becomes not only shortened, but also thicker, giving more mass to unit length. At the same time, since the external force acting on T, pulling it externally, is counteracted in part by the contraction force f_v of the body, the force X_c acting on the cover is less than X_t, and the difference is large if f_v is large. For a given f_t, the cover therefore is more slack, i.e., the longitudinal tension X_c is smaller, when the vocalis is in contraction.

---

* For that situation, we also have to consider feedback conditions. Thus a distinction of so-called isotonic vs. isometric contraction may involve differences in effective elastic properties of the pertinent muscle. Apart from such further details, our model illustrates that realistic situations are neither isometric nor isotonic.

Our model in Fig.1 gives us a more quantitative picture. For the body, the force X_b that is exerted inward on the boundary walls by this structure, we assume a linear approximation

$$X_b = k_b(x-x_b) + f_v \quad (1),$$

where x_b is the natural length of the body (i.e. the length of the body when it is separated from the cover and $X_b=0$). For the cover, similarly,

$$X_c = k_c(x-x_c) \quad (2).$$

For the external system between the walls T and C, we have

$$X_t = k_t(y-y_o) + f_t \quad (3).$$

The condition of equilibrium gives us

$$X_t = X_b + X_c \quad (4).$$

Also, given _a_ as a constant distance,

$$x + y = a \quad (5).$$

We are now interested in X_c as a function of f_v and f_t, the effective contraction forces. From the set of equations above, we can readily derive

$$X_c = K(f_t-f_v) + C \quad (6),$$

where K and C are constants containing elastic constants. Specifically

$$K = \frac{k_c}{k_b + k_c + k_t} \quad (7).$$

It can be seen from (6) that the vocalis contraction counteracts the external pull such that only the difference f_t-f_v contributes to the increase of the stretching force X_c of the cover. The larger the stiffness of the cover, i.e. the larger k_c in comparison with other stiffnesses, the larger this contribution is. In other words, if the cover is inherently compliant, within a range of its stretched length, most of the external force pulling the vocal cord outward would be counteracted by the body,

exception is mass-occupying lesions

whether by its passive stiffness or by muscle contraction force. If the vocalis contraction is sufficiently large in comparison with the external pull, then regardless of the cover stiffness, the cover is slack, i.e. it does not exert any significant (positive) pulling force X_c onto its boundaries (A and T).

Since the cover is entirely passive, its longitudinal state is completely specified by its length. Its lateral displacement depends on the thickness of the body and is not represented in the one-dimensional model of Fig.1b. This displacement, which is perpendicular to the tissue fiber direction, does affect the longitudinal condition, but only as a second-order effect that can be ignored for our purpose. As for the perpendicular movement, if the external force f_t is kept constant, the vocalis contraction results in medial approximation of the vocal cord surface via two mechanisms, (1) medial displacement of the cover due to the thicknening of the body, and (2) thickening of the cover itself. In comparison with a condition of smaller f_v and the same f_t, the body is relatively stiff with respect to lateral displacement of its surface due to the dependence of elastic constants on contraction.

The stiffness of the cover, with respect to its lateral displacement near the midpoint of the glottis, is to the first order of approximation proportional to the tension X_c. But X_c is in turn a linear function of $f_t - f_v$ for small changes of f_t and f_v, provided the lateral movement is not impeded by the boundary of the body. This is probably not true in general, however, since the body must be essentially in contact with, or sufficiently close to, the cover. Vertical movements of the cover, on the other hand, are relatively free. The slack cover presumably can slide more freely alongside the body surface, perhaps causing considerable nonuniformity in thickness of the cover along the vertical surface contour. Also, at the upper edge of the vocal cord, even the horizontal excursion of the cover is presumably relatively free, as can be seen in Fig.2.

Thus, for relatively small values of $f_t - f_v$ and even for a rather large longitudinal tension X_t of the vocal cord if both f_t and f_v are large, large wavelike motion of the slack cover can be expected, with a significant upward transportation of the cover mass that causes a formation of a relatively sharp and medially sucked-in edge at the upper surface of the glottis (Kirikae 1943, Hirano 1977; Baer 1975). For this to happen, of course, the adduction must not be too strong. The apparent lateral movement of the vocal fold surface below the upper edge level may or may not be associated with large lateral movements of the body surface via body deformation, a question still to be answered by actual observation. The larger f_v for a given f_t, the smaller the vibratory movement of the body would be. A downward pull on the cover by external forces, as shown by the vertical arrow at the bottom of Fig.2, either by the trachea directly or by an upward pull of the entire larynx by the upper structures relative to the trachea (Maeda 1976, Stevens 1977), will impede the production of the wave-like movement of the cover in the frontal plane.

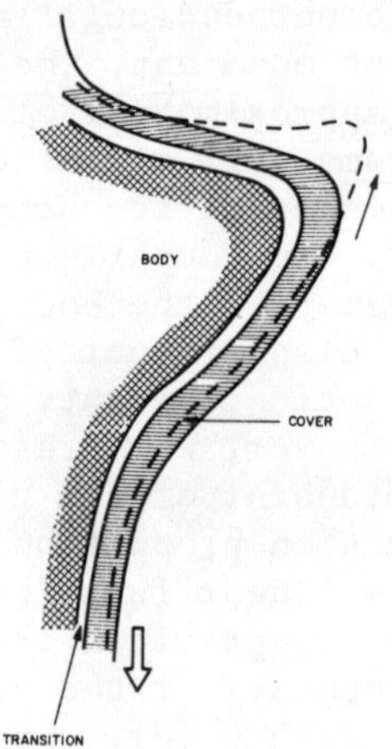

Fig.2. Schematic cross-section of vocal fold showing body, transition, and cover. The dashed line and upper arrow show the kind of sliding motion that is postulated to occur between cover and body. The possibility of a vertical force on the cover is indicated by the arrow at the bottom.

IMPLICATIONS, REMARKS

The adjustment of the vocal cords with a relatively strong vocalis contraction is appropriate for maintaining voice in chest register, particularly for loud heavy voice in the medium pitch range (Hirano, discussion in the meeting). Large excursions of the vocal cords are accompanied by a complete glottal closure for a considerable portion of the vibratory cycle. This would also effectively cause, via aerodynamic effects interacting with the slack cover, an abrupt voice onset with a quick and large opening movement of the upper edge of the vocal cord, provided that the degree of vocal fold adduction is appropriate. Vocal fry may be an extreme case of this category, with a very small f_t-f_v value.

If f_t-f_v is large, on the other hand, the cover stiffness with respect to perpendicular (i.e. lateral or vertical) movement is large, and the cover is less free from the constraints of the body. If f_v is small enough, it must be the case that the perpendicular stiffness of the body is mostly determined by its longitudinal tension, showing a linear dependence of stiffness on f_t (compare the vibration of stretched rubber bands). The body (together with the accompanying cover) will affect the vibration pattern by its own deformation; there is little effect of body-cover separation. In this mode, the adducting effect of the vocalis contraction is also weak, and other means of adduction, via the lateral cricoarytenoid and the interarytenoid muscles will have to be enhanced, if the same glottal distance is to be obtained as in the case of a stronger f_v. The cover also is expected to be thinner. Some EMG data provide us with interesting materials for discussion of the functions of different adductors. (See Fujimura (1979) for a review.)

In the model depicted in Fig.1, we assumed that the elastic constants (stiffness k's) were given at fixed values. This assumption is valid only for a small range of the contraction force, f_t or f_v. The stiffness k_t or k_b represents not only the passive elasticity of the muscle with no contraction, but also must represent the increase of longitudinal stiffness when the muscle contracts. Thus, strictly, k_b and k_t are functions of f_v and f_t, respectively. Also, the passive elements themselves exhibit nonlinearity at a large value of tension. The linear analysis we have given above, however, is valid for considering incremental effects, given appropriate values of stiffness for the levels of forces under consideration, and thereby should be useful for understanding the essence of the problem*. The first approximation is that the state of the cover is uniquely determined by its length. In this case, there is only one independent variable that determines the characteristics of voice, whether pitch, voice quality or intensity, as far as the condition of the cover is concerned. If the body stays still without significant deformation, rigorously speaking an unrealistic assumption, the only remaining factors will be the degree of adduction and aerodynamics**. The second approximation may consider vertical stretch of the cover, affecting stiffness with respect to both longitudinal stretch and perpendicular displacement (cf. Kakita, Chapter 25 of this book). This adjustment could give an independent control of cover stiffness.

When the body participates in vibration to a considerable degree, on the other hand, body stiffness with respect to lateral movement becomes important as one of the factors that determine vibration characteristics. The body will play an active role in vibration in the sense that there is considerable energy transfer between the two structures. It may be the case that direct stiffness control, taking care of the effects of simultaneous contraction of the cricothyroid as well as the vocalis, via feedback (see footnote above concerning the comment of Abbs), gives the best control of vibration mode, whereas $f_t - f_v$ as another variable controls pitch more directly. The body stiffness may be related to a quantity more like $f_t + f_v$ than $f_t - f_v$. We

---

* Abbs in the meeting pointed out the possibility that via stiffness control of the vocalis and the cricothyroid muscles, a relatively independent control of stiffness for the cover and body may be achievable (cf. Chapter 16 in this book).

** Hirano mentioned the following qualitative (gross) observation (see Fig.3): (a) When both cricothyroid (CT) and vocalis (VOC) activities are very weak, the deformation (movement) of the body and that of the cover are almost identical. This condition occurs in low and soft heavy voice or modal voice. (b) When VOC activity is very strong relative to CT activity, the deformation is much greater for the cover than for the body. The movement takes place almost exclusively in the cover. This condition occurs for loud heavy voice at middle pitch range. (c) When VOC activity is more dominant than CT activity, deformation is greater in the cover than in the body. Most heavy voices appear to fall under this condition. (d) When CT is active while VOC is almost relaxed, both the cover and the body are equally stiffened. The deformation of the cover and the body is minimum. This condition occurs in falsetto.

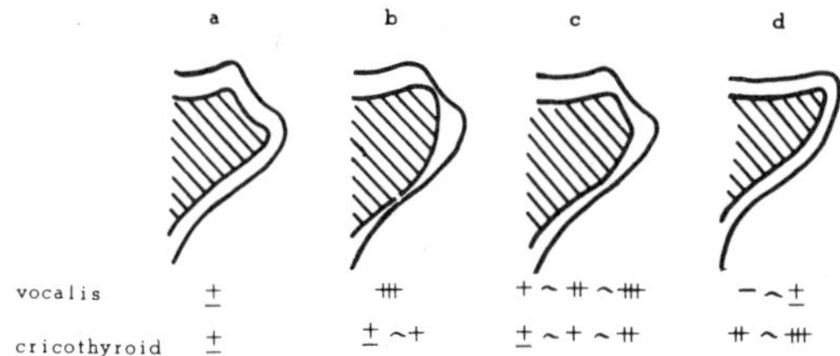

Fig.3. Schematic (exaggerated) drawings of cross-sectional shapes of the body (shaded) and the cover. The signs + and - indicate relative degrees of contraction of the vocalis and cricothyroid muscles. (Figure courtesy of M. Hirano.)

have to wait for further studies before we can suggest factual relevance of such possibilities.

It should also be mentioned that our model assumes a simplification by ignoring many secondary contributions from structures not mentioned in the model. For example, the fixed boundaries A and C in Fig.1a are in reality not rigid. The cartilages not only move slightly in response to the force applied by the pertinent muscles, but they may also be affected in their relative longitudinal positions by other external factors. These may include the state of the interarytenoids, strap muscles, etc., because the linkage between the cartilages is not as simple and rigid as depicted in this figure. All these secondary effects presumably will not affect the essence of the vibration characteristics except one that we will mention below. They will slightly modify relations between effective parameters, such as spring constants in the functional model, and directly observed physical properties of separate anatomical structures. In other words, constants have to be evaluated empirically for various ranges of physiological conditions in direct reference to the specific model.

At this point, we would like to mention one possible deviation from our picture above that can have important consequences with respect to our model interpretation. Lindqvist-Gauffin (1972) (also see Gauffin, 1977) proposed, based on fiberscopic observation, a pitch lowering mechanism in the form of contraction of the pharyngeal constrictors. It is interesting to note that this mechanism of shortening the vocal cord by external forces is, in terms of Fig.1(b), equivalent to the contraction of the vocalis muscle, as far as its effects on the cover characteristics are concerned. Because of the dependence of the elastic property on contraction, the elastic characteristics of the body itself will be different depending on the choice of the causal mechanism. Also, a quick and transient vocalis contraction probably does not result in a uniform shortening/thickening of the vocal cord, in particular the cover. The dynamic characteristics of the cover may vary depending on whether the response is due to a change in the massive pharyngolaryngeal structures or to a fast-acting vocalis muscle contraction. Vocalis contraction is probably more related to subtle adjustments, such as register control and quick triggering actions of the vocal cord vibration (modal change), rather than simple pitch control (Fujimura, 1979).

Even though only the difference between the cricothyroid and vocalis (or pharyngeal constrictor) muscle contractions is the primary variable in determining the cover condition with respect to its longitudinal stretching (and thereby pitch), voices with different degrees of training, for example, could choose different ranges of contraction levels. This would result in variations of the dynamic characteristics, including stability and vocal efficiency.

REFERENCES

Baer, T. (1975) Investigation of phonation using excised larynxes, Ph.D. dissertation, MIT.

Fujimura, O. (1979) Physiological functions of the larynx in phonetic control. In <u>Current Issues in the Phonetic Sciences</u>, Harry and Patricia Hollien (eds.), Amsterdam: John Banjamins B.V., Vol. 1. 129-164.

Gauffin, J. (1977) Mechanisms of larynx tube constriction. <u>Phonetica</u> 34, 307-309.

Hirano, M. (1977) Structure and vibratory behavior of the vocal folds. In <u>Dynamic Aspects of Speech Production</u>. M. Sawashima and F.S. Cooper (eds.), Tokyo: University of Tokyo Press, 13-30.

Kirikae, I. (1943) A study on the vibration of the human vocal cords in phonation and the timing relations of the glottal opening-closure by the use of a laryngeal stroboscopic motion picture technique. J. Japan Soc. Oto-Rhino-Laryngology 49, 236-268.

Lindqvist-Gauffin, J. (1972) A descriptive model of laryngeal articulation in speech. QPSR. 2/3, Royal Institute of Technology, Stockholm, 1-9.

Maeda, S. (1976) A characterization of American English intonation. Ph.D. dissertation, MIT.

Stevens, K.N. (1977) Physics of laryngeal behavior and larynx modes. Phonetica 34, 264-279.

Titze, I.R. and Talkin, D.T. (1979) A theoretical study of the effects of various laryngeal configurations on the acoustics of phonation. J. Acoust Soc. Am. 66, 60-74.

DISCUSSION

Sawashima: I quite agree with your point that we have to be careful about the interpretation of the body-cover model. However, I cannot quite agree with you on the point that the body may remain still during vocal fold vibration.

Fujimura: I am not assuming that, but mention it as a possible idealization. At one extreme we can consider such a possibility, whereas at the other extreme we can probably consider functional nonseparation of body and cover. The latter may well be the case for some of the vibration modes, such as falsetto, for example.

Sawashima: There should be some situations in between these tow conditions.

Fujimura: It is probably true that reality lies somewhere in between, but which extreme idealization is more realistic depends very crucially on the mode of vibration we are talking about. Whether or not either assumption is justifiable is an empirical issue. For example, Professor Saito's X-ray data (Chapter 8 of this book) could give us some evidence (or counter-evidence) to support the assumptions.

Stevens: It seems safe to say, then, that in any mode of vocal fold vibration, the cover is always involved in its entirety. But as I understand it, vibration penetrates only a millimeter or two into the body. In a sense, then, what we are doing by adjusting the tension of the body is to change the amount of penetration of the vibration into the body. In effect, we are changing the boundary conditions, or the tissue impedance, of the body.

Fujimura: That is correct.

Abbs: Is it possible for contracting muscle to be lengthened while it is contracting? If this is the case, your model suggests that one could independently control the stiffness of the cover and the body.

Fujimura: That is correct. I was intrigued by your notion of stiffness control this morning (Chapter 16 of this book). It could be the case that, when the cover is independent from the body, as exemplified by contraction of the vocalis and relaxation of the cricothyroid, the state of the cover would be entirely dependent on length. That would mean that stiffness control as such would not play as important a role. On the other hand, if the cover and body are moving together, the stiffness of the body will determine to a large extent the stiffness of the entire vocal cord. Then it might be sensible to talk about stiffness control.

Abbs: I was thinking that the situation might be such that the vocalis contraction and body stiffness need not be tied together. A contracting muscle can be lengthened, and therefore we can control the stiffness of the cover with the cricothyroid and the stiffness of the body with the vocalis without being concerned about length constraints. This would offer a greater freedom in control. As I understand it, those two muscles often contract together. Only one of them may be lengthening, or there may be an isometric contraction in both. We don't often know which one of those conditions exists. It offers an elegance of independent control that is very intriguing. The control of stiffness via feedback to the vocalis would be of value in the sense that, if you pull the vocalis from its rest position into a lengthened position, where its muscle force would reduce substantially by virtue of the length-tension curve, you would have a mechanism whereby you could maintain the stiffness. Even though the folds were lengthened substantially, the body would still be independently controlled automatically.

Fujimura: That depends on the control mechanism. When a phonetic gesture requires control of two muscles at the same time, what will be the principle to determine balance between the muscle contractions? At this moment it is rather hard to say, but the stiffness control certainly gives us a good possibility.

Abbs: Do you think the trained singer develops the same degree of adjustments in the cricothyroid and vocalis whenever he sings a given tone, or, if your derivation is correct, is he able to use more or less of one or the other, thereby achieving some degree of freedom in the adjustment $f_t - f_v$?

Fujimura: I expect training would give the singer more freedom.

Abbs: One of the things that we have talked about with people working in the motor skills area may be applicable here as well. To illustrate, I can pick up a glass of water a number of different ways, but if I wish to optimize speed and accuracy, I wouldn't do it very well unless I practiced again and again. When I am trained to do the task, I do it principally in one manner. Likewise, a skilled athlete does it in one way because he is optimizing for speed, or accuracy, or whatever optimization one might want to use. This principle might be true also in terms of the different kinds of adjustments one can make as a trade-off between vocalis and cricothyroid.

Hirano: When a singer changes the intensity of the voice with the same fundamental frequency, one can see the change in muscle activity in spite of the fact that the fundamental frequency is kept constant (Chapter 12 of this book). This is one example which shows the possibility that you can have different kinds of combinations of muscle activity.

Ishizaka: What is the relation between the longitudinal stiffness of the cover and the velocity of the shear wave along the cover in the vertical direction? Also, what is the relation between the velocity of the shear wave and the fundamental frequency?

Fujimura: These two things are not necessarily related because the shear wave propagation you are talking about is transverse. On the other hand, the tension you are talking about is longitudinal.

Ishizaka: The cover stiffness you mentioned would not be longitudinal stiffness?

Fujimura: No. When we discuss the vibration mode, what matters is the effective transverse properties, not the longitudinal properties. The longitudinal stiffness of the cover is represented by the spring in my picture.

That is perhaps misleading. But I switched the topic from that picture to something else. When we talk about wavelike motion of the membrane, we are concerned with transverse movement rather than longitudinal movement.

Ishizaka: There are two shear waves, one propagating in the longitudinal direction, and one in the transverse direction.

Fujimura: But the longitudinal wave probably does not contribute directly to the vibration of the vocal cord.

Ishizaka: That is my concern.

Fujimura: Perhaps I could clarify my statement by saying that the term "transverse" could mean either vertical or lateral.

Titze: I think this is an important point. Even though we are talking about transverse movement (lateral and vertical), the total restoring force is a combination of lateral and longitudinal stiffness. Imagine, for the moment, that the vocal folds behave like a balloon filled with water. The analogy is incomplete unless we also include longitudinal fibers within the balloon. The "string-like" restoring forces of the fibers in the longitudinal direction may be more significant than the lateral coupling between the fibers and the fluid. What needs to be established, in terms of measurement, is how the transverse stiffness varies as a function of longitudinal stiffness for a given state of longitudinal contraction.

Fujimura: The first part of my paper was concerned with that problem, and I apologize for not making that clear. But the wavelike motion is strictly separate from the longitudinal consideration. Parametrically it is related. In finding the equilibrium state of the system, we have to consider the longitudinal stiffness. After that, what matters is the perpendicular movement.

Akazawa: Are these the important variables in control in voice production: the position of T and the stiffness of both muscles?

Fujimura: That is correct. The position of T is a function

of both f_v and f_t.

Akazawa: Which is more important, the position of T or the stiffness of the system?

Fujimura: As far as the cover motion is concerned, the stiffness doesn't come into the picture very strongly, as the formula in the paper shows. All that matters is the difference between f_t and f_v and two constants K and C, both depending on the elastic constants of the system. So if we talk about the effect of contracting forces, then what matters is really only the difference between the two forces. In that sense, both contraction forces contribute equally, after the geometric transformation.

Akazawa: For example, in a model system, the position of a limb is usually the controlled variable. If both muscles are contracting, the stiffness of the limb is also controlled.

Fujimura: That is true. But notice that I'm really talking about the passive element, i.e. the cover, which doesn't contain any muscle at all. That is a peculiarity of the system. So once you set the length of that passive element, the passive element doesn't have anything to control. The contraction forces may both be large, but if the differences are very small the contraction doesn't affect the movement of the cover at all. That is really the point I was trying to make.

Strong: This has been a most informative afternoon for me, and highly instructive. But, obviously, there are some huge problems that exist because of the diversity of our backgrounds. Now to show you the depth of my naiveté, I will address a question to you, Dr. Titze. You might be able to address it most easily. We always need a model. If we have something we don't understand, we need to model it. In a clinical situation we need an animal model to test out a new hypothesis, or form of treatment. After testing the model it is easier to proceed. Now, could you tell me why we must have an abstract kinetic mathematical model? For example, are we hopeful that the construction of the mathematical model will allow us to determine whether or not the body shares distortion with other layers? I'm using that as an example. Is that a realistic hope? If we get the proper model, will you be able to tell us for certain the reasons why the body must share in the distortion during a single oscillation? What are we going to do with this model when we've got it? This is naive, so you must bear with me. Don't forget that clinicians are poorly versed in mathematics and physics, as a group, except for a few who have made the transition between the two.

Titze: With regard to the first part of your question, it is realistic to assume that, if the model is properly constructed, we can tell how much of the body is involved. With regard to the second part of the question, what are we going to do with the model, I can think of almost a myriad of applications. We should be able to predict, for example, the changes in vibrational mode if one puts a nodule, or some other kind of defect, in a certain portion of the tissue. We should be able to predict life-span changes if we know to what degree, histologically, the layers of the tissue change with age. We assess the corresponding changes in the mechanical properties, put them in the model, and simulate intensity and fundamental frequency changes. These are two examples. I think we can think of many more.

Strong: That's exactly what I needed.

Fujimura: I can add another example. I said I wasn't sure if the idealization of "cover only" for vibration is realistic. We can test this hypothesis, I hope, with Dr. Titze's model by making the body stiff enough, perhaps infinitely stiff, to see what happens. There may be some technical limitations. Nevertheless, we can idealize the realistic system and then continuously move from the idealization to a realistic situation in order to observe the continuity of this change. That would contribute to the understanding of inherent mechanisms. I think in order to understand something that is complex, we need to oversimplify the situation. If the oversimplification makes the entire picture different, then of course the oversimplification makes no sense. That kind of effect of oversimplification can be tested by modeling, provided the model proves to be appropriate.

Abbs: I don't know if this applies to the area of otolaryngology, but I have a colleague at the University of

Wisconsin who has a very complex mathematical model of the spine. He is at this time using this model in conjunction with orthopedic surgeons. Before they cut a ligament in the spine, or make some other change, they first simulate the effect of the change on the model. I wonder if at some time we might see the situation whereby we would all have a little box with Ingo Titze's model in it, and perhaps use it as an aid to model the pre-surgical or post-surgical state. I suspect it would be something that would be very useful.

Strong: I would be the first one to place an order for one.

V. VIBRATION MODES AND VOICE QUALITY

Section Editor: Martin Rothenberg

Syracuse University,
Syracuse, New York, USA

CHAPTER 20
VIBRATION MODES IN RELATION TO MODEL PARAMETERS

Kenneth N. Stevens

Massachusetts Institute of Technology,
Cambridge, Massachusetts, USA

THE CONCEPT OF QUANTAL STATES IN SPEECH PRODUCTION AND PERCEPTION

The production of speech consists of movements of the articulatory structures so as to achieve an ordered succession of target configurations or target states. A target is achieved through the realization of a particular state or configuration of some articulatory structure or group of structures. One example of such a target is the configuration of the lips when they are closed or almost closed to form a labial consonant such as [p b m f v w]. A target that involves the state of a group of articulatory structures is the articulatory activity that produces a complete closure of the vocal tract at some point between the larynx and lips, without specifying which structure is forming the closure. The group of speech sounds [p t k b d g] have in common this articulatory property of complete closure of the vocal tract.

A phonetic segment is characterized in the articulatory domain by the simultaneous or nearly simultaneous occurrence of target configurations or states of several different structures. Thus, for example, for the segment [b] the following targets are involved: (1) a complete closure is made in the vocal tract at some point along its length; (2) the lips are involved in forming a constriction; (3) pressure is built up in the mouth, creating a force against the inner surfaces of the vocal tract; (4) the vocal folds are in a configuration that will result in vocal-fold vibration if a flow of air through the glottis is created. Some of these target states also play a role in producing other segments. Consequently a rather large number of different phonetic segments can be described by different combinations of a relatively small number of target states each involving different groups of articulatory structures. Each of the target states specifies a class of segments the members of which have this common articulatory property. The labial consonants listed above from such a class. Other classes include [p b m t d n k g ŋ] (complete closure of the vocal tract); [p b f v t d s z k g] (pressure build-up in the vocal tract); [b d g v z i ɑ u...] (Vocal folds in a position appropriate for vibration).

The various target states are binary in the sense that the articulatory system is either instructed to achieve the state or is not so instructed. For example, the lips either are or are not involved in producing the segment, or the vocal folds either vibrate or do not vibrate when a pressure drop is applied across the glottis. In a sense, then, we can regard the articulatory structures as being controlled in a manner that gives rise to quantal articulatory modes or states. A class of phonetic segments that have a certain articulatory target state in common is said to be characterized by a particular phonetic <u>feature</u>. Thus a phonetic segment can be described in terms of a bundle of such features (Jakobson, Fant, and Halle, 1963; Chomsky and Halle, 1968, Jakobson and Waugh, 1979).

Each of the various target articulatory configurations and states gives rise to sounds with particular acoustic properties. Thus, for example, when a member of the class of stop consonants is produced at the beginning of a syllable, the sound that results has a time interval of relatively low amplitude followed by a rather abrupt increase in amplitude. Another example is the class of labial consonants, for which the spectrum of the sound sampled in the vicinity of the consonantal release exhibits a diffuse spread of sound energy across a wide frequency range, with the amplitudes of the spectral peaks showing a rather flat or slightly falling contour in the amplitude-frequency domain. Thus in addition to being defined in terms of quantal articulatory targets and states, the various phonetic categories or features also have specific acoustic correlates. It is assumed that the auditory system makes some kind of distinctive response when the sound has a particular acoustic property corresponding to one of these phonetic classes. The acoustic property that marks a particular feature usually occurs at some point or narrow region of the stream of sound that constitutes an utterance.

The regions where these properties reside are joined smoothly together by appropriate acoustic material, and this joining material does not generally contain information that unambiguously identifies a feature.

In view of these remarks, it would appear that the properties of the speech production and speech perception systems determine the inventory of speech sounds that are used to define the oppositions that can occur in language. The sounds that are selected for use in forming these oppositions are those for which there are, in some sense, distinctive or "natural" target configurations or states for the articulatory structures and that give rise to acoustic properties to which the auditory perception system responds in a distinctive manner (Stevens, 1972).

The number of features that are used to describe the universal set of oppositions that can exist in language seems to be in the range 10 to 20. In a particular language, not all of the possible combinations of these features are used to form oppositions. When a particular opposition _is_ used in a language, a well-defined acoustic property usually appears in the sound to indicate the presence of the feature. On the other hand, when a feature is _not_ used to mark an opposition in the language, then one of the polar acoustic properties that would occur if that feature were present is not necessarily achieved. The acoustic properties relevant to that feature are free to be influenced by the context, and often exhibit acoustic attributes intermediate between the extreme values that would occur if that feature were being used to mark an opposition in the language.

PHONETIC CLASSES DEFINED IN TERMS OF LARYNGEAL STATES

We return now, then, to an examination of the behavior of the larynx as a mechanism for generating speech sounds with different acoustic properties. If the larynx behaves in the same way as other articulatory structures (and there is no reason to believe that it should behave differently), then we would expect to find certain quantal modes or states or configurations of the larynx, each giving rise to a sound output with distinctive properties. The distinctive property corresponding to a particular configuration or state will be manifested most clearly when the presence or absence of that state defines an opposition in the language. Thus examination of how the larynx behaves in any one language will not necessarily give a complete picture of all the possible various distinctive states or acoustic consequences of these states that are available for use in language. As in the case of phonetic categories involving structures other than the larynx, we assume that the phonetic categories that are defined in terms of laryngeal target configurations are represented in terms of binary oppositions.

If we knew enough about the larynx and the way it is controlled during speech, we should, in principle, be able to predict what are the probable target states of the laryngeal structures that will give rise to sounds with distinctive properties. (See, for example, Catford, 1964; Lindqvist, 1969; Halle and Stevens, 1971; Ladefoged, 1971; Ladefoged, 1973; Stevens, 1977; Painter, 1978.) Unfortunately our knowledge of larynx behavior is not sufficiently complete to permit this kind of prediction to be made without indulging in some speculation. Hopefully some of the findings with regard to vocal-fold anatomy, physiology, and modelling, reported at this conference, will bring us closer to these objectives. Some modes of larynx behavior can, however, be predicted from what we know about larynx phsiology. For others, we can, in fact, be guided in what to look for by examining the acoustic correlates of the categories of speech sounds in various languages that make use of distinctive laryngeal states. By observing these acoustic manifestations, we might be able to make inferences about how the larynx is being manipulated during speech.

The voiced-voiceless distinction. One major opposition involving larynx configurations is that which distinguishes voiced from voiceless segments. This distinction is utilized in a large number of languages. Basically, for voiced segments the vocal folds are vibrating to produce low-frequency periodicity, whereas for voiceless segments they are not. In the case of nonobstruent segments such as vowels (that is, sounds that are produced with an open air passage, without pressure buildup behind a constriction), the periodicity is continuous through the sound, and the presence or absence of periodicity is easily observed and detected. For obstruent segments, on the other hand (i.e., those involving a buildup of pressure in the mouth behind a constriction), periodicity is not normally maintained throughout the closure or constricted consonantal interval. The presence or absence of low-frequency periodicity is detected, then, at the boundaries where rapid changes between obstruent and nonobstruent configurations occur. If there is low-frequency periodicity in the nonobstruent region immediately adjacent to the obstruent configuration (for example, immediately following the release of the consonant into the following vowel), then the segment is voiced. This low-frequency periodicity will occur if the vocal folds are in a configuration appropriate for voicing immediately preceding the time the obstruent is formed or at the instant of release of the obstruent. If there is no low-frequency periodicity in the vicinity of the consonant release, then the segment is voiceless.

We know enough about the mechanism of vocal-fold vibration to be able to state roughly the conditions under which vibration can and cannot occur (Ishizaka and Matsudaira, 1968; Halle and Stevens, 1971). In general, vocal-fold vibration will not occur if the vocal folds are abducted or are tightly adducted and if, in addition, the vocal-fold surfaces are stiffened. The exact combinations of conditions under which vibration occurs have never been spelled out quantitatively in detail, and further studies with models are needed in order to specify these conditions.

Breathy voice and creaky voice. Another aspect of laryngeal behavior that plays a role in creating phonetic contrasts in a number of languages is the adjustment of the mode of vocal-fold vibration that gives rise to modifications in the waveform of each pulse of air flowing through the glottis. Thus, for example, there are languages that distinguish two words which native speakers of English or Japanese would regard as having identical meaning, but for one of the words the vowel is produced with a breathy voice and for the other the vowel is produced with a more "normal" voice. Acoustic measurements indicate that the vowel produced with breathy voice, sometimes called a murmured vowel, has a spectrum with more low-frequency energy in relation to high-frequency energy (Fischer-Jorgensen, 1967). Schematic representations of the glottal configuration, the waveform of one glottal pulse, and the spectrum of the glottal output for a normal voice and for a breathy voice are shown in parts (a) and (b) of Fig.1. Apparently the breathy vowel is produced with the vocal folds partially abducted, particularly in the region of the arytenoid cartilages. Thus there is never a time during the vibratory cycle when the glottis is closed, and hence there is never a time when the flow of air through the glottis drops drops to zero, as the figure shows. A further consequence of the partially abducted configuration is that there is not an abrupt discontinuity in the slope of the waveform of the glottal airflow since there is not an abrupt closure of the glottis at all points along its length simultaneously. Apparently when the glottal configuration is adjusted so that it is wider at the posterior end than at the anterior end, and such that there is never complete closure at the posterior end, then conditions become favorable for producing a glottal waveform that does not have abrupt discontinuities in slope, and hence has a spectrum with greater low-frequency relative to high-frequency energy.

Another mode of vocal-fold vibration that is used to produce distinctive differences between vowels in some languages is referred to as creaky voice (Ladefoged, 1971; 1973). The glottal configuration and acoustic characteristics for this mode of glottal vibration are schematized

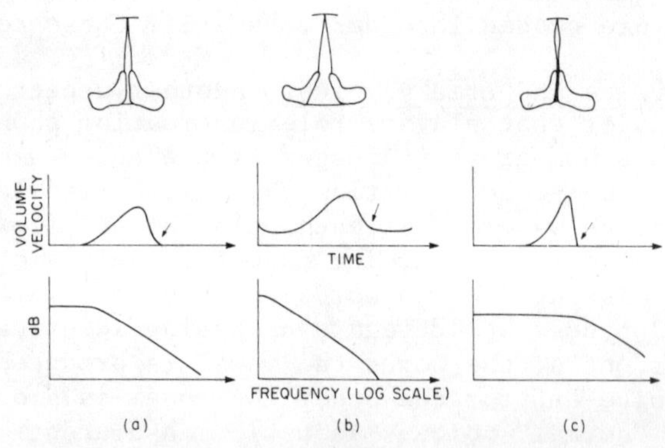

Fig.1. Sketches of glottal configurations (upper row), of glottal volume velocity for one cycle of vibration (middle row), and spectrum of glottal pulse (bottom row) for three adjustments of adduction or abduction: neutral position (a); spread arytenoid cartilages (b); and constricted glottis (c). The arrows indicate the region of the waveform where the abruptness of cessation of airflow influences the relative amount of spectral energy at high frequenceis.

in part (c) of Fig.1. It has been suggested that creaky voice is produced by forcing the vocal folds together, so that during a cycle of vibration the glottis opens only along a portion of the vocal-fold length. Each glottal pulse is rather short in relation to the period of vibration, with the result that the waveform of glottal airflow is relatively rich in high-frequency energy.

Registers and tones. Another important way in which the larynx is manipulated to produce different phonetic contrasts in language is through adjustment of the frequency of vibration (F_o) of the vocal folds. There are many languages in the world that distinguish between words that have a different fundamental frequency contour on the vowel or vowels but are otherwise phonetically the same. The fundamental frequency on the vowel, or the tone as it is sometimes called, may be relatively level or it may show a rising or falling contour. In the case of the level tones, linguists have noted that as many as four different levels of F_o may be contrasted in a particular language. (There is, in fact, some disagreement as to whether this number is four or five, but recent work seems to favor the specificcation of four levels.) (Yip, 1980). When the contour is rising or falling, the linguistic description is in terms of a sequence of target frequencies so that, for example, a particular falling tone may have a decreasing fundamental frequency from level 4 to level 1, or from level 3 to level 1 in a four-level system (where the levels of the tones of increasing frequency are numbered from 1 to 4). The entire system of tones is complicated by the fact that, in the course of a sentence, there is a gradual drifiting downwards in frequency of all the tones, so that, for example, a high tone at level 4 at the beginning of a sentence tends to have a higher fundamental frequency than a level-4 tone toward the end of the sentence.

Apparently, then, tone languages operate as though there were four different target states for the larynx, giving rise to the four level tones. A rising or falling tone can be described as a movement between two of these target states. Superimposed on these tones is a gradual, continuous downward drift of the fundamental frequency during a sentence.

What are the physiological correlates of these target states corresponding to the different tones? At first glance, the concept of quantal target states with corresponding frequencies of vibration seems counterintuitive. We may tend to think of the frequency of vocal-fold vibrations as being controlled primarily by adjusting the longitudinal tension of the vocal folds. It would appear that this tension can be adjusted continuously, giving rise to continuous changes in the fundamental frequency. In such a view, there would be little basis for a preference for one value of tension over another, except possibly at the extremes of minimally small or maximally large tension. In a singing mode, in fact, the goal is to be able to produce a continuous range of frequencies without apparent abrupt shifts in mode at any point along this continuum. In speech, however, it is postulated that for certain languages with particular tone contrasts preferred target states for the vocal folds are specified within the vowels throughout a sentence, and these give rise to particular target frequencies of vibration depending on the locations within the sentence.

The linguistic evidence seems to suggest that the four tones can be described in terms of two binary features (Yip, 1989). On the basis of this evidence, then, there would appear to be two different mechanisms that are responsible for generating the different tones in tone languages. Different combinations of these two binary features would give rise to four different values of fundamental frequency.

One of these mechanisms is probably the adjustment of the longitudinal tension of the vocal folds to either a tense condition or a slack condition. These two values of tension are presumably achieved principally by appropriate maximal or minimal contraction of the cricothyroid muscle. The other mechanism is one that can presumably operate whether the vocal folds are in the tense state or in the slack state, and gives rise to a high and a low "register". (The term register is used here in a different sense from its use in describing vocal-fold vibration during singing.) Several possible mechanisms for achieving these two registers might be suggested, and are illustrated in Fig.2: (1) adjustment of the vertical rather than the horizontal tension of the vocal folds, possibly through adjustment of the vertical position of the larynx; (2) adjustment of the thickness of the vocal folds, the thick or more massive condition resulting in a mode of vibration with out-of-phase movements of the relatively thick superior and inferior edges of the folds, and the thin or less massive condition resulting in participation of just the vocal ligament and a small region of each fold inferior to the ligament; (3) manipulation of the angle

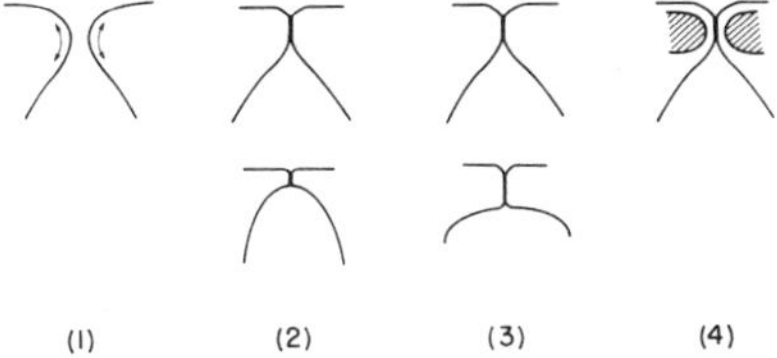

Fig.2. Schematic representation of some suggested modifications of the vocal-fold configuration that could lead to different modes of vibration or "registers," upon which changes in longitudinal tension could be superimposed. (1) Changes in vertical tension; (2) changes in vocal-fold thickness or region of contact; (3) changes in angle of inferior surface in relation to a vertical plane in the midline of the glottis; (4) changes in stiffness of the body in relation to the cover.

of the inferior surfaces of the folds in relation to the midline; (4) manipulation of the stiffness of the body of the vocal folds in relation to the cover (Hirano, 1974). These suggestions are, of course, highly speculative, and need to be refined or new hypotheses need to be made as new evidence emerges from the physiological and modelling studies. As noted above, whatever these mechanisms for producing tone are, they are superimposed on a gradually changing condition that is responsible for the slow downward drift of F_0 during a sentence. A language like English does not have contrasting tones, and consequently the fundamental frequency is not so tightly constrained as it is in tone language. Fundamental frequency is, however, used to mark word and sentence stress. There is evidence that the fundamental frequency contour in English sentences can be explained by postulating just one feature that specifies either a high or a low tone (Pierrehumbert, 1980).

CONCLUDING REMARKS

The main point of these remarks is that studies of the way the larynx is used to produce phonetic contrasts in language may guide us in our search for an understanding of the details of larynx behavior when we generate speech.

A particular gap in our knowledge is the nature of the states of the vocal folds that underlie the contrasts involving tones in languages that utilize these contrasts.

ACKNOWLEDGMENTS

Advice from Moira Yip and Morris Halle in developing the ideas in this paper is gratefully acknowledged. Preparation of the paper was supported in part by Grant NS-04332 from the National Institutes of Health.

REFERENCES

Catford, J.C. (1964) Phonation types: The classification of some laryngeal components of speech production. In In Honour of Daniel Jones, D. Abercrombie, D.B. Fry, P.A.D. MacCarthy, N.C. Scott, and J.L.M. Trim (eds.) London: Longmans 26-37.

Chomsky, N. and Halle, M. (1968) The Sound Pattern of English New York: Harper and Row.

Fischer-Jørgensen, E. (1967) Phonetic analysis of breathy (murmured) vowels in Gujarati. Annual Rep. Inst. Phon. Univ. of Copenhagen. 2, 35-85.

Halle, M. (1962) Phonology in generative grammar. Word 18, 54-72.

Halle, M. and Stevens, K.N. (1971) A note on laryngeal features. Quarterly Prog. Rep. Res. Lab. Electron. M.I.T., 101, 198-213.

Hirano, M. (1974) Morphological structure of the vocal cord as a vibrator and its variations. Folia Phoniatrica 26, 89-94.

Ishizaka, K. and Matsudaira, M. (1968) Analysis of the vibration of the vocal cords. J. Acoust. Soc. Japan 24, 311-312.

Jakobson, R., Fant, G. and Halle, M. (1963) Preliminaries to Speech Analysis. Cambridge, Mass.: M.I.T. Press.

Jakobson, R. and Waugh, L.R. (1979) The Sound Shape of Language. Bloomington, Indiana: Indiana University Press.

Ladefoged, P. (1971) Preliminaries to Linguistic Phonetics. Chicago: University of Chicago Press.

Ladefoged, P. (1973) The features of the larynx. Journal of Phonetics 1, 73-83.

Lindqvist, J. (1969) Laryngeal mechanisms in speech. Quarterly Prog. and Status Rep., Speech Transm. Lab., Royal Inst. Technol., Stockholm 2/3: 26-32.

Painter, C. (1978) Implosives, inherent pitch, tonogenesis and laryngeal mechanisms. Journal of Phonetics 6, 249-274.

Pierrehumbert, J. (1980) The phonology and phonetics of English intonation. Ph.D. thesis, Massachusetts Institute of Technology.

Stevens, K.N. (1972) The quantal nature of speech. In Human Communication: A Unified View, E.E. David, Jr. and P.B. Denes (eds.) New York: McGraw-Hill, 54-66.

Stevens, K.N. (1977) Physics of laryngeal behavior and larynx modes. Phonetica 34, 264-279.

Yip, M. (1980) The tonal phonology of Chinese. Ph.D. thesis, Massachusetts Institute of Technology.

DISCUSSION

Fujimura: If I understand correctly, you would predict that, in the production of tones, there would be quite systematic and significant deviations of cricothyroid muscle activity from the pitch curve, depending on selection of the so-called register. Is that correct?

Stevens: I prefer to think of the physiological correlates of the features as being related to the states or configurations of the structures used in speech production, rather than to the contraction of particular muscles. In the case of the features corresponding to tones, it would be convenient if contraction of vocalis muscle and of cricothyroid muscle represented two independent mechanisms giving rise to two features, but that is probably not the case. I would not be surprised, then, to find that the same cricothyroid activity in two different "registers" could give rise to different fundamental frequencies of vibration.

Fujimura: I am not familiar with data on the control of fundamental frequency in so-called tone languages. But there must be some kind of physiological correlates for the features of tone. If these correlates are not some kind of muscle activity or the contraction states of particular muscles, then one might expect something like stiffness control of particular components of the vocal folds.

Hirose: We have done some experiments in which we looked at EMG signals from laryngeal muscles for Thai, which is a tone language. Thai may not be a good example of a language that has four levels of tone, but at least it has some contour tones and some level tones. We found that the cricothyroid activity pattern was very well correlated with the pitch curve. In addition, we often notice that the strap muscles appear to play a role in enhancing very quick pitch drops of the type that occur in falling contour tones. However, I'm not sure that this type of muscle control would be true for all tone languages.

Baer: I can verify that the cricothyroid and strap muscles

both participate in pitch control. Incidentally, Thai has three level tones and two contour tones.

Sawashima: Does anyone have EMG data showing that vocal-fold tension may be elevated for voiceless consonants as compared to voiced consonants?

Hirose: At this conference I have pointed out that in some cases of voiceless consonant production there is increased cricothyroid activity, and this might be related to the pitch elevation sometimes associated with voicelessness. But I am not certain if this cricothyroid activity is directly related to the increase in terms of vocal fold stiffness.

Stevens: In English (and apparently in some other languages) you do usually observe an elevation in pitch following a voiceless consonant. The question is: what is the mechanism for that elevation? Is it because of the aspiration, such that spreading the vocal folds alone causes F_o to go up? Or is there some change in the surface properties of the vocal fold structures that causes the increase in F_o? My impression from Dr. Titze's modelling work is that if you spread the vocal folds apart without making other changes, and if they continue to vibrate, the frequency does not change very much. If this is true, then the pitch rise for voiceless consonants would have to be explained in terms of stiffness changes of some kind.

Titze: I have a question about the state of adduction-abduction which you have called breathy. I would like to know what is the <u>perceptually</u> significant correlate of this feature. Is it the presence of noise due to turbulence or is it the greater spectral slope (similar to the slope that occurs in a higher pitch range for falsetto)? If you were to remove or filter out all the noise, would you still identify the same feature?

Stevens: There have been some acoustic data for so-called breathy vowels (from Fischer-Jorgensen, referred to in my paper) - incidentally sometimes called <u>murmured</u> vowels. The consistent acoustic correlate seems to be a greater amplitude of the fundamental component, and not the presence of noise. However, the perceptual experiments have not been done.

Titze: In a sense, then, breathy voice is a kind of low-frequency falsetto, because it has a similar spectrum shape. I think that singers are able to carry the same falsetto production through the entire pitch range of the voice - all the way from an extremely high pitch to virtually as low a pitch as they can achieve with chest register, but with a much more rapidly falling spectrum shape.

Rothenberg: With regard to the perceptual correlates of the spread vocal-fold configuration, I can report on some impressions from speech synthesis experiments, using the voice source that I helped to put in the Stockholm speech synthesizer. If you change the spectrum for an [h] type sound in an utterance like [aha] and you remove the noise, it sounds like a very nice [h]. For a short [h], then, changes in the spectrum slope are sufficient to produce a very natural sound. For a long [h], as in an extended [ahhha], it sounds unnatural unless you insert some noise. In a sense, it is not unexpected that turbulence is needed for a long [h], since, if you don't insert turbulence you are going to lose air rapidly from the lungs. Thus for a long [h], turbulence is expected, but for a short [h] it is not needed in order to produce a natural sound.

CHAPTER 21
ACOUSTIC INTERACTION BETWEEN THE GLOTTAL SOURCE AND THE VOCAL TRACT

Martin Rothenberg
Syracuse University,
Syracuse, New York, USA

INTRODUCTION

Though the glottal sound source is often considered to have a volume velocity waveform independent of the supralaryngeal configuration during vowel-like sounds, it has long been suspected that the separation of sound source and vocal tract can lead to a significant error in the estimation of voice quality (Fant, 1960; Flanagan 1968). It is generally realized that there can be appreciable first formant energy absorbed by the glottis during the open phase of the glottal cycle, and that this energy can cause oscillations on the glottal flow (volume velocity) waveform and a change in the frequency and damping of the formant. However, it is not generally recognized that this interaction can also have a strong effect on the overall waveshape of the glottal pulse, and, in particular, on the amount of high frequency energy generated at the instant of vocal fold closure.

High speed and stroboscopic motion pictures of the glottis during chest voice have generally yielded a rather symmetrical, triangular waveform for the projected glottal area, as, for example, in the samples shown by Dr. Hiroto in Chapter 1 of this book. On the other hand, measurements of the glottal flow waveform by inverse-filtering the sound pressure or the flow at the mouth have often shown a markedly unsymmetrical waveform, with a slowly-rising glottal opening phase and a sharply terminating glottal closing phase (for example, see Miller, 1959; Holmes, 1962; and Rothenberg, 1973). The glottal flow waveforms in simulation studies have usually shown these same characteristics, as we have seen in the contribution to this conference by Dr. Ishizaka and Dr. Titze (Chapters 17 and 18 of this book). This dissymmetry of the glottal flow waveform can be an important determinant of voice quality in that it increases the high frequency energy of the waveform, as compared to the projected area waveform, and concentrates the energy in the glottal closed phase, during which the vocal tract is most efficient (Fant, 1979).

Of the possible causes for this flow dissymmetry, the following three appear to me to be the most likely to be significant:

(1) a non-invariant relationship between projected glottal area and glottal flow conductance (the reciprocal of flow resistance) due to the different vocal fold configurations that exist during the opening and closing phases,

(2) the small component of air flow which is due to the air displaced by vocal fold motion (Rothenberg, 1973; Rothenberg and Zahorian, 1977),

(3) the effect of the supraglottal acoustic impedance.

The relationship between projected glottal area and flow conductance is likely to be significant in determining voice quality under some conditions. We will not consider this factor further in this paper, however, and we make the common first-approximation assumption that the relation between glottal conductance and projected glottal area is invariant.

Since the air displaced by vocal fold motion tends to decrease the glottal flow as the folds separate, and increase the flow as the folds come together (as in a hand clap), this component will tend to cause a dissymmetry of the type we are discussing. A simple calculation shows that the component will be small, but not necessarily negligible (Rothenberg, 1973. See also the simulation result by Flanagan and Ishizaka (1978).) However, in this paper we will not consider this component further, and we will study, instead, the effect of the third factor. We will consider the effect of supraglottal loading on the glottal waveform, using a model which is valid at the fundamental frequency and lowest order harmonics, since it is these components which most strongly influence the overall waveshape of the glottal pulse. Our comments will be restricted to acoustic interaction and not include the effect that the supraglottal pressure variations might have on the motion of the vocal folds.

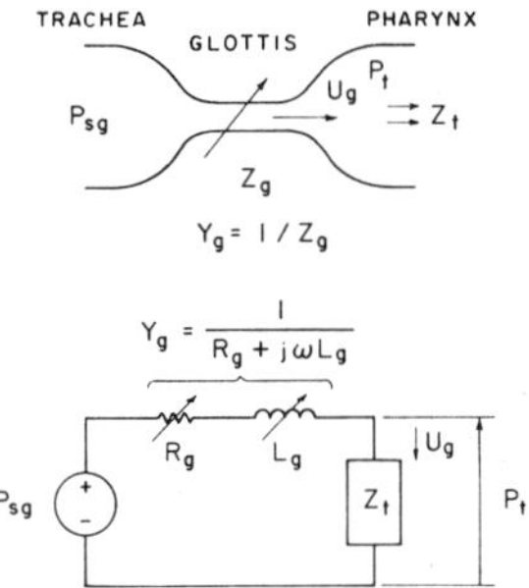

Fig.1. Simplified linear model for the glottal source.

A MODEL FOR SOURCE-TRACT ACOUSTIC INTERACTION

Figure 1 shows a simple linear, lumped-parameter model for the glottis and the supraglottal vocal tract. The elements in the model are in standard electrical circuit form, but are defined acoustically as follows:

Z_g = glottal impedance (The dissipative part of the glottal impedance is termed the glottal resistance.)
Y_g = glottal admittance (The dissipative part of the glottal admittance is termed the glottal conductance.)
U_g = glottal volume velocity
P_{sg} = subglottal pressure
Z_t = impedance of the supraglottal vocal tract as seen by the glottis
P_t = supraglottal pressure

In this paper, we will consider the subglottal pressure to be constant and the glottal inertance L_g to be zero. The glottal admittance will then be a pure conductance that is the inverse of the glottal resistance R_g and is equal to $U_g/(P_{sg}-P_t)$. In the following theoretical development, we will initially consider this admittance to have the symmetrical, triangular shape shown at the upper right in Fig.2, as the vocal folds open and close during the glottal air pulse. Though this representation does not properly reflect the flow dependency of the glottal resistance (which, for larger glottal areas causes the differential or small-signal flow resistance to be somewhat higher than the resistance defined by pressure/flow, and causes both measures of resistance to increase with volume velocity for a given glottal area), it should yield a good approximation to the actual glottal flow for small values of Z_t, if the variation in projected glottal area is approximately triangular (Flanagan 1958).

In the common assumption of independence between the glottal source and the vocal tract, the supraglottal impedance Z_t is considered negligible compared to Z_g, and therefore, as shown in the curve for $R_t = 0$ in Fig.2, the glottal air flow would have the same shape as the glottal admittance function Y_g. In the figure, the pressure, admittance and time scales are normalized to arbitrary units ($P_{sg} = 1$, Y_g maximum = 1, pulsewidth = 2).

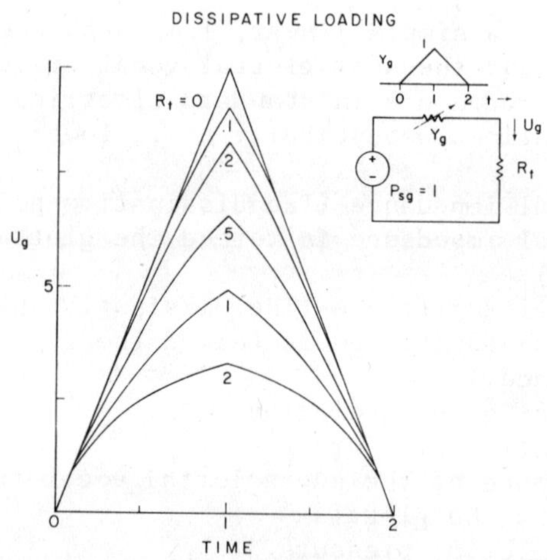

Fig.2. Computed glottal air flow with a dissipative supraglottal impedance and a triangular variation in glottal admittance.

In looking at the effect of a non-negligible Z_t, let us first assume Z_t to be purely dissipative, as shown in Fig.2, for some representative values of R_t. In this case, the air flow U_g is given by

$$U_g(t) = \frac{P_{sg}}{R_g(t) + R_t} = \frac{P_{sg}}{\frac{1}{Y_g(t)} + R_t} \,. \tag{1}$$

At the initiation and termination of the air flow pulse, R_g is high and dominates R_t, and the resulting flow is similar to that which would occur with no R_t. However, as R_g decreases (and Y_g increases) the flow becomes limited by R_t. For high values of R_t, the flow U_g approaches a rectangular pulse of amplitude P_{sg}/R_t, as it is "switched" on and off by the onset and offset of Y_g. This rectangular pulse will have a much higher ratio of high-frequency energy to low-frequency energy than would be the case with R_t equal to zero (the non-interactive model).

A reactive supraglottal impedance will also cause an increase in the proportion of high frequency energy, The way in which this change occurs, however, is different from that for the dissipative case. If the lowest supraglottal resonance (the first formant F_1) is higher than the voice fundamental frequency F_0, as is usually the case, the supraglottal loading will be inertive at frequencies between F_0 and F_1. In addition, in a more accurate representation the inertive component of the glottal impedance would be added to the load impedance in determining the flow, thus increasing the importance of the effect of inertive loading. In this paper, we will present a mathematical analysis for only the case of an inertive reactance, assuming, for simplicity, that Z_t is due to a pure inertance L_t, so that $Z_t(\omega) = j\omega L_t$.

Figure 3 shows our simplified model with an inertive supraglottal loading of magnitude L_t. The flow U_g for this model is governed by the following differential equations:

$$L_t \frac{dU_g}{dt} + \frac{U_g}{t} = 1, \quad \text{for } 0 \leq t \leq 1, \tag{2A}$$

$$L_t \frac{dU_g}{dt} - \frac{U_g}{t-2} = 1, \quad \text{for } 1 \leq t \leq 2, \tag{2B}$$

with the added condition that $U_g(0) = 0$.

As can be verified by substitution in the equations, the solution for this set of differential equation is

$$U_g = \frac{t}{L_t + 1} \quad \text{for } 0 \leq t \leq 1. \tag{3A}$$

For $1 \leq t \leq 2$ the solution has two forms, depending on the magnitude of L_t:

$$U_g = \begin{cases} \dfrac{2L_t}{L_t^{\,2} - 1} (2-t)^{1/L_t} - \dfrac{2 - t}{L_t - 1} & \text{for } L_t \neq 1 \\ [\frac{1}{2} - \ln(2-t)]\ (2-t) & \text{for } L_t = 1 \end{cases} \tag{3B}$$

These functions are plotted in Fig.3 for some representative value of L_t. It can be seen that inertive loading would tend to give the flow pulse its often-noted skew to the right and rapid termination. Since the high frequency energy produced at a discontinuity of slope tends to be proportional to the change of slope at the discontinuity, the high frequency energy produced at the termination of the glottal pulse can be greatly increased by inertive loading. The terminal slope increases rapidly with L_t, even at values of L_t which do not drastically reduce the peak amplitude of the flow waveform. This differs from the dissipative case, in which a steep termination is obtained only by limiting the pulse height, i.e., in which the proportion of high frequency energy is increased by reducing the low frequency energy (which varies with the pulse height). In the inertive case, there is an actual increase in high frequency energy caused by the loading.

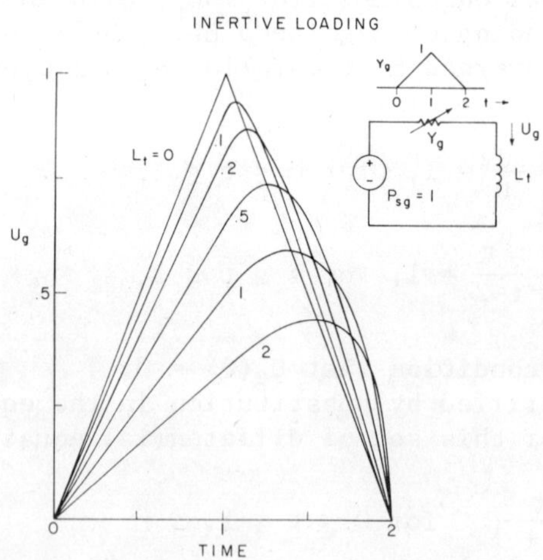

Fig.3. Computed glottal air flow with an inertive supraglottal impedance and a triangular variation in glottal admittance.

It can also be seen in Fig.3 that the response between t = 0 and t = 1 is a linear increase in flow with a smaller slope than for the non-interactive case. Thus the high frequency energy produced at the onset of the glottal pulse is reduced. In the limit, with high values of L_t, U_g approaches a "sawtooth" or "ramp" waveform with a linear increases from zero flow at t = 0 to a peak flow of $2/(L_t+1)$ at t = 2, followed by a sudden decrease to zero flow at t = 2. The spectrum of such a pulse falls off at only 20 dB/decade compared to the 40 dB/decade fall-off for the triangular pulse that occurs with $L_t = 0$.

However, the increase of high frequency energy produced by the glottal closure is not just an asymptotic affect that is present only with high values of L_t. The increase of terminal slope occurs with relatively small values of L_t, and in fact, the terminal slope becomes infinite for values of L_t greater than unity. This result can be seen from the time derivative of $U_g(t)$. For $1 \leq t \leq 2$ the derivative is

$$\frac{dU_g}{dt} = \begin{cases} \dfrac{1}{L_t - 1} - \dfrac{2}{L_t^2 - 1}(2-t)^{\left(\frac{1}{L_t} - 1\right)} & \text{for } L_t \neq 1 \\[2ex] \dfrac{1}{2} + \ln(2-t) & \text{for } L_t = 1 \end{cases} \qquad (4)$$

For $0 \leq t \leq 1$ the slope is $1/(L+1)$ for all values of L. Thus the slope at the onset of air flow decreases gradually with L_t, while the terminal slope increases rapidly for values of L_t approaching unity as the term $1/(L_t-1)$ increases and dominates the second term. For $L_t > 1$ the second term becomes infinite as t approaches 2, since $(\frac{1}{L_t} - 1)$ is negative.

Inertive loading also delays the peak of the volume velocity flow. For the simple model of Fig.3, the time at which U_g is maximum can be calculated by setting the time derivative equal to zero and solving for t. This procedure yields:

$$t \text{ at } U_g \text{ maximum} = \begin{cases} 2 - \left[\dfrac{L_t+1}{2}\right]^{\frac{L_t}{1-L_t}} & \text{for } L_t \neq 1 \\[2ex] 2 - e^{-1/2} = 1.39 & \text{for } L_t = 1 \end{cases} \qquad (5)$$

To show the effect of inertive loading with an admittance waveform that is more rounded near the peak than is a triangle, Fig.4 gives the flow that would result if Y_g were one-half cycle of a sinusoid. Since we have not derived a closed-form solution for this case, the curves were obtained by means of a digital simulation of the differential equation. With the sinusoidal admittance, the peaks of the flow waveforms become more rounded than for the triangle, especially for small values of L_t. In addition, the peak of the flow waveform is delayed somewhat more, as a function of L_t, than for the trangular admittance function, and the value of L_t at which the derivative at t = 2 becomes infinite appears to be somewhat less than unity. Otherwise, the responses for the sinusoidal and triangular cases are very similar. The insensitivity of the general form of the volume velocity to the details of the glottal admittance function with higher values of L_t supports our assumption that a rough approximation to the actual admittance can be informative.

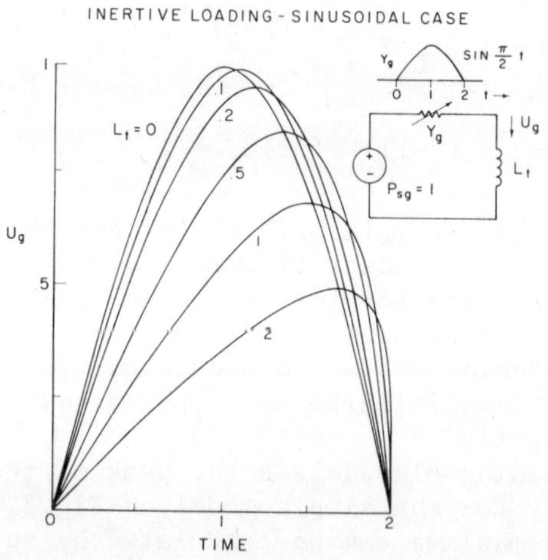

Fig.4. Computed glottal air flow with an inertive supraglottal impedance and sinusoidal variation in glottal admittance.

Another simplification that we have made in modeling the glottal admittance waveform has been to assume that the admittance before and after the glottal pulse is zero. Inverse-filtering studies and motion pictures of the glottis during voicing have shown that there is often a patent air path between the arytenoid cartilages. This flow path would tend to show up in our model as a fixed impedance (or admittance) in parallel with the time-varying component. In the non-interactive model, the result would be primarily to offset the flow waveform from zero flow, without much change in the shape of the glottal pulse. However, with inertive loading assumed, the added admittance would alter the form of the differential equation and therefore affect the pulse waveshape, primarily near the onset and offset of the glottal pulse. To see in more detail what the effect of such glottal "leakage" might be, we have, in Fig.5, inserted a fixed admittance, $Y_{g-\ell}$, of 0.2 times the amplitude of the time-varying component of Y_g, Y_{g-ac}, in parallel with the time varying component. In doing this, we have again assumed a linear model for the glottal admittance and neglected the inertive component. Offsets of this magnitude are commonly observed during inverse-filtering of oral air flow, and may be much larger in pathological voice, or, naturally, during breathy voice. The general result of this glottal leakage is to cause a gradual onset of the glottal flow pulse, and a more gradual offset, with less high frequency energy produced at both locations.

The reduction of high frequency energy at the instant of glottal closure is of special interest because of its strong potential affect on voice quality. Without "leakage," the high frequency energy is produced by the sealed glottis forcing the flow to zero, in opposition to the influence of the inertance, which acts to continue the flow. With leakage, the decrease in Y_g stops when U_g is still decreasing slowly. At that instant the glottal flow pattern changes to a more gradual, exponential decay, with a time constant ($Y_{g-\ell}L_t$). It may be significant that, according to this simple model, the stronger the source-tract interaction (the higher the value of L_t) the greater is the degradation of the high frequency energy caused by $Y_{g-\ell}$. In other words, according to this model, inertive loading of the glottal source will cause an increase in high frequency energy on glottal closure only if there is very little air leakage during the interval of vocal fold closure.

Before turning to the experimental corroboration of acoustic loading effects on the glottal waveform, we should note that the above theoretical development has been for a symmetrical glottal admittance pulse. Though a symmetrical pulse (whether triangular or sinusoidal)

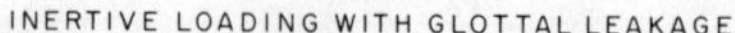

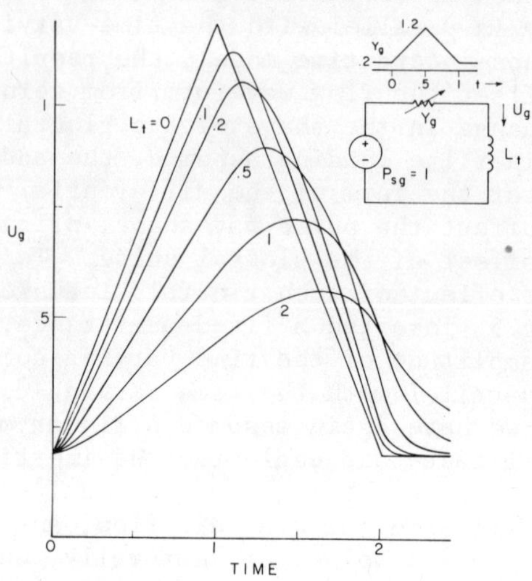

Fig.5. Computed glottal air flow with an inertive supraglottal impedance and a triangular variation in glottal admittance. An incomplete glottal closure is simulated by adding a fixed glottal conductance to the triangular variation.

may be a good first approximation to admittance functions derived from projected area measurements, there may be a good deal of dissymmetry in individual cases. To see how such dissymmetry could interact with loading effects, we solved the differential equation resulting from the triangular admittance function pulse used for Fig.3 (having a total width or duration of two, a peak value of unity, and no "leakage"), but with the peak occurring at some arbitrary time T_m, instead of at $t = 1$. If T_m is between zero and one, the admittance function tilts to the left, and if T_m is between one and two, the tilt is to the right, with $T_m = 1$ being the case illustrated above in Fig.3. The differential equations for U_g would then be:

$$L_t \frac{dU_g}{dt} + \frac{T_m}{t} U_g = 1, \quad \text{for } 0 \leq t \leq T_m \tag{6A}$$

$$L_t \frac{dU_g}{dt} + \frac{2-T_m}{2-t} U_g = 1, \quad \text{for } T_m \leq t \leq 2 \tag{6B}$$

As long as L_t is not exactly equal to unity (since L_t = 1 results in an indeterminacy in the solution form) the solution to these equations is

$$U_g = \frac{t}{L_t + T_m} \qquad \text{for } 0 \leq L \leq T_m \tag{7A}$$

$$U_g = K(2-t)^{\frac{2-T_m}{L}} + \frac{2-t}{L - 2 + T_m}$$

$$\text{for } T_m \leq t \leq 2, \tag{7B}$$

where

$$K = \frac{2L(2 - T_m)^{\frac{T_m - 2}{L}}}{L^2 + 2(T_m - 1)L + T_m^2 - 2T_m} \tag{7C}$$

As for the special case of T_m = 1 (a symmetrical pulse), the onset of the pulse is linear, and the offset is steeper than the onset. However, the skew of the admittance pulse is now a function of both L_t and T_m. We illustrate this by showing that the "critical" value of L_t, i.e., the value above which the derivative becomes infinite at t = 2, will vary with T_m. The relationship can be derived by first differentiating U_g in the interval $T_m \leq t \leq 2$:

$$\frac{dU_g}{dt} = \frac{K(T_m-2)}{L_t}(2-t)^{\frac{2-T_m-L_t}{L_t}} + \frac{1}{L_t-2+T_m} \tag{8}$$

As t approaches two, this function becomes infinite for values of T_m and L_t that make the exponent in the first term negative. This occurs for values of L_t greater than $(2 - T_m)$. Thus, if the admittance pulse is skewed to the right ($T_m > 1$) the flow termination will become infinite at smaller values of L_t, and vice-versa. For example, if $T_m = 4/3$, for a rather high but possibly attainable opening time to closing time ratio of two, the critical value of L_t is reduced to 2/3 as compared to the value of unity that holds for the symmetrical admittance function.

THE MEASUREMENT OF SOURCE-TRACT ACOUSTIC INTERACTION

Though an inertive loading of the glottal source would produce flow waveforms very much like those observed by using standard inverse-filtering techniques, given a symmetrical variation of glottal admittance, it still remains to be shown that this type of glottal-supraglottal interaction is significant in such activities as speech or singing. There are a number of ways that we can study this during actual vocalizations. The most direct method might be to measure Z_t somehow, but this requires the measurement of the pressure just above the glottis, and is difficult to implement. (However, see Dr. Koike's Chapter 14 in this book.)

Using another approach, we have attempted to implement a "nonlinear inverse filter" in which some of the effects of the glottal-supraglottal interaction are removed (Rothenberg and Zahorian, 1977). The resulting waveform, shown in Fig.6, is more directly related to Y_g than is the actual flow U_g. To aid in visualizing the assymetry of each waveform, the connected lines above the waveform were drawn in to match the maximum slopes of the rising and falling segments, neglecting the oscillations at the frequency of the first formant in the case of the linear filter. It can be seen that in this case the supraglottal impedance did cause an alteration of U_g similar to that produced by inertive loading in our model.

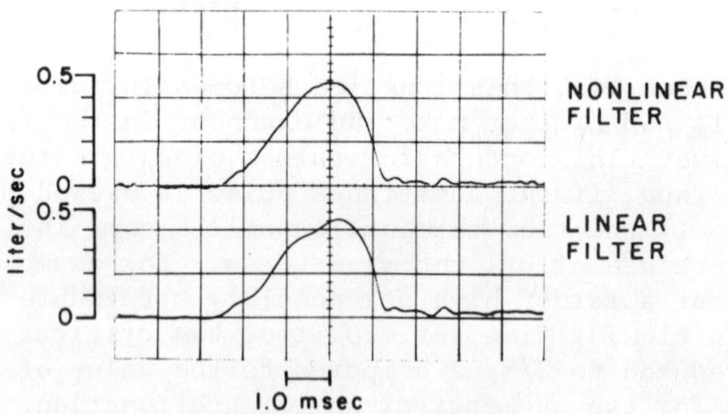

Fig.6. Nonlinear inverse filtering of a spoken vowel [æ]. The top trace shows the output of the time-varying nonlinear inverse filter. The bottom trace shows the output of the time-invariant inverse filter. (From Rothenberg and Zahorian, 1977).

Another approach in measuring the affect of Z_t is to change Z_t while keeping the glottal area function approximately invariant. One way this can be done is by changing the vowel value. In the exampel in Fig.7, the glottal flow was measured by inverse filtering oral air flow, while vocal fold movements were monitored by simultaneously recording the vocal fold contact area (VFCA) waveform obtained from a Laryngograph (Fourcin, 1974). The VFCA waveform is shown inverted in the figure, since the Inverse VFCA waveform tends to rise and fall with the glottal air flow. The samples shown in the figure were from the center of the vowel in the nonsense syllable /b Vowel p/ in the syllable sequence /b a p b æ p ---/. Each row in the figure represents one such sequence, with the first two sequences (top two rows) spoken slowly enough so that each vowel had a distinct steady-state segment, while the last sequence (bottom row) was spoken at a natural rate. Vocal effort was at a moderate conversational level. The stop consonants help assure a good velopharyngeal closure during the vowel, which is important for accurate inverse filtering. Filter parameters corresponding to the frequency and damping of the first three formants were adjusted manually during a repetitive playback of the vowel sample, using the VFCA waveform as an aid in defining the glottal closed and open periods (Rothenberg, 1979). The low-frequency response limitation of the standard automatic amplitude control and high-pass filtering in the Laryngograph probably caused a slight falling of the Inverse VFCA trace during the glottal open phase, but this distortion should be similar for all samples.

Except perhaps for the first (topmost) repetition of /a/ and the second (middle) repetition of /æ/, a constancy of the VFCA waveform between samples suggests that the differences in the U_g waveform were not caused by different vibratory patterns of the vocal folds. We refer here to the general shape of the waveform and not the amplitude, since the waveform amplitude depends on the larynx position relative to the electrodes, and therefore can vary with the vowel articulation.

If the two samples having a non-representative VFCA waveform are ignored, the figure shows that, of the vowels tested, those with a constriction closer to the glottis and a higher first formant (at the left in the figure) tended to have a glottal flow waveform which was more skewed to the right, with a steeper flow termination, and therefore might be expected to have more high frequency

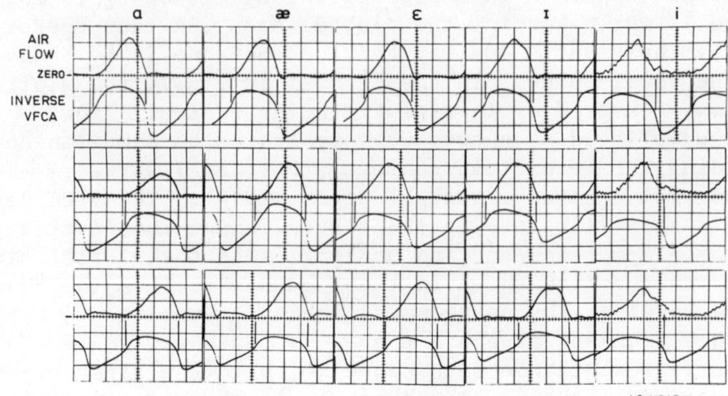

Fig.7. Glottal volume velocity as a function of vowel value for a single male adult speaker. The vertical lines indicate the approximate beginning and end of the primary glottal opening movements, as measured from the vocal fold contact area (VFCA) waveform using the model presented in Rothenberg (1979). Upper curves: Glottal air flow obtained by inverse filtering oral air flow. Lower curves: Inverse vocal fold contact area from a Laryngograph. The different rows represent different repetitions of the vowel sequences. Note: A slight negative overshoot after the glottal closing phase may be due to a damped mask resonance near 1200 Hz. This artifact can be removed with a more complex inverse filter.

energy generated by the termination of the glottal closure. In fact, for the /i/ samples shown, the sharpest discontinuity in waveform slope, and therefore greatest production of high-frequency energy, appears to be at the peak of the waveform, and not at the instant of glottal closure. The overall shapes of the flow waveforms in Fig.7 are roughly similar to those produced by the model in Figs. 3 and 4, as inertive loading is varied, except for the added oscillations at the first formant frequency. The oscillatory component of the interaction is not included in our simple model. Though there was considerable waveform variability between speakers, the general trend toward more dissymetry with vowels closer to /a/ was also found in the samples from two other speakers tested, one male and one female.

These results are at least roughly consistent with calculations made from a simple model of the vocal tract. For a lossless supraglottal vocal tract 17 cm long, with a uniform area of 5 cm^2, the impedance Z_t will be inertive for frequencies below the first formant frequency of 500 Hz (or, more precisely, below a frequency just slightly under the first formant). The magnitude of this impedance will be approximately 8 tan (ω/2000) in either acoustic ohms or units of cm H_2O per liter/sec. In order to represent the actual vocal tract impedance below F_1 by a pure inertance, it is necessary to find a linear approximation to the actual impedance function. Assuming that in our example the frequencies between 125 Hz and 375 Hz, representing an F_0 of 125 Hz and the second and third harmonics, are of most interest, we can make a linear approximation by estimating L_t as the derivative of $|Z_t|$ with respect to ω at some intermediate frequency, say 250 Hz:

$$L_t \approx \frac{d|Z_t|}{d\omega} = \frac{d}{d\omega}\left[8 \tan \frac{\omega}{2000}\right] \text{ at } \omega = 250(2\pi) \quad (6)$$

$$= 0.008 \text{ at } \omega = 250(2\pi)$$

To normalize L_t to the scales used for Figs.2, 3, and 4, it is necessary to multiply by the actual maximum glottal admittance (or conductance, ignoring L_g) and divide by the actual time for one-half the glottal pulse (approximately 2 ms at F_0 = 125 Hz). In calculating interactive effects, the differential conductance $dU_g/d(P_{sg} - P_t)$ should be used. For a flow of 500 mℓ/sec and a maximum glottal area of 0.16 mm^2, typical adult male values, the maximum glottal conductance would be approximately .05 in cgs units, as computed from $A^2/\rho U_g$ (Flanagan, 1958; Fant, 1960). Defining $\overline{L}_t$ as the value of L_t normalized to the scales used for Figs.2,3, and 4, we obtain:

$$\overline{L}_t \text{ (normalized)} = L_t \text{ (actual)} \times \frac{.05}{.002} = 0.2 \; . \quad (7)$$

Vowels with a higher F_1 would be expected to yield a value of $\overline{L}_t$ that is valid over a wider frequency range, since more harmonics would be included before F_1 is surpassed and the reactance becomes compliant. In addition, vocal tract configurations in which the pharynx is more constricted than for a neutral vowel might be expected to lead to a higher value of $\bar{L}_t$. Since the value of $\bar{L}_t$ also depends upon the maximum glottal admittance, a vocal fold vibratory pattern that resulted in a wider than average glottal opening would also increase $\bar{L}_t$, as would the inertive component of an unusually pronounced constriction at the entrance to the larynx or at the false vocal folds. Thus a value of $\bar{L}_t$ of at least 0.5 for a back vowel such as /a/ in some speakers is not inconceivable. Any glottal inertance would add to this figure.

Finally, we have also tested for the presence of supraglottal loading effects by comparing vocalizations made with air and with a large proportion of helium mixed with the air. By reducing the acoustic inertance in the vocal tract, the helium would be expected to reduce any supraglottal loading effect, if present. (Though, unlike the change of vowel value, the use of inspired helium also affects the glottal inertance. To affect only the acoustic loading, it would be necessary to introduce the helium only into the supraglottal pathway.) Figure 8 shows the general result we obtain. Both waveforms in the figure were obtained by inverse filtering the oral volume velocity for a male adult holding a vocal tract position for an /æ/ vowel. The fundamental frequency in each case was about 110 Hz. It can be seen that the symmetry of the waveform increases significantly with helium displacing some of the air.

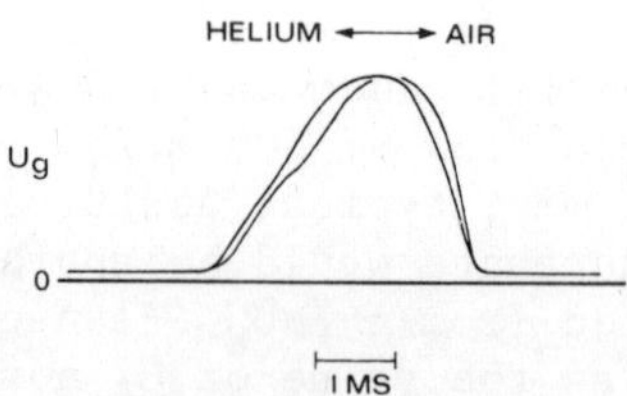

Fig.8. Glottal waveforms obtained by inverse filtering glottal air flow with air and with a large proportion of helium mixed with the air.

CONCLUSIONS

It appears that the often-noted skewing of the glottal flow waveform which results in the primary vocal tract excitation being at the instant of glottal closure can be caused by a combination of factors, including dissymmetry in the glottal admittance function, air displaced by vocal fold motion, and acoustic interaction with the supraglottal impedance. The inertance of the glottal slit may also be a factor, at least at the smaller glottal openings, when this inertance is largest.

To study the effect of acoustic interaction, we have defined a normalized supraglottal inertance $\overline{L}_t$ which approximates the actual loading of the glottis at frequencies between F_0 and F_1, assuming F_1 is appreciably larger than F_0. This model for the supraglottal loading indicates that for a symmetrical triangular admittance pulse the effect of acoustic interaction becomes large if $\overline{L}_t$ is close to or exceeds unity, since at $\overline{L}_t = 1$ the derivative of the glottal flow becomes infinite at the instant of glottal closure. This critical value of $\overline{L}_t$ will vary with the symmetry and general shape of the admittance pulse, but appears to remain in a range of roughly 0.5 to 2.0 for the type of admittance variation to be found in normal speech. The model also indicates that at higher values of $\overline{L}_t$ the volume velocity waveform tends to have a characteristic shape which is rather insensitive to the details of the glottal admittance function.

A rough analysis of the magnitude of the supraglottal vocal tract impedance shows that values of $\overline{L}_t$ of at least 0.5 are not implausible, with the value in any given case being a function of the vowel value, the maximum admittance of the glottis during the glottal cycle and the configuration of the larynx above the vocal folds.

A simple representation of the glottal admittance function that would result from an incomplete vocal fold closure during the glottal cycle indicates that this factor is also important, in that it can appreciably modify the effect of source-tract acoustic interaction. However, small leakage paths may not be as significant as our results in Fig.5 suggest, since we have neglected the glottal inertance, a factor that could be relatively large with a small opening.

Our results demonstrate that acoustic interaction can cause the glottal source waveform to vary widely as a function of vowel value and F_0, since the first formant must be high compared to F_0 in order for the supraglottal loading to be inertive at an appreciable number of glottal harmonics, and because the magnitude of the impedance below F_1 varies as a function of vowel value. It is also possible that different pronunciations (allophonic variations) of the same vowel phoneme can result in appreciably different source spectra because of differences in the impedance seen by the glottis. The degree to which this phenomenon can explain differences in voice quality in speech and singing would be an interesting subject for future research.

ACKNOWLEDGMENTS

The work described here was supported by research grant NS08919 from the National Institutes of Health. James T. Mahshie assisted in the experimental work, and the author was fortunate to have the help of Wilbur R. LePage in the solution of the differential equations.

REFERENCES

Fant, G. (1960) Acoustic theory of speech production. s-Gravenhage: Mouton.

Fant, G. (1979) Glottal source and excitation analysis. Royal Inst. of Tech. (Stockholm): Speech Trans. Lab., Quart. Prog. and Stat. Rep. 1/1979, 85-105.

Flanagan, J.L. (1958) Some properties of the glottal sound source. Journ. Speech and Hearing Res. 1, 99-116.

Flanagan, J.L. (1968) Source-system interaction in the vocal tract. Ann. N.Y. Acad. Sci. (Sound Production in Man), 155, 9-17.

Flanagan, J.L. and Ishizaka, K. (1978) Computer model to characterize the air volume displaced by the vibrating vocal cords. J. Acoust. Soc. Am. 63, 1559-1565.

Fourcin, A.J. (1974) Laryngographic examination of vocal fold vibration. In Ventilatory and phonatory control mechanisms, B. Wyke (ed.) Oxford: Oxford University Press, 315-333.

Holmes, J.N. (1962) An investigation of the volume velocity waveform at the larynx during speech by means of an inverse filter. In Proc. IV Int. Congr. Acoust,

Copenhagen, Denmark, Aug. 1962.

Miller, R.L. (1959) Nature of the vocal cord wave. J. Acoust. Soc. Am. 31, 667-679.

Rothenberg, M. (1973) A new inverse-filtering technique for deriving the glottal airflow waveform during voicing. J. Acoust. Soc. Am. 53, 1632-1645.

Rothenberg, M. (1979) Some relations between glottal air flow and vocal fold contact area. In National Institutes of Health, Proceedings of the Conference on the Assessment of Vocal Pathology (to be published).

Rothenberg, M. and Zahorian, S. (1977) Nonlinear inverse filtering technique for estimating the glottal area waveform. J. Acoust. Soc. Am. 61, 1063-1071.

DISCUSSION

Ishizaka: Dr. Rothenberg has clearly demonstrated the interaction between glottal flow and the vocal tract with the minimum use of mathematics. He represented the glottal impedance in terms of a two-terminal impedance for simplicity.

J.L. Flanagan and I have examined, by computer simulation, the contribution of the displacement flow produced by the vibrating vocal cords to glottal flow, U_g, and output sounds (Flanagan and Ishizaka, 1978). I would like to show how the displacement flow will affect glottal flow, which is skewed in the clockwise direction through the interaction with the vocal tract, just as Dr. Rothenberg has demonstrated.

In order to consider the displacement flow, the compressibility of air in the glottal slit should also be taken into account, because the air in the glottis behaves like a cushion. Therefore, the glottal impedance will be represented as a four-terminal network instead of the two-terminal impedance.

Figure A shows such a four-terminal representation of the glottal impedance corresponding to the two-mass approximation of the vocal cords. In the figure, the time rate of air volume displaced by lateral motion of the masses m_1 and m_2 (see Fig.1 of Chapter 17), are represented by the current (flow) sources, U_{x1} and U_{x2}, respectively. Similarly, the volume flows owing to longitudinal motion of the masses are represented by the current sources, U_{y1} and U_{y2}, respectively. And the time-varying compliance and loss of a small cavity formed by each opposing mass pair are represented as C_i and G_i, i = 1, 2. The serial impedances are the same as those of the two-terminal impedance representation. Namely, they are time-varying and R_c, R_{i2}, and R_e are flow-dependent resistances. This vocal cord model has been incorporated in a computer model of the subglottal system and the vocal tract with yielding walls. And we have made a computer simulation of speech production to assess the influences of the displacement flows and the shunt elements upon glottal flow and output sounds.

Figure B shows the computed waveforms for glottal area A_g and glottal volume flows U_g, with and without the displacement flow and the shunt admittances. In

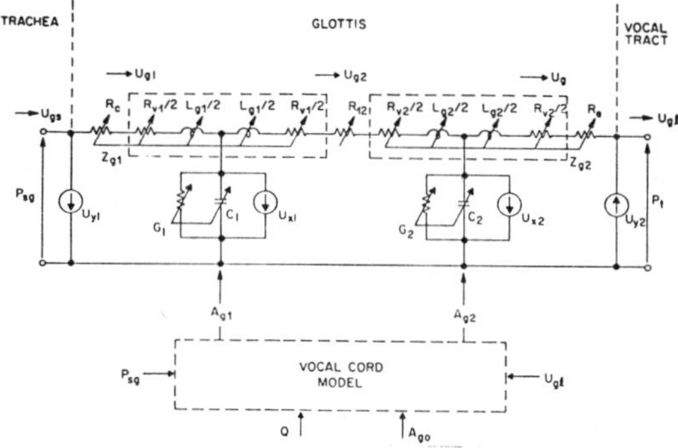

Fig.A. Representation of glottis by an equivalent network with two terminal pairs. The areas of the two sections of the glottis, A_{g1} and A_{g2} are controlled by the vocal cord model at the bottom.

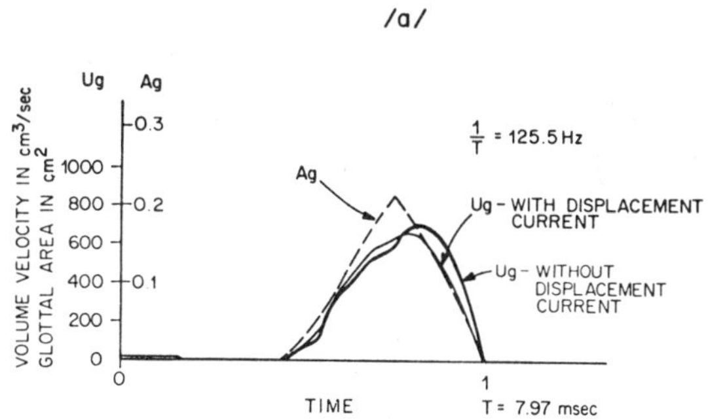

Fig.B. Computed waveforms of the glottal area A_g and glottal volume velocity U_g, with and without displacement current, for two-mass model of vocal folds driving a vocal tract in /a/ configuration.

this case, in order to examine the influence of lateral displacement flow alone, the longitudinal displacement flow sources are set to zero; $U_{y1} = U_{y2} = 0$. The vocal tract is configured for the vowel /a/. The A_g waveform shown by the broken line is nearly triangular in shape. The U_g waveform without the lateral displacement sources and the shunt elements shown by the heavy solid line shows a steeper slope than that of the A_g waveform at the closing phase, just as Dr. Rothenberg has shown. In addition, the interaction of the vocal resonances with U_g is indicated by the fine structure in the U_g waveform. On the other hand, the U_g waveform with the displacement flow sources and the shunt elements, shown by the light solid line, has a less sharp slope at closing phase, more similar to that of the A_g waveform. We can also observe the non-zero displacement flow, of the order of 20 cc/sec (beginning at the time origin of the figure), corresponding to the air squeezed out of the glottal orifice by the m_2 pair after the m_1 pair has collided and reduced A_g to zero area. Although it is not shown in the figure, upward motion of the vocal cords during the glottis-closed interval also produces the non-zero displacement flow, which is of the same order as that owing to lateral motion of the vocal cords.

Figure C also shows the same waveforms for the neutral schwa vowel / ə / in the same format as in Fig.B.

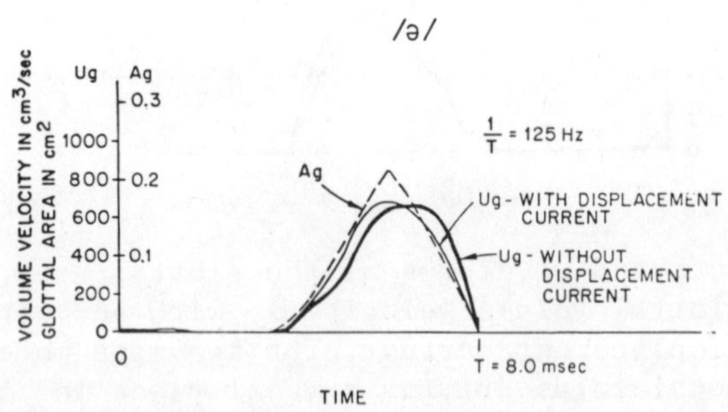

Fig.C. Same as Fig.B, except for / ə / configuration.

The U_g waveform with the lateral displacement sources and the shunt elements is again less sharp at the closing phase. However, we also notice a change in the fine structure in the U_g waveform for the vowel / ə /, because the fine structure is conditioned largely by the acoustic interaction at the lowest formant frequency.

Figure D shows the computed waveforms for the supraglottal pressure P_1, transglottal pressure $P_{sg} - P_1$, subglottal pressure P_{sg}, and glottal volume flow U_g. The vocal tract shape is for the schwa / ə /. The lung pressure, P_s, smoothly reaches the steady state value of 8 cm H_2O after about 10 msec from the time origin, as shown by the dotted line. The P_{sg} waveform is in good agreement with clinical direct measurements on a laryngectomized subject (Sawashima et al., 1964) and also with indirect measurements with an accelerometer attached to the neck (Stevens, 1972). The P_t waveform reflects directly the vocal tract resonances and is relatively similar to that of the output sound pressure. The transglottal pressure, $P_{sg} - P_1$, which activates the glottal flow, shows large pressure variations. However, because the predominant subglottal pressure variation is mainly excited at glottal closure and almost decays during the closed interval, the subglottal pressure variations are little reflected in the U_g wave, as we have seen in the previous figures. This fact gives a rationale for the disregard of the subglottal pressure variation or the subglottal system in calculating glottal flow approximately.

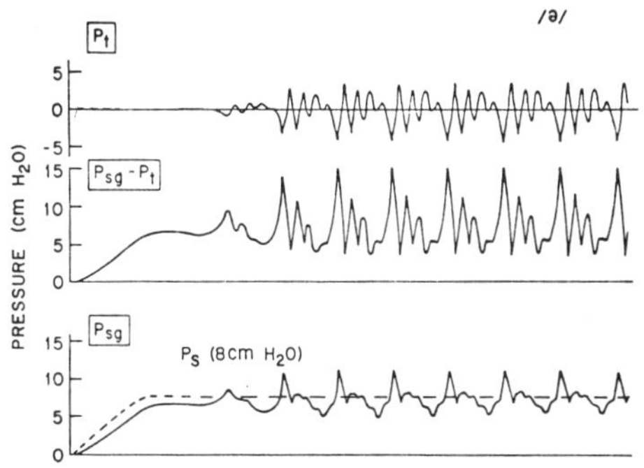

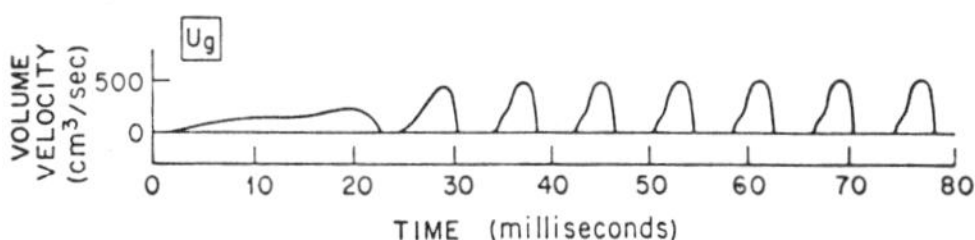

Fig.D. Computed waveforms for supraglottal pressure (P_t), transglottal pressure (P_{sg}-P_t), subglottal pressure P_{sg}, and glottal volume flow U_g, for two-mass model of vocal folds driving a vocal tract in / ə / configuration.

REFERENCES

Flanagan, J.L. and Ishizaka, K. (1978) Computer model to characterize the air volume displaced by the vibrating vocal cords. J. Acoust. Soc. Am. 63, 1559-1565.

Sawashima, M., et al. (1964) Subglottal pressure during phonation. Jpn. J. Logoped. Phoniatr. 5, 84-85. (In Japanese.)

Stevens, K.N. (1972) Personal communication. The data were later published in the following: W.L. Henke, Signals from external acceleometers during phonation, M.I.T. Res. Lab. Electron., Q. Prog. Report No. 114, 224-231 (Oct. 1974).

CHAPTER 22
ABDUCTION-ADDUCTION OF THE GLOTTIS IN SPEECH AND VOICE PRODUCTION

M. Sawashima and H. Hirose

Research Institute of Logopedics and Phoniatrics, Faculty of Medicine, University of Tokyo, Tokyo, Japan

Abduction-adduction of the glottis is a basic action of the laryngeal adjustments both for airway protection and voice production. In the study of speech production, this action has generally been recognized as an important "laryngeal feature" for phonetic distinctions (Ladefoged, 1973; Stevens, 1977; Fujimura, 1979; Swashima, 1979).

It is well known that the abduction-adduction of the glottis is achieved by the movements of the arytenoid cartilages on the surface of the cricoarytenoid joint. Studies of the functional anatomy of the cricoarytenoid joint in human larynges (Sonesson, 1958; von Leden and Moore, 1961; Frable, 1961; Takase, 1964) have revealed that the main part of the joint movement is a rotating motion of the arytenoid cartilage around the longitudinal axis of the joint. Other possible movements of the arytenoid cartilage are a small degree of sliding motion along the longitudinal axis of the joint surface of the cricoid cartilage and some rocking motion with a fixed point at the attachment of the posterior cricoarytenoid ligament. Contrary to the descriptions in some classical textbooks, there should be no rotating motion of the arytenoid around the axis which is vertical to the joint surface of the cricoid cartilage. The results of these studies were summarized elsewhere (Sawashima, 1974). Movements of these cartilages are controlled by the abductor and adductor muscles of the larynx. The functions of these muscles in speech are discussed in Chapter 11 of this book, by Hirose and Sawashima.

In this paper, the authors will concentrate on the apparent movement of the glottis in the abduction-adduction dimension. Among the various methods, the most reliable and straightforward method for observing the glottal condition, especially in the abduction-adduction dimension, is the use of a laryngeal fiberscope, the instrumentation and technique of which were reported elsewhere (Sawashima, 1977). In the following sections, results of fiberscopic observations of the glottis in various languages and phonetic conditions so far obtained are presented.

GLOTTAL ABDUCTION IN VOICELESS SOUNDS

An ordinary laryngoscopic view during normal phonation in the modal or the chest register is shown in Fig.1a. The laryngeal view for the deep inspiration is seen in Fig. 1b, where the vocal folds are fully abducted. In quiet respiration, the vocal folds are at the position which is approximately halfway to full abduction. Figure 2 presents a series of successive frames of a laryngeal cine film taken at a rate of 24 frames per second during the initiation of phonation. From left to right in the figure, the vocal folds are first set to the adducted or the so-called neutral position, and then are set into vibration by the transglottal air flow. The transglottal air flow may also generate the vocal fold vibration with the glottis abducted to a certain extent. The resultant voice is a so-called breathy voice or a murmur.

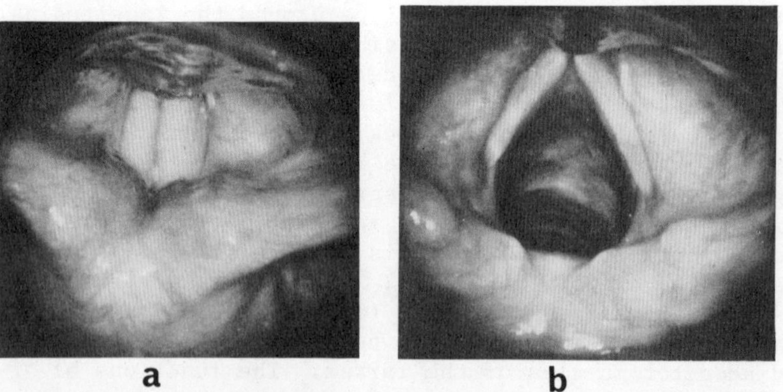

Fig.1. Laryngoscopic view for normal phonation (a) and deep inspiration (b).

The general picture of the glottal condition in the abduction-adduction dimension is that the glottis is closed or nearly closed for voiced sounds while it is open for voiceless sounds, the extent of the glottal opening varying with different phonemes and phonological environments. Figure 3 shows the glottal view in articulation of /s/ in Japanese. It is clearly shown that the glottis is fairly open for the fricative sound. It also appears that the distance between the vocal processes of the arytenoid cartilages gives a good measure of the abduction and adduction of the glottis.

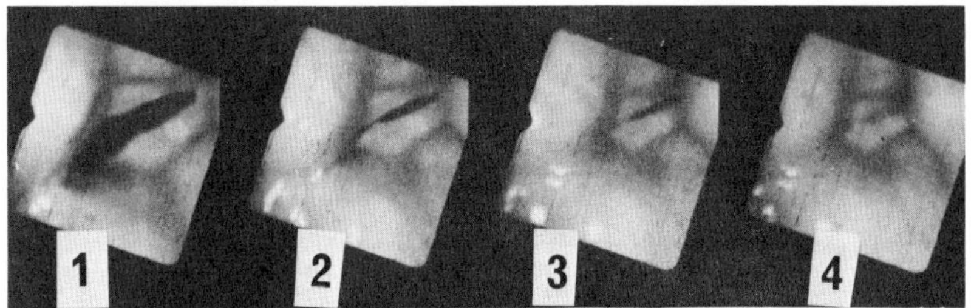

Fig.2. Successive frames of a laryngeal cinefilm during the initiation of phonation.

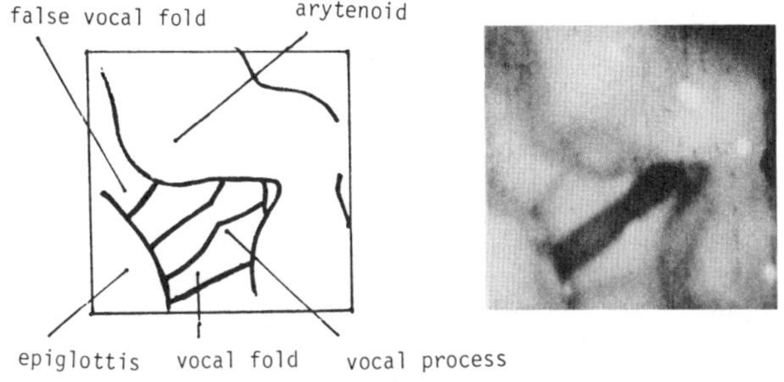

Fig.3. Fiberscopic view of the larynx for the /s/ in Japanese.

Figure 4 shows the time course of the glottal aperture obtained from fiberscopic laryngeal films in utterances of Japanese words [se:se:], [ke:ke:] and [te:te:] in a frame sentence. In each graph, the ordinate indicates the glottal width at an arbitrary scale, and the abscissa indicates the time course represented by the interval (20 msec) of each frame of the film.

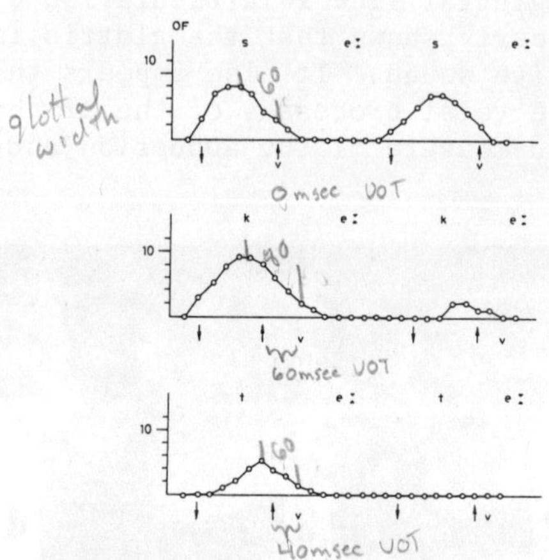

Fig.4. Opening and closing process of the glottis for Japanese voiceless consonants. The glottal width is plotted on the ordinate to an arbitrary scale. The points on the horizontal time scale are separated by 20 msec. The arrows indicate times of oral closure and release for the consonants and the V's indicate times of voicing onset.

The arrows under each graph indicate the times of the oral closure and release for the consonants, and V's indicate the times of the voicing onset for the following vowels. The time course shows a rather simple pattern that usually has a single peak in the glottal width for each consonant. For the word-medial [k], the glottal width is far smaller than that for the initial [k]. For the [t], there is no apparent glottal opening in the word-medial position for this subject. Selected frames of the laryngeal films in correspondence with the sound spectrograms of speech for utterances of [ke:ke:] and [te:te:] are shown in Figs.5 and 6 respectively.

Peak values of the glottal width for Japanese voiceless sounds examined in four Japanese subjects are summarized in Fig.7 (Sawashima et al, 1976). In the figure, horizontal bars in each item represent the entire ranges of the

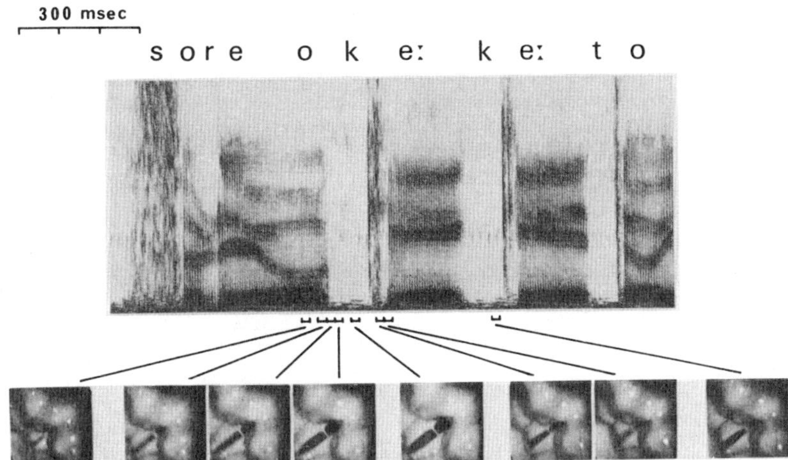

Fig.5. Selected frames of a laryngeal film and a sound spectrogram of an utterance of [ke:ke:] in a frame sentence.

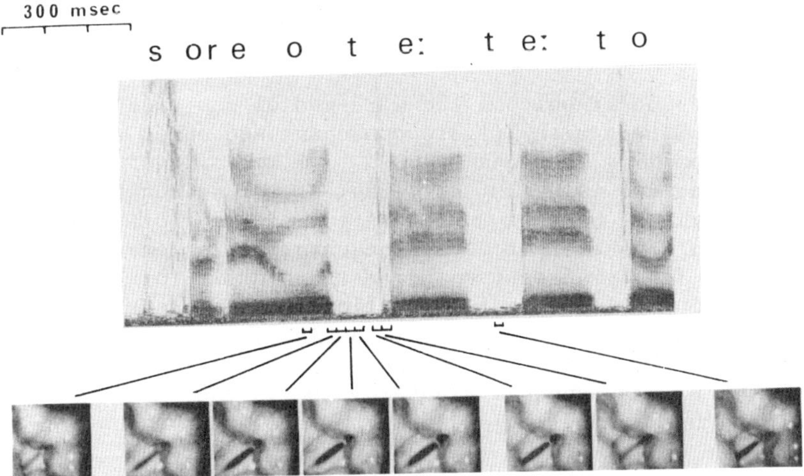

Fig.6. Same as Fig.5 for [te:te:].

sample variations and filled circles indicate the mean values. At the bottom of each column is an arbitrary scale representing the value of the glottal aperture, the leftmost end of the scale indicating an apparently closed glottis. In the leftmost column listing the sounds, (I) and (M) indicate initial and medial positions, respectively. Sounds with doubled phonetic symbols are the geminate

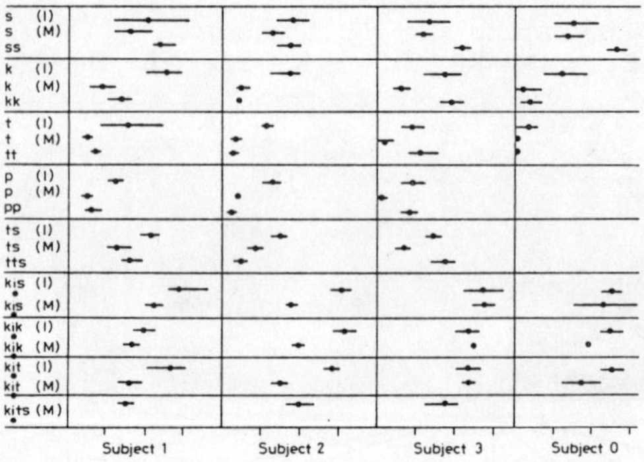

Fig.7. Maximum glottal aperture for Japanese voiceless sounds. The horizontal scale is arbitrary. Means and ranges over 4-6 utterances are represented by the points and the horizontal bars. Data for initial (I), medical (M), and, in some cases, geminate consonants are given.

sounds which occur only in the word-medial position in Japanese. Sounds with [i̥] are consonant sequences with unvoiced vowel [i̥] between them.

Comparing the values of different items, we can find a characteristic pattern in the extent of the glottal abduction for Japanese voiceless consonants. In general there is a fairly large opening of the glottis for [s] in both word-initial and medial positions. In stops the opening is definitely larger for the initial position than for the medial position. The glottal opening for the affricate [ts] also shows a greater value in the intial position than in the medial position. For the geminate stops, the extent of the glottal opening is as small as word-medial non-geminate stops except for subject 3. In subject 3, the glottal opening for the geminate stop is comparable to that of the initial non-geminate stop. It is also noted that consonant combinations involving the voiceless [i̥] show a glottal opening the extent of which is as large as, or even larger than, that for the fricative [s]. It is known that the vowel [i] becomes voiceless in the Tokyo dialect when it is placed between voiceless consonants. Although there is no phonemic distinction between the voiced and unvoiced vowels, the latter is acoustically characterized by turbulent noise generated in the vocal tract, and the laryngeal adjustment for this sound appears to be identical to that for the voiceless fricative [s]. The laryngeal adjustment for the [s] is also used for the fricative sound [h], although this sound becomes voiced in the intervocalic position as is discussed later.

Averaged time curves for each of the stops and the affricate for the three subjects are displayed in Fig.8.

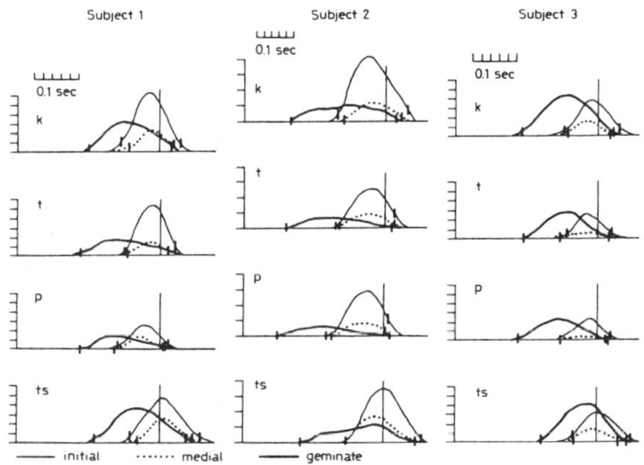

Fig.8. Time courses of glottal aperture for Japanese stops and affricates. The vertical scale is arbitrary, and the time scale is shown at the top of each column. Times of voicing offset and onset are marked by short vertical lines, and the curves are aligned relative to the release time of the supraglottal closure. Data represent means for 4-6 utterances.

In the figure, each of the averaged curves is lined up at the point where the oral closure is released. A vertical line in each graph indicates the line-up point. Short vertical bars on each curve delimit the time interval of the voiceless segment. In non-geminate stops, the oral release is observed to take place after the peak glottal width is reached. In the affricate, which is characterized by the fricative noise following release of the stop closure, the oral release takes place around the time point where the peak glottal width is reached. In both the stops and affricate, there is little difference between the initial and medial position in the timing of the oral release relative to the glottal abduction-adduction movements, although the glottal width at the oral release is greater for the initial position than the medial position. There is also little difference in the voice onset time between the two conditions. In the geminate consonants, there is a longer duration of the stop closure and of the glottal separation. Near the end of the stop closure and after the release, however, the curves of the geminates become almost identical with those of the medial non-geminates.

There are languages such as Korean, Hindi, and Chinese, which have a phonemic distinction between aspirated and unaspirated voiceless stops. Figure 9 shows the time curves of the glottal width for the aspirated (denoted as t^h) and unaspirated (denoted as t) dental stops in Mandarin (Iwata and Hirose, 1976). The curves are lined up at the oral release indicated by the vertical line. On each curve, a solid arrow indicates the voice offset and a dashed arrow indicates the voice onset for the following vowel. In the aspirated stop, there is a great extent of glottal abduction after the oral closure. It is noted that the oral release takes place at or before the time point where the maximum glottal width is reached. This type of glottal time curve results in a large value of the voice onset time. The glottal time curve for the unaspirated stop, in contrast, shows a very small aperture during the oral closure. The glottis is nearly closed at the oral release, the time point of the voice onset being immediately after the release. Observations on Fukienese (Iwata et al, 1979), Korean (Kagaya, 1974; Hirose et al, 1974; Sawashima and Park, 1979) and Hindi (Kagaya and Hirose, 1975) revealed the same pattern in this respect. A similar contrast is also observable between /p/ and /b/ in Danish in word-initial position (Fischer-Jørgensen and Hirose, 1974).

In American English, where there is no phonemic distinction between aspirated and unaspirated stops, a greater glottal abduction with a greater degree of aspiration is observed for prestressed voiceless stops as compared to the corresponding poststressed stops (Sawashima, 1970). In French voiceless stops also, the amount of the glottal abduction for the voiceless stop varies according to the stress conditions (Benguerel et al, 1978).

Based on his cinefluorographic observation of the la-

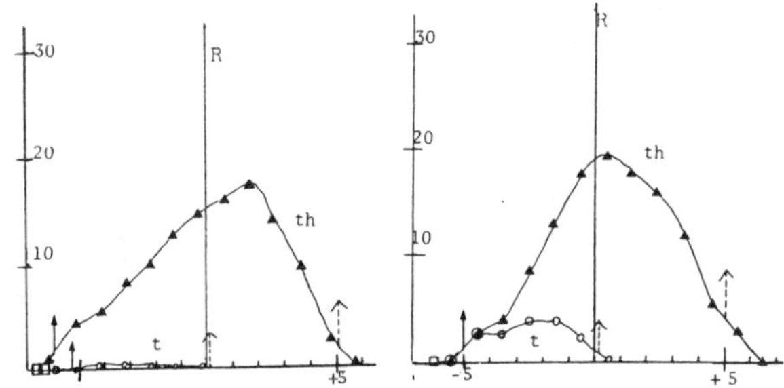

Fig.9. Time courses of glottal aperture for Mandarin stops (t, t^h). The frame numbers on the abscissa are at intervals of 20 msec.

ryngeal adjustments for Korean stops, Kim (1970) stated in his theory of aspiration that the extent of aspiration is determined by the glottal aperture at the moment of articulatory release. Our fiberscopic data appears to be basically in agreement with Kim in this respect as far as the voiceless stops are concerned.

Observations of the glottal conditions for Japanese voiceless sounds and sound sequences have suggested that a glottal time curve for a certain sound sequence may be interpreted as a succession of the glottal adjustments for each of the constituent sounds. Here the coarticulatory effect of the neighboring sounds and sound modifications at some higher level in the process of speech production should be taken into account.

Figure 10 shows the glottal time curves for [ʃi̥ss] of /siQseH/ and [ʃi̥pp] of /siQpeH/ in two subjects, M.S. and H.H. (Sawashima and Hirose, 1978). The time curves for /siQseH/ tend to show two peaks. It may be assumed that the first peak corresponds to the [ʃi̥] and the second peak to the [s] of the third mora. The time curves for /siQpeH/ are considered to be more distinct in the sense that the initial peak should correspond to the [ʃi̥] and the following part to the [pp]. It is interesting to refer to the recent study on consonant sequences in American English (Yoshioka et al, 1979). According to the results, the glottal time curve for a consonant sequence such as /sk/ shows a single peak when the sequence is placed word-initially or finally without an intervening word boundary. In contrast, the time curve shows two peaks for each of the /s/ and /k/ when a word boundary is placed between them.

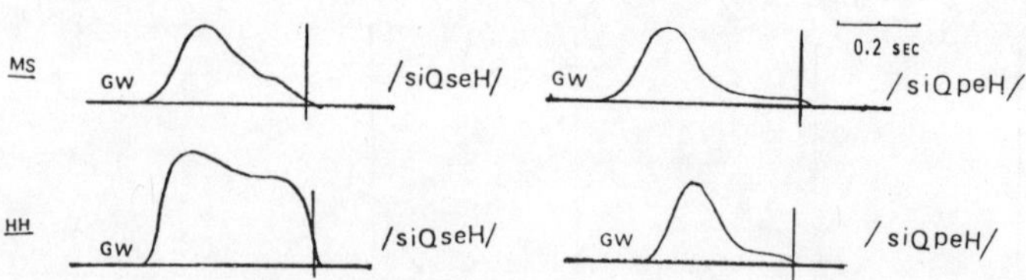

Fig.10. Time courses of glottal aperture for voiceless sound sequences in Japanese.

ACTION OF THE FALSE VOCAL FOLDS AND SUPRAGLOTTAL LARYNGEAL STRUCTURES FOR VOICING DISTINCTION

It is well known that the glottal stop is characterized by a laryngeal gesture for achieving cessation of voicing with the glottis closed. Some languages have a phonemic distinction between the glottal stop and other voiceless stops. Fukienese has the glottal stop as one of the four syllable final applosives. The laryngeal gesture for this sound is characterized by an adduction of the false vocal folds or a sphincteric constriction of the supraglottic laryngeal structures (Iwata et al, 1979). It has been observed that in American English the glottal stop gesture is used in certain environments for the voiceless stops which are otherwise produced with glottal abduction (Fujimura and Sawashima, 1971).

A lesser degree of supraglottic constriction with a closed glottis may be associated with laryngealization as claimed by Gauffin (1977). It is not clear at present, however, whether this type of constriction holds for "creaky voice" or not.

Another typical example of the supraglottic laryngeal constriction is observed in whispering, particularly in stage whispering (Weitzman et al, 1976). Figure 11 shows tracings of laryngeal pictures for the vowels /i/ and /u/ in stage whispered speech. Here the glottis is abducted, but a strong constriction of the supraglottic structures including the arytenoid masses, the false vocal folds and the epiglottis is evident so that only a small portion of the glottis in the vicinity of the vocal processes is visible. Antero-posterior laryngography have revealed that the false vocal folds press directly the upper surface of the vocal folds in stage whisper. Thus the supraglottic constriction for whispering is considered to contribute toward preventing glottal vibration by the transglottal air flow and also to facilitate the generation of turbulent noise.

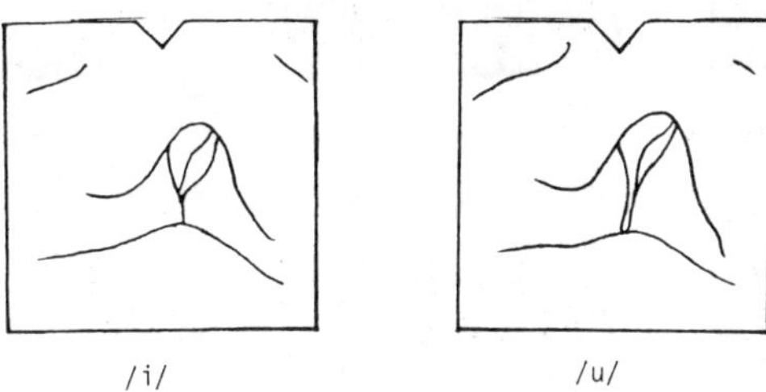

Fig.11. Tracings of the glottal views for stage whispered vowels.

GLOTTAL ABDUCTION-ADDUCTION AND VOICING DISTINCTION

As is well known, the voiced vs voiceless distinction is achieved by control of the laryngeal conditions in combination with the aerodynamic conditions at the glottis. Figure 12 shows photoelectric glottograms of syllables containing voiced and voiceless consonants. Abduction-adduction of the glottis as well as the glottal vibration is recognized in each trace. The test syllables are embedded in a frame sentence "ii ___ desu" (It is a good ___). It is noted that /h/'s are in the intervocalic position and are voiced in spite of a fairly large glottal opening. In /h/, there is no articulatory constriction and the resulting fast air flow through the glottis enables the vocal folds to maintain vibration. For the second /t/ of /te te/, in contrast, the vocal fold vibration ceases immediately after the oral closure in spite of a very small glottal aperture. The oral closure prevents the air from passing through the glottis. A gradual cessation of the vocal fold vibration in /s/ also reflects the aerodynamic condition caused by the oral constriction. It is apparent that the crucial factor in the voicing distinction for these consonants is the aerodynamic condition at the glottis rather than the extent of the glottal abduction. An aerodynamic effect on the vocal fold vibration with the closed glottis is observable in the glottograms for voiced consonants. For the /d/, there is a decrease

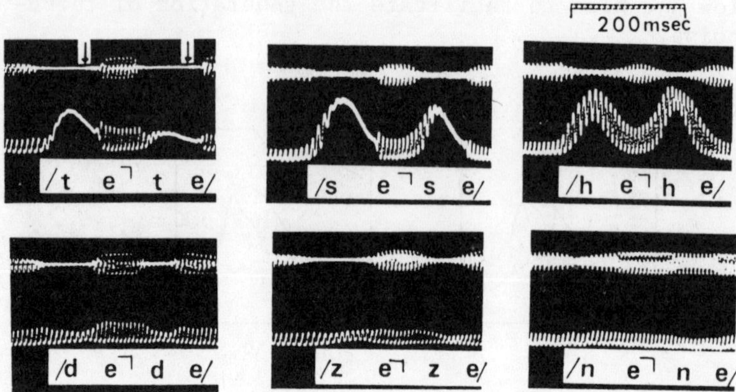

Fig.12. The lower trace in each panel displays photoelectric glottograms for Japanese consonants. The upper trace is the acoustic waveform.

in both the amplitude and frequency because of the oral closure. For the /n/, however, no such change is observed because of the nasal passage remaining open for the air flow.

Figure 13 shows glottal time curves for Hindi stops (Kagaya and Hirose, 1975). In this particular language, there is a four-way distinction in stop consonants; voiceless unaspirated, voiceless aspirated, voiced unaspirated and voiced aspirated. Time curves for voiceless stops show identical patterns to those of other languages as described before. The voiced unaspirated stop shows the glottis closed through the consonant period. In a voiced aspirated stop, the glottis is closed during the oral closure until it begins to open at or before the oral release, the peak glottal width being reached after the oral release. The glottal vibration is maintained throughout the consonantal period. The closed glottis in the early part of the consonantal portion is considered to be identical to the unaspirated voiced stop and the open glottis in the latter part after the release is considered to be identical to the voiced /h/. It is noted here that the closed glottis would be necessary for maintaining vocal fold vibration in the presence of a vocal tract constriction which causes an unfavorable aerodynamic condition for maintaining the glottal vibration.

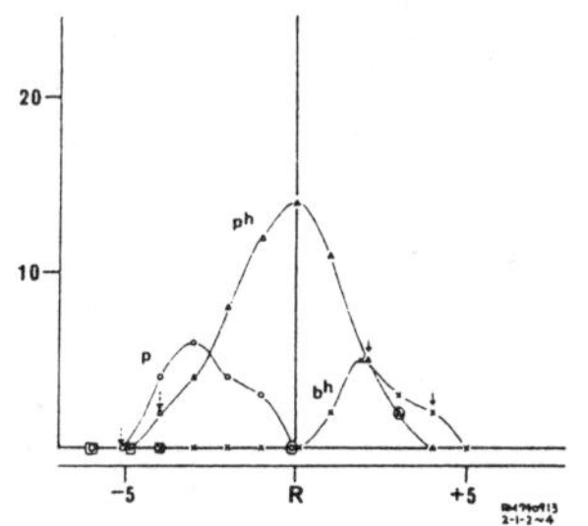

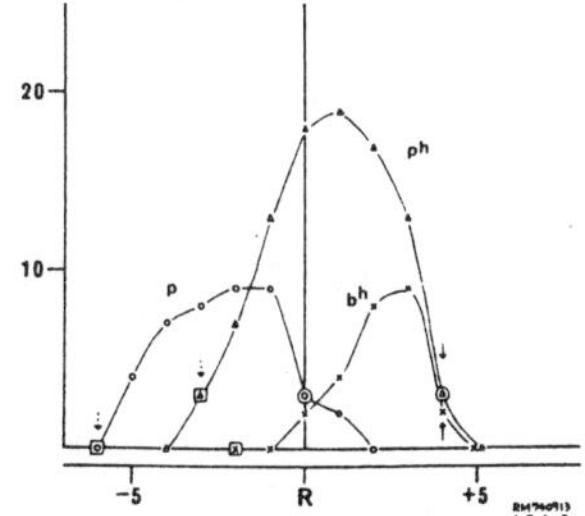

Fig.13. Time curves of glottal aperture for Hindi stops. The spacing between points is 20 msec.

The contribution of the supraglottic laryngeal structures in creating the voicing distinction was mentioned before. Another possible feature contributing to the voicing distinction is the stiff-slack dimension of the vocal folds (Halle and Stevens, 1971). This problem is in part related to the electromyographic study of the laryngeal muscles (Chapter 11 of this book), and further study is needed in this respect.

ACKNOWLEDGMENT

This work was in part supported by a Grant-in-Aid for Co-operative Research (No. 337040), the Ministry of Education, Science and Culture, Japanese Government.

REFERENCES

Benguerel, A.P., Hirose, H., Sawashima, M. and Ushijima, T. (1978) Laryngeal control in French stop production: A fiberscopic, acoustic and electromyographic study. Folia Phoniatrica 30, 175-198.

Fischer-Jørgensen, E. and Hirose, H. (1974) A note on laryngeal activity in the Danish "stød". Haskins Laboratories. SR 39/40, 255-259.

Frable, M.A. (1961) Computation of motion of cricoarytenoid joint. Arch. Otolaryng. 73, 551-556.

Fujimura, O. (1979) Physiological functions of the larynx in phonetic control. In Current Issues in the Phonetic Sciences. H. Hollien and P. Hollien (eds.) Amsterdam: John Benjamins B.V., 129-163.

Fujimura, O. and Sawashima, M. (1971) Consonant sequences and laryngeal control. Ann. Bull. RILP. 5, 1-6.

Gauffin, J. (1977) Mechanism of larynx tube constriction. Phonetica 34, 307-309.

Halle, M. and Stevens, K.N. (1971) A note on laryngeal features. Q. Prog. Rep. Res. Lab. Electron. M.I.T. 101, 198-213.

Hirose, H., Lee, C.Y. and Ushijima, T. (1974) Laryngeal control in Korean stop production. J. Phonetics 2, 145-152.

Iwata, R. and Hirose, H. (1976) Fiberoptic and acoustic studies of Mandarin stops and affricates. Ann. Bull. RILP., 10, 47-60.

Iwata, R., Sawashima, M., Hirose, H. and Niimi, S. (1979) Laryngeal adjustments of Fukienese stops - Initial plosives and final Applosives. Ann. Bull. RILP., 13, 61-81.

Kagaya, R. (1974) A fiberoptic and acoustic study of the Korean stops, affricates and fricatives. J. Phonetics 2, 161-180.

Kagaya, R. and Hirose, H. (1975) Fiberoptic, electromyographic and acoustic analysis of Hindi stop consonants. Ann. Bull. RILP., 9, 27-46.

Kim, C.W. (1970) A theory of aspiration. Phonetica 21, 107-116.

Ladefoged, P. (1973) The features of the larynx. J. Phonetics 1, 73-83.

Leden, H. Von and Moore, P. (1961) The mechanism of the cricoarytenoid joint. Arch. Otolaryng. 73, 541-550.

Sawashima, M. (1970) Glottal adjustments for English obstruents. Haskins Laboratories SR 21/22, 180-200.

Sawashima, M. (1974) Laryngeal research in experimental phonetics. In Current Trends in Linguistics, Vol. 12, T.A. Sebeok (ed.) The Hague: Mouton, 2302-2348.

Sawashima, M. (1977) Fiberoptic observation of the larynx and other speech organs. In Dynamic Aspects of Speech Production M. Sawashima and F.S. Cooper (eds.) Tokyo: University of Tokyo Press, 33-46.

Sawashima, M. (1979) Laryngeal control for voicing distinctions: A review of recent works. Ann. Bull. RILP., 13, 23-26.

Sawashima, M., Hirose, H. and Niimi, S. (1976) Glottal conditions in articulation of Japanese voiceless consonants. XVI Int. Congr. Logopedics and Phoniatrics. Interlaken 1974, Basel: Karger, 409-414.

Sawashima, M., Hirose, H. and Yoshioka, H. (1978) Abductor (PCA) and adductor (INT) muscles of the larynx in voiceless sound production. Ann. Bull. RILP., 12, 53-60.

Sawashima, M. and Park, H.S. (1979) Laryngeal adjustments for syllable final stops in Korean: Some preliminary results of fiberoptic observation. Ann. Bull. RILP., 13, 83-89.

Sonesson, B. (1958) Die funktionelle Anatomie des Crico-arytenoid-gelenkes. Zschr. Anat. Entw. 121, 292-303.

Stevens, K.N. (1977) Physics of laryngeal behavior and larynx modes. Phonetica 34, 264-279.

Takase, S. (1964) Studies on the intrinsic laryngeal muscles of mammals: Comparative anatomy and physiology. Otologia (Fukuoka) 10, Suppl. 1. (in Japanese).

Weitzman, R.S., Sawashima, M., Hirose, H. and Ushijima, T. (1976) Devoiced and whispered vowels in Japanese. Ann. Bull. RILP., 10, 61-80.

Yoshioka, H., Löfqvist, A. and Hirose, H. (1979) Laryngeal adjustments in the production of consonant clusters and geminates in American English. An extended version of the paper presented at the 97th ASA Meeting, Cambridge, Mass. (June, 1979).

DISCUSSION

Fujimura: In your data comparing word-initial and medial /t/'s in Japanese, as presented in Fig.6, I notice a relatively large glottal opening in the membranous portion for the medial /t/ in spite of the small distance between the vocal processes. The glottis also seems to be much shorter in this case. Are there any EMG data showing different muscle gestures, e.g. less CT contraction for the word-medial case? Also, the glottal area from an acoustic point of view is not as small as your plotting suggests for medial /t/ for this reason. Do you think the arytenoidal adduction/abduction is more relevant than the opening area, for example in accounting for the extent of aspiration?

Hirano: The glottal appearance for the medial /t/ you showed in Fig.6 is different from that for vowels. Although the tips of the bilateral vocal processes are approximated, there is a tiny chink at the membranous portion of the glottis. I am very much interested in the activities of the laryngeal muscles for this glottal appearance.

Sawashima: As far as our EMG studies are concerned, there are no data showing more activity of CT for word-initial voiceless stops than for word-medial ones. Our data indicated rather opposite tendency, i.e., more suppression of CT activity for the word-initial position than for the medial position. The activity of VOC also indicates the same tendency.

A spindle shaped glottal opening at the membranous portion is usually noted in the laryngeal gesture for vowel production when there is no transglottal air flow. The situation is the so-called neutral position as seen in the third frame of Fig.2. In the word-medial /t/ of Fig.6, the distance between the vocal processes is so small that there is no apparent gap to be measured. However, the glottal adduction is not so complete as in vowel production. In other words, there is a very small degree of abduction of the arytenoids controlled by the abductor and adductor muscles. Also, the activity of VOC is suppressed for the consonant as compared to the vowel. These conditions may account for the glottal chink which is larger than that of the so-called neutral position, although it is still "tiny" according to Dr. Hirano.

The apparent difference in the antero-posterior dimension of the larynx cavity between the initial and medial /t/'s should be attributed to some mechanisms other than those controlled by the intrinsic laryngeal muscles.

As for the second question of Dr. Fujimura, I may not be able to give a straightforward answer concerning the point whether or not the arytenoidal adduction/abduction is more relevant than the glottal area in accounting for the acoustic output. I simply say that the arytenoidal adduction/abduction is a basic mechanism in controlling the glottal area.

CHAPTER 23
ANALYSIS OF PITCH CONTROL IN SINGING

H. Fujisaki, M. Tatsumi, and N. Higuchi

Faculty of Engineering,
University of Tokyo, Tokyo, Japan

INTRODUCTION

Needless to say, changes in the voice fundamental frequency play important roles both in speech and in singing. In many spoken languages, temporal patterns of the fundamental frequency are major manifestations of the suprasegmental structure of a spoken message and are used to convey both lexical and syntactic information, while in some languages they carry even segmental information. Their role in singing is also crucial since they carry the melodic information. Studies of fundamental frequency control (henceforth pitch control) in speech and singing are thus quite important in elucidating the underlying mechanism by which such information is encoded and transmitted to a listener.

The dynamic process of pitch control in speech has been studied rather extensively. For example, the fundamental frequency contours (henceforth pitch contours) of spoken words and sentences were analyzed and modeled by Fujisaki and others (Fujisaki and Nagashima, 1969; Fujisaki and Sudo, 1971), separating features that are related to the linguistic content of an utterance from those related to the voice control mechanism. This approach has been applied to analysis of the word accent both in Japanese and in English (Fujisaki and Sugito, 1978; Hirose, Fujisaki, and Sugito, 1978), as well as of the sentence intonation of Japanese (Fujisaki, Hirose, and Ohta, 1979). The dynamic characteristics of the larynx in rapid pitch changes were also studied by Ohala and Ewan (1973), indicating a tendency for the transition time to be unaffected by the magnitude of the pitch change. On the other hand, studies of pitch control in singing have been rather scarce. The speed of rapid pitch changes in singing, however, was investigated recently by Sundberg (1979) in an experiment in which the subjects were asked to alternate repeatedly between two given pitches in a legato-like performance. His results show mean response times of about 50 to 80 msec with systematic changes due to differences in sex and in professional training.

It is to be expected, however, that the speed (hence the response time) of pitch changes will certainly depend on the expression, on manner of performance, and possibly on tempo. The purpose of the present study is to analyze the characteristics of pitch transitions from one note to another under various conditions of singing, using techniques already developed for the analysis of pitch contours of speech.

MATERIALS AND SUBJECTS

The material for the present study consisted of a number of two-note sequences sung with the vowel [a] in various manners of performance (i.e., in various degrees of articulation of the two notes). They were: a) a note with an _appoggiatura_, b) two notes sung in _staccato_, c) two notes sung in _non legato_, d) two notes sung in _legato_, and e) two notes sung in _portamento_. Since, however, the two notes sung in _staccato_ are generally separated by a silent gap of considerable duration, they were left out of the subsequent analysis. The subjects were two females with a similar range and quality of voice. One (Subject MT) was a voice trainer with 10 years of professional training in singing herself, and the other (Subject YS) was a student in a conservatory of music with three years of training in singing. The pitches of the two notes were selected to suit their voice range, and the intervals were either a musical fourth (A_4 - D_5) or an octave (D_4 - D_5). The sequences were produced in both directions, upward and downward. Each sequence was repeated several times in 3/4 time with a M.M. setting of 100 except in the case of _portamento_ where the beat was approximately M.M. 80. These sequences were sung at three levels of volume: forte _(f)_, _mezzopiano_ _(mp)_, and _pianissimo_ (pp). At least _five_ samples were collected for each of the conditions and subjects. For the sake of comparison, speech materials were also recorded. They were isolated utterances of the two words in the Tokyo dialect of Japanese: "ame" [ame] (candy) and "ame" [ame] (rain). These two words possess an identical phonemic structure but differ in the accent type manifested mainly in their pitch contours, the former being the "low-high" type and the latter being the "high-low" type.

METHOD OF ANALYSIS

The analysis of pitch transitions in singing involves two stages of processing, i.e., (1) extraction of the fundamental frequency trajectory, and (2) extraction of the parameters of the trajectory.

Extraction of the Fundamental Frequency Trajectory

The fundamental periods are detected pitch synchronously using both short-term autocorrelation analysis and waveform peak detection. These fundamental periods are converted to fundamental frequency values, which are further smoothed and interpolated to produce a trajectory (henceforth F_0 - trajectory) uniformly sampled at intervals of 10 msec.

In the sung materials, a trajectory thus extracted usually consists of an initial segment which is quasi-stationary except for the case of *appoggiatura*, and a transitional segment characterized by a smooth movement toward a stationary final segment. The initial and final segments are usually accompanied by a *vibrato*, i.e., an almost periodic modulation of the fundamental frequency, whose amplitude is considerably diminished in the transitional segment. As pointed out by Vennard (1967) and Sundberg (1979), the *vibrato* generally aligns in phase with the transition. Although the analysis of the interaction between these two components is certainly worthwhile, we are concerned here only with the transient component whose parameters reflect the characteristics of the pitch control mechanism.

Extraction of the Parameters of an F_0 Trajectory

The extraction of the parameters of an observed F_0 trajectory is based on an approximate functional formulation (model) of the process of its production. Our previous studies on pitch contours of speech suggest that a proper formulation of the F_0 trajectory in singing should be based on the logarithmic scale of the fundamental frequency.

They also suggest that the transient component can be regarded as the response of the pitch control mechanism to a hypothetical command to switch notes. If we assume the command to be a step function, the pitch control mechanism can be functionally approximated by a second-order linear system, and the F_0 trajectory of a two-note sequence may be represented by

$$\ln[F_0(t)/F_i] = \ln(F_f/F_i)\ f(\beta,\ \gamma,\ t)\ u(t), \qquad (1)$$

where

$$f(\beta,\gamma,t) = 1 - \left[\cos \beta\sqrt{1-\gamma^2}t + \frac{\gamma}{\sqrt{1-\gamma^2}} \sin \beta\sqrt{1-\gamma^2}t\right] \times \exp(-\beta\gamma t), \quad \text{for } \gamma<1,$$

$$= 1 - (1+\beta t)\exp(-\beta t), \quad \text{for } \gamma=1,$$

$$= 1 - \left[\cosh \beta\sqrt{\gamma^2-1}t + \frac{\gamma}{\sqrt{\gamma^2-1}} \sinh \beta\sqrt{\gamma^2-1}t\right] \times \exp(-\beta\gamma t), \quad \text{for } \gamma>1,$$

$u(t)$ denotes the unit step function, F_i and F_f respectively denote the initial and final values of the transition, and β and γ are parameters characterizing the second-order linear system. In particular, γ is the damping factor and the three conditions for γ in the above equations correspond to the under-damped, the critically-damped, and the over-damped cases, respectively. The origin of the time axis is selected at the onset of the transition.

Although it is possible to measure such characteristics as the rise/fall times directly from an F_0 trajectory, the above formulation gives us more insight into the underlying mechanism of pitch control. Parameters such as β and γ can be obtained from a measured F_0 trajectory by finding its best approximation given by the above equations, which can then be used to determine the rise/fall times. For the sake of comparison with the results obtained by Ohala and Ewan (1973) and by Sundberg (1979), we adopt here the same definition of rise/fall time as in their studies. Namely, the rise/fall time is defined as the time required for the pitch to change from 1/8 to 7/8 of the total range of transition.

The above formulation for the F_0 trajectory of sung notes follows the same line of thought as that for the F_0

trajectory of a spoken word, except that in the latter we assume an additional "voicing component" of the following shape

$$g(t) = h(t - t_i) - h(t - t_f), \quad (2)$$

where

$$h(t) = A_v \alpha t \exp(-\alpha t) u(t),$$

which serves as the baseline upon which the accent component is superposed on the logarithmic scale of the fundamental frequency. In Eq. (2), A_v and α respectively denote the amplitude and the rate of change of the voicing component, while t_i and t_f denote the onset and the offset of the command for voicing. Thus the method of analysis for the speech material is essentially the same as that for the sung material except for the addition of parameters characterizing the voicing component.

RESULTS

Figure 1 illustrates one example each of pitch transitions across the interval of a fourth (A_4 - D_5) in the sung material of Subject MT produced at <u>mezzopiano</u> under eight different conditions, i.e., upward and downward transitions sung at four different degrees of articulation (<u>appoggiatura</u>, <u>non legato</u>, <u>legato</u>, and <u>portamento</u>). The symbol (+) indicates a value of the fundamental frequency sampled at 10 msec intervals on the measured F_0 trajectory, while the curve in each panel indicates the best approximation based on Eq.(1) of the preceding section. These and other results of analysis indicate that the model adopted in the present study can provide very good approximations to almost all the F_0 trajectories observed, and hence its parameters can be regarded as good indices for the dynamic properties of the pitch control mechanism.

Quite naturally, the rate of pitch change is seen to vary to a large extent with the degree of articulation, and also to vary with the direction, i.e., a downward transition is faster than an upward transition especially in <u>appoggiatura</u> and in <u>non legato</u>. The F_0 trajectories are clearly under-damped in these fast transitions, while they are almost critically damped in normal and slower transitions (<u>legato</u> and <u>portamento</u>). The <u>vibrato</u> component,

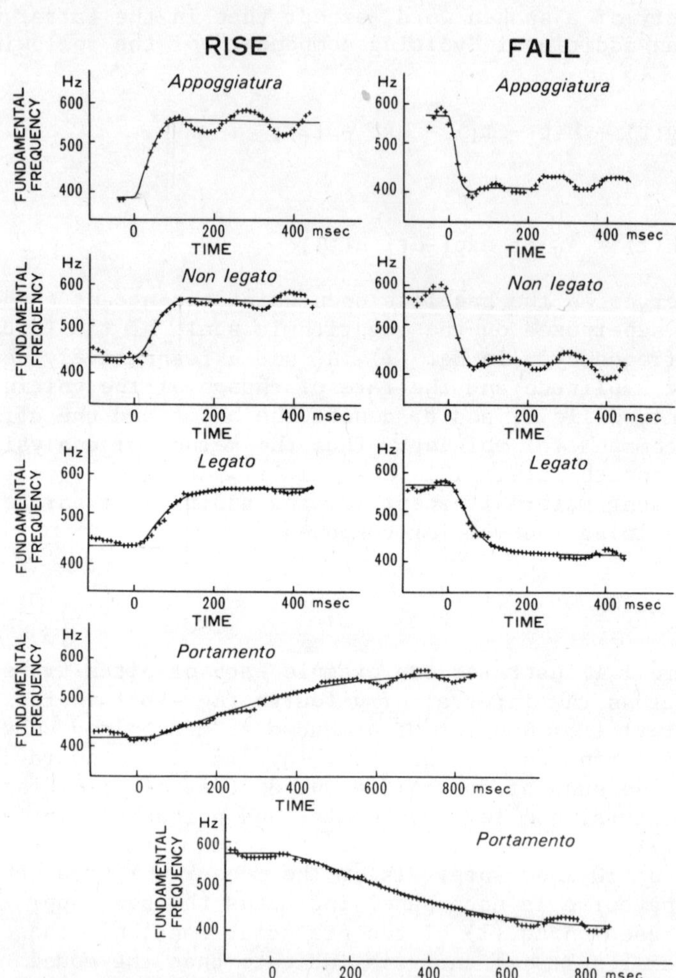

Fig.1. Analysis of F_0 trajectories in singing. Typical results obtained from samples of two-note sequences separated by an interval of a fourth (Subject MT).

which appears as deviations of the measured points from the smooth trajectory given by the model, seems to be suppressed during the transition.

Figure 2 shows one example each of the pitch contours of the speech material uttered by the same subject, together with the best approximations produced by the model of the word pitch contour under the assumption of critical damping.

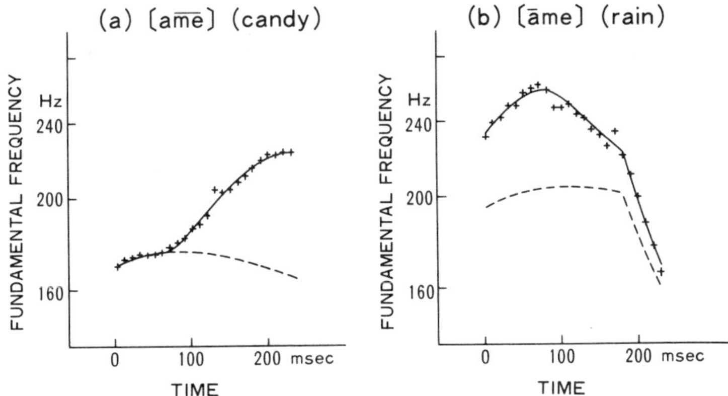

Fig.2. Analysis of F_0 trajectories in speech. Results obtained from (a) [amē] (candy) and (b) [āme] (rain) uttered by Subject MT.

Table 1 lists the mean values of β and γ averaged over several samples each of the eight conditions, obtained from the analysis of the material sung by MT, together with the mean rise/fall times τ* defined in the preceding section and calculated from β and γ. For the sake of comparison, parameter values obtained from the speech material are also listed. The rise/fall times for the speech material were also calculated from β and γ, disregarding the existence of the voicing component. The rate of transition in the spoken material is considerably slower than that of the pitch transition in legato singing.

The mean values of β and γ are plotted in Fig.3 on the β - γ plane to illustrate the differences in the characteristics of the pitch transition in the eight conditions of singing. There exists a high negative correlation between the two parameters.

The mean rise/fall times for the upward and downward transitions over the interval of a fourth are compared in Fig.4 for each of the four manners of performance, while those for transitions over the interval of an octave are compared in Fig.5 for appoggiatura, non legato, and legato. From Figs.4 and 5 it can be seen that mean rise/fall times are not much affected by the pitch interval between the two notes, as already pointed out by Ohala and Ewan (1973) as well as by Sundberg (1979).

Table 1. Characteristic parameters and rise/fall times of F_0 trajectories in singing and in speech. The results for singing are from two-note sequences separated by an interval of a fourth (Subject MT).

	Rise			Fall		
	β (sec^{-1})	γ	τ* (msec)	β (sec^{-1})	γ	τ* (msec)
Appoggiatura	40	0.76	54	75	0.50	20
Non legato	38	0.85	67	57	0.77	38
Legato	27	0.85	91	33	0.94	87
Portamento	6.8	0.95	419	6.9	0.93	409
Speech	18	1.00	167	18	1.00	171

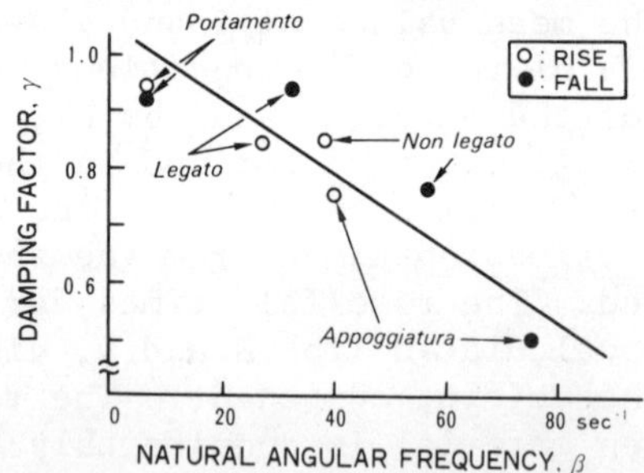

Fig.3. Parameters of various F_0 trajectories in singing. The results are from two-note sequences separated by an interval of a fourth (Subject MT).

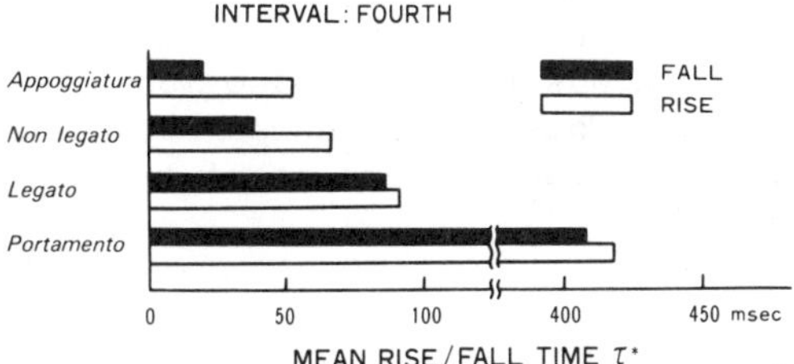

Fig.4. Rise/fall times of F_0 trajectories in singing. The results are from two-note sequences separated by an interval of a fourth (Subject MT).

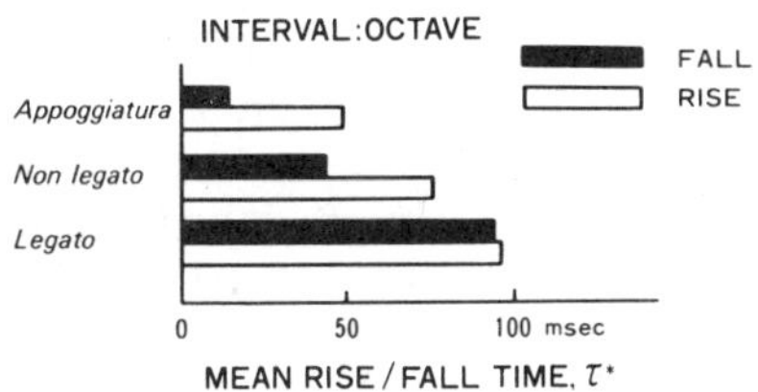

Fig.5. Rise/fall times of F_0 trajectories in singing. The results are from two-note sequences separated by an interval of an octave (Subject MT).

Analysis of materials sung at different levels indicated that changes in the volume do not appreciably affect the rate of transition in most cases. Exceptions are the downward pitch transitions in the case of appoggiatura and non legato, where a marked increase was observed in the rate of transition when going from mezzopiano to forte. In fact, a fall time of as short as 17 msec was observed in one sample of appoggiatura sung by MT, though with a considerable amount of overshoot due to insufficient damping.

All the foregoing results were obtained from the analysis of materials sung by MT, but the results for the other subject YS also showed similar tendencies. Comparison of results for the two subjects indicates that the differences in the parameters of pitch transition are rather small in slower transitions, but become more marked in rapid transitions. For example, the minimum rise/fall time observed for YS was 36 msec, which was twice as long as the minimum value for MT. The variability of the final value of the pitch transition was also found to be somewhat greater in YS. These differences may be ascribed to differences in the period and amount of training in the two subjects.

DISCUSSION

Although the present study is concerned mainly with a descriptive analysis of the dynamic characteristics of pitch control in singing, the results can be interpreted to shed light on the underlying mechanism of pitch control both in speech and in singing.

The essential features of the present analysis are the success in:

(1) the functional formulation of the dynamic characteristics of pitch control on a logarithmic scale of fundamental frequency, and

(2) the approximation of the F_0 trajectory in terms of the response characteristics of a second-order linear system.

Although these results were obtained empirically, we will now present our interpretations based on some theoretical considerations and published data on the physical properties of skeletal muscles.

The closeness of approximation of (logarithmic) F_0 trajectories by our model strongly suggests that the logarithmic fundamental frequency may actually reflect the mechanical motion of an element in the laryngeal mechanism which, from the point of view of pitch control, can be approximated by a second-order linear system. More specifically, we present the following hypotheses and show evidence supporting these hypotheses.

Hypothesis (1). The logarithm of fundamental frequency varies linearly with the displacement of a point in the laryngeal structure.

Hypotheses (2). The displacement of the point reflects the mechanical motion of a mass element connected with stiffness and viscous resistance elements.

Supporting evidence for Hypothesis (1) can be found in the stress-strain relationship of muscles. Although we do not have data from the vocalis muscle, the following experimental relationship has been known to apply between the tension T and the elongation x of skeletal muscles in general (Buchthal and Kaiser, 1944; Sandow, 1958):

$$T = a\,(e^{bx} - 1). \tag{3}$$

In the present study, we regard x as the elongation of the vocalis muscle due mainly to the displacement of its anterior end. If $e^{bx} >> 1$, the above equation can be approximated by

$$T = a\,e^{bx}. \tag{4}$$

On the other hand, the frequency of vibration of strings as well as membranes with simple structures varies generally in proportion to the square root of their tension. (Slater and Frank, 1933). This relationship will hold even for the vibration of the vocal fold which can be regarded as an elastic membrane as a first-order approximation. Thus $f_0 = c_0\sqrt{T}$ (5)
From Eqs.(3) and (4) we obtain

$$\ln f_0 = \frac{b}{2}x + \ln(\sqrt{a}\cdot c_0), \tag{6}$$

where, strictly speaking, c_0 also varies slightly with x, but the overall dependency of $\ln f_0$ is primarily determined by the first term on the right-hand side of Eq.(6).

Hypothesis (2) can be supported by the analysis of the mechanical properties of the laryngeal structure whose major elements are shown in Fig.6. If we adopt a coordinate system fixed to the cricoid cartilage (and the trachea which is connected more or less tightly with the cricoid), the thyroid cartilage can be regarded as one major mass element supported by two stiffness elements (the cricothyroid and the vocalis muscles) and rotating around the cricothyroid joint with a viscous resistance. The two stiffness elements are also accompanied by viscous resistances which represent their internal losses. If we denote the angular displacement of the thyroid by θ, its rotation can be described by the following equation of motion:

$$I\ddot{\theta} + R\dot{\theta} + (c_1K_1 + c_2K_2)\theta = \tau(t), \tag{7}$$

where I represents the moment of inertia, R represents the combined viscous loss, K_1 and K_2 represent the stiffness of the cricothyroid and the vocalis muscles, and $\tau(t)$ represents the torque caused by the contraction of the cricothyroid muscle. Since the anterior end of the vocalis

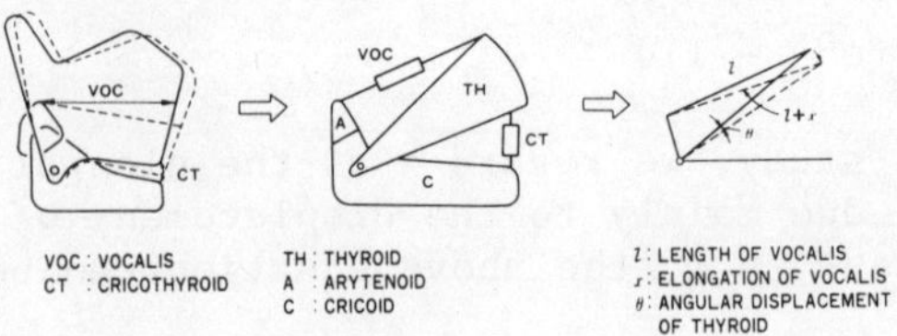

Fig.6. Simplified laryngeal structure showing only those elements that exert dominant influences on the dynamics of the voice fundamental frequency.

muscle is fixed at a point on the thyroid cartilage, the relationship between x and θ for small angular displacements of the thyroid cartilage is given approximately by

$$x = c_3\ \theta. \tag{8}$$

For a unit-step forcing function u(t), x can then be given by

$$x = c_4\ f(\beta,\ \gamma,\ t)\ u(t), \tag{9}$$

where $f(\beta,\ \gamma,\ t)$ is the same as in Eq.(1), and

$$\beta = \sqrt{\frac{c_1K_1 + c_2K_2}{I}}, \qquad \gamma = \frac{R}{2\sqrt{I\ (c_1K_1 + c_2K_2)}}\ .$$

Equations (6) and (9) with initial and final conditions will lead to Eq.(1).

As one of the possible ways to control the rate of pitch transition, we may assume that only the stiffnesses of the related laryngeal muscles are changed. In this case, the following hyperbolic relationship is expected to hold between β and γ,

$$\beta\cdot\gamma = R/2I. \tag{10}$$

While the results of Fig.3 indicate a definite negative correlation between β and γ, the relationship is not strictly hyperbolic. The relatively large value of γ for larger β (appoggiatura) can be ascribed to the increase of viscous resistance within the muscle itself in the case of stronger contraction (Mashima, et al., 1973; Akazawa, 1980), while the tendency of γ to approach 1 for smaller values of β (*portamento*) may be the consequence of better coordination between antagonistic muscles to accomplish optimal control.

On the other hand, differences in the rate for upward and downward transitions can be explained by referring to the stress-strain relationship of Eq.(3). The incremental stiffness, as given by $\partial T/\partial x$, is obviously greater at larger values of x. Since the initial value of x is greater in the downward transitions, the stiffness is greater and hence produces a larger value of β than in the upward transitions.

CONCLUSIONS

Dynamic characteristics of pitch control in singing have been investigated using techniques already developed for the analysis of pitch control in speech. It was found that the trajectory of the voice fundamental frequency in transitions from one note to another, when expressed in logarithmic units, can be approximated very well by the step response function of a second-order linear system. The parameters of the model were determined by a method of successive approximation to the measured F_0 trajectory, and were used to represent the dynamic characteristics of vocal pitch control. In general, our results on *legato* singing were in agreement with the findings of Ohala and Ewan (1973) as well as with those of Sundberg (1979). On the other hand, it was found that under certain conditions the rise/fall times of pitch transition in singing could be much shorter than 50 msec, which is the smallest value reported by these investigators. The speed of pitch transition in speech was shown to be considerably lower than that found in *legato* singing. Furthermore, an interpretation of the observed dynamic characteristics in terms of a possible underlying mechanism of pitch control has been presented on the basis of two hypotheses, supported by some physiological data and theoretical considerations.

ACKNOWLEDGMENT

The authors are grateful to Dr. K. Akazawa for helpful comments on the preliminary version of the paper.

REFERENCES

Akazawa, K. (1980) Personal communication.

Buchthal, F. and Kaiser, E. (1944) Factors determining tension development in skeletal muscle. Acta Physiol. Scand. 8, 38-74.

Fujisaki, H., Hirose, K. and Ohta, K. (1979) Acoustic features of the fundamental frequency contours of declarative sentences in Japanese. Annual Bulletin, Research Institute of Logopedics and Phoniatrics, Faculty of Medicine, University of Tokyo 13, 163-173.

Fujisaki, H. and Nagashima, S. (1969) A model for synthesis of pitch contours of connected speech. Annual Report, Engineering Research Institute, Faculty of Engineering, University of Tokyo 28, 53-60.

Fujisaki, H. and Sudo, H. (1971) A model for the generation of fundamental frequency contours of Japanese word accent. J. Acoust. Soc. Japan 27, 445-453.

Fujisaki, H. and Sugito, M. (1978) Analysis and perception of two-mora word accent types in the kinki dialect. J. Acoust. Soc. Japan 34, 167-176.

Hirose, K., Fujisaki, H. and Sugito, M. (1978) Word accent in Japanese and English: A comparative study of acoustic characteristics in disyllabic words. J. Acoust. Soc. Am. 64, Suppl. 1., S114.

Mashima, H., Akazawa K., Kushima, H. and Fujii, K. (1973) Graphical analysis and experimental determination of the active state in frog skeletal muscle. Jap. J. Physiol. 23, 217-240.

Ohala, J. and Ewan, W. (1973) Speed of pitch change. J. Acoust. Soc. Am. 53, 345(A).

Sandow, A. (1958) A theory of active state mechanisms in isometric muscular contraction. Science 127, 760-762.

Slater, J.C. and Frank, N.H. (1933) Introduction to Theoretical Physics. New York: McGraw-Hill.

Sunberg, J. (1979) Maximum speed of pitch changes in singers and untrained subjects. J. Phonetics 7, 71-79.

Vennard, W. (1967) Singing- the Mechanism and the Technic (revised edition). New York: Carl Fischer, Inc.

DISCUSSION

Abbs: The data presented by Dr. Fujisaki would further emphasize the need for a fast muscle involved in the lowering of vocal fundamental frequency. As shown by Partridge (1966), when a muscle is activated and the activation signal is suddenly reduced in rate, the force of contraction is not reduced until that stimulation rate goes below a certain threshold. This would seem to rule out a muscle relaxation for pitch lowering.

Hirose: Regarding the difference in the speed of rise and fall of pitch, it must be mentioned that activation of muscle is achieved by asynchronous excitation of many different motor units, whereas at the time of relaxation all the units can stop their activity almost synchronously. This may explain, at least in part, the difference in rise and fall times.

Baer: As Sundberg suggested, there is a possibility that the faster speed for pitch lowering might be due to activity of the aryepiglottic sphincter. This hypothesis calls for physiological measurements. There is a developing literature that suggests that shelted muscle systems become organized to act as mass-spring systems. This description would be consistent with your functional model, if the analogy held for the pitch-control muscle system.

Fujimura: I think there possibly is a different explanation of the difference between ascent and descent in speed: it is easier and more accurate to predict the resulting pitch by adjusting muscle gestures without audio feedback if the target pitch is in the lower region than in the higher region, and therefore one has to rely partially on feedback in going up to a high value. This could be tested by using ascending and descending gesture with the same target pitch, or by asking to sing in both directions as rapidly as possible without specifying the target.

Fujisaki: I also believe that the rate of increase or decrease of muscular tension will contribute to the difference in speed of pitch rise and pitch fall. The main point of my analysis, however, is that the difference can be explained on the basis of the inherent nonlinearity of stress-strain relationship of the vocalis muscle itself. The rate of change in muscular tension may only have a secondary effect on the rate of pitch transition, as long as the former can be regarded to be much faster than the time constant of the mechanical system in the larynx. I would also like to add that, after the Kurume Conference, my colleagues at the University of Tokyo actually made measurements on the vocal fold length using a stereoendoscope while a subject produced vowels at various pitch. Their results clearly indicate that, at least in the chest register, the relationship between the vocal fold length and the logarithm of voice fundamental frequency can be regarded as linear (K. Honda et al., Measurement of laryngeal structures during phonation by use of a stereoendoscope, Annual Bulletin, Research Institute of Logopedics and Phoniatrics, University of Tokyo, No. 14, pp. 73-78, 1980).

VI. ESTIMATION OF PHYSICAL PROPERTIES OF CONSTITUENT STRUCTURES FROM MEASUREMENTS AND MODELS

Section Editor: Osamu Fujimura

Bell Laboratories,
Murray Hill, New Jersey, USA

CHAPTER 24
MECHANICAL PROPERTIES OF THE VOCAL FOLD: MEASUREMENTS IN VIVO

T. Kaneko, K. Uchida, H. Suzuki, K. Komatsu, T. Kanesaka, N. Kobayashi, and J. Naito

Department of Otolaryngology,
School of Medicine, Chiba University,
Chiba, Japan

I. INTRODUCTION

Detailed analysis of the mechanism of vocal fold vibration, together with that of the articulation system, is essential to the study of phonation. Detailed observation of vocal fold vibration has been reported by employing such techniques as stroboscopy, high speed cinematography, electroglottography, photoelectroglottography, and ultra-sonoglottography. To understand the physical mechanism of vocal fold vibration, however, measurements of the mechanical properties of the vocal fold are needed. The mechanical properties, such as effective stiffness, damping ratio etc., have been measured in excised larynges but not in the living human larynx. To know the mechanical properties of the vocal fold during phonation at various pitches is a key point in clarifying the vibration mechanism of the vocal fold. In the present study, we will demonstrate a new method of measuring the resonance characteristics of the vocal fold in vivo. Our ultrasonic pulse method makes it possible to measure the mechanical properties of the vocal fold without inserting any instruments into the larynx, and without causing pain.

II. PRINCIPLES

Anatomically, the vocal folds are attached to the framework of the thyroid cartilage through laryngeal muscles and soft tissue, which may be interpreted as a mass-spring system with loss (resistance). In other words, we can simplify the situation and assume that a mass is attached to the framework through a spring and resistance in a single vibration system. The surface position of the vocal fold can then be represented by the position of the mass element, or the length of the spring. When the framework is driven by an oscillator to cause a sinusoidal displacement at a certain frequency, the system is set into a forced oscillation, and a sinusoidal movement of the mass is observed with the same frequency. At a certain frequency, the mass-spring system may show resonance, and a particularly large amplitude of vibration may be observed in the movement of the mass. According to this principle, the resonance frequency and the Q value for the vocal fold can be estimated. The Q value of resonance is defined by the following equations:

$$Q = \frac{f_0}{|f_1 - f_2|} = \frac{f_0}{\Delta f},$$

where f_1 and f_2 are the frequencies at which $1/\sqrt{2}$ of the amplitude at the resonance frequency, f_0, is observed, and Δf is the difference between these frequencies, or the bandwidth. Because the amplitude of displacement of the vocal fold provoked by this forced oscillation is very small, and cannot be recorded by regular ultrasonoglottography, a new variant of the so-called M-mode display has been devised for this study.

III. APPARATUS

A block diagram of the apparatus is shown in Fig.1. The apparatus is roughly divided into two systems: the ultrasonic and vibrator systems.

1. Ultrasonic System

The equipment used for the ultrasonic system is almost the same as that used for ultrasonoglottography. (See Chapter 9 of this volume.) However, the use of the equipment is quite different. The equipment used consists of a multivibrator (repetition frequency 5000 Hz), and an ultrasonic reflectoscope. A pulse-modulated ultrasonic beam is irradiated from the transducer, and the reflected echoes from the margin of the vocal fold are received by the same transducer. Each reflected echo is selected by an echo-selector, is sent to a cathode ray oscilloscope

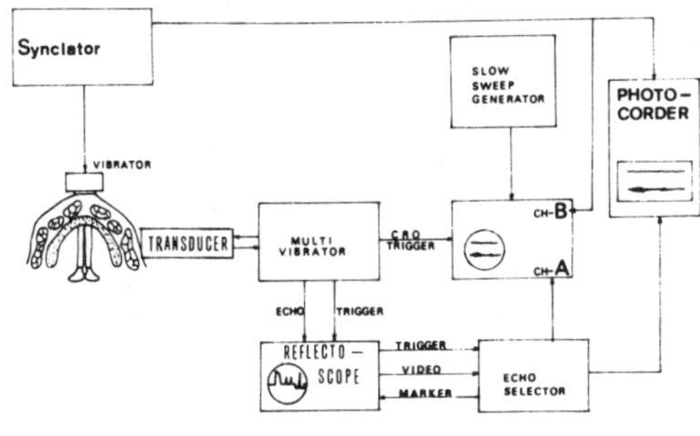

Fig.1. Block diagram of system for observing movement of vocal folds in response to a vibrating stimulus.

(channel A), and is swept by a slow sweep generator. As a recorder, an electromagnetic oscilloscope (photocorder) is used. For observing the minute displacement of the vocal fold caused by the forced oscillation given to the framework, we display the amplitude of the echo signal as a function of frequency (or time as the experimenter manipulates the frequency control of the oscillator for the vibrator input). The vibration of the vocal fold results in a periodic change of the surface angle with respect to the incident ultrasonic beam within each vibration cycle, and at a certain phase of the vibration, an optimal angle gives rise to a peak of the detected amplitude of the echo signal. This peak amplitude in the display varies as the vibration frequency is changed, and shows resonance near the resonance frequency of the biomechanical system, if the incident beam is directed appropriately, such that the right-angle reflection of the vocal fold surface at the selected portion of the vocal fold is achieved only as the result of vocal fold deformation due to its induced vibration (forced oscillation)[*1]. By this method, resonance patterns observed in the echoes from the vocal fold and the thyroid cartilage can be recorded simultaneously.

2. Vibrator System

For the vibrator system, a low-frequency sinusoidal oscillator and a mechanical shaker (Wilcoxon model Z602) were utilized. The frequency of the oscillator was manually changed from 30 to 300 Hz. The shaker had resonances at 60 Hz and 400 Hz*2.

IV. METHOD OF EXAMINATION

The subject was laid down in a supine position with his chin up so that the outline of the thyroid cartilage could be seen clearly. The transducer was placed on the thyroid lamina in order for the ultrasonic beam to irradiate the margin of a vocal fold perpendicularly. If the ultrasonic beam is correctly directed to the vocal fold, the vibration echo can be detected during phonation. The vibrator was pressed lightly on the skin over the midline of the thyroid cartilage, and used to provoke an oscillation with frequencies ranging from 30 to 300 Hz continuously. The resonance pattern of the vocal fold was recorded in the quiet inspiratory phase and in the phase of phonation neutral (without expiratory air flow) at several pitches.

V. RESULTS

The following items have been examined:

1) Relationship between the resonance patterns of the thyroid cartilage and the vocal fold.
2) Influences of the site of the vibrator application on the resonance pattern of the vocal fold.
3) Influences of the site of the transducer and the manner of its application on the observed resonance pattern of the vocal fold.
4) Resonance patterns of the vocal fold in an excised human larynx.
5) Differences in the resonance pattern of the vocal fold by sex and age during "quiet" respiration.
6) Resonance pattern of a vocal fold for the phonation neutral gesture (without expiratory air flow).

1. Relationship between the Resonance Patterns of the Thyroid Cartilage and the Vocal Fold

In order to examine the resonance relationship between the thyroid cartilage and the vocal fold, the echoes from the thyroid cartilage and the vocal fold were selected simultaneously using two echo selectors. The former echo can be observed approximately at a time that corresponds to a roundtrip of the sound pulse for a distance of 5 mm, and the latter at a time for approximately 20 mm. After selecting these echoes, the thyroid cartilage was driven by a shaker during quiet respiration.

The resonance frequency observed in the pulse wave reflected from the thyroid cartilage was usually found to be between 70 and 80 Hz, and the apparent Q-value between 2 and 3, while the resonance frequency for the vocal fold was found to be in the range of 110-120 Hz, with a Q between 4 and 6. Typical recordings are shown in Fig.2.

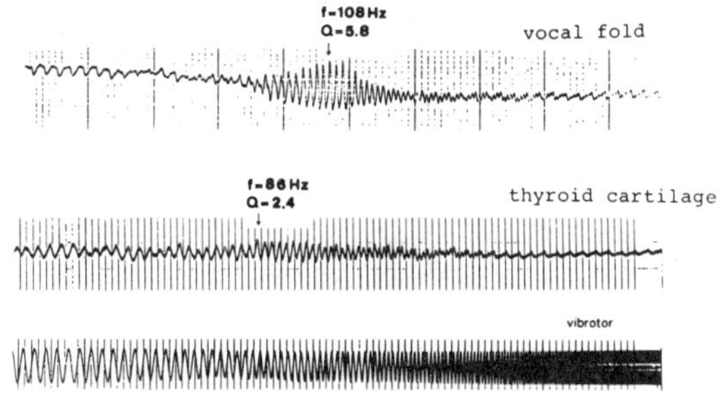

Fig.2. Simultaneous recordings of the resonance waveforms of the vocal fold and the thyroid cartilage. The signal applied to the vibrator, showing the gradually increasing frequency of the vibrator input, is shown in the bottom trace.

2. Influences of the Site of the Vibrator on the Resonance Pattern of the Vocal Fold

The resonance characteristics of the vocal fold were examined when the vibrator was placed on different points of the thyroid lamina. The vibrator was placed either on the midline or on the thyroid lamina ipsilaterally or contralaterally to the transducer.

Little change was found in the resonance characteristics of the vocal fold. The resonance pattern was always obtained in the range of 100-110 Hz during quiet respiration. Therefore, in the main experiments, the vibrator was always placed on the midline of the thyroid cartilage.

3. Influences of the Site of the Transducer on the Resonance Pattern of the Vocal Fold

Variation of the vocal fold resonance characteristics was examined by directing an ultrasonic beam to the anterior, middle, and posterior parts of the vocal fold.

Little difference was observed regardless of the site of the transducer. Therefore, the middle part of the vocal fold was always chosen for the measurement of the response and the determination of resonance.

4. Resonance Patterns of the Vocal Fold in an Excised Human Larynx

Similar examinations were performed in excised human larynges for which the posterior commissure was open. Resonance frequencies and apparent Q-values in the excised larynges were approximately 100 Hz and 2.2-2.9, respectively (Fig.3).

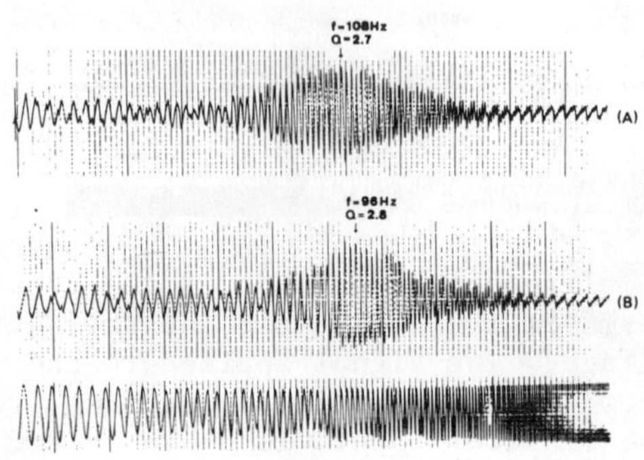

Fig.3. Resonance waveforms of vocal folds for two excised human larynges for a configuration in which the posterior commissure was open. The vibrator signal is show at the bottom.

5. Difference in the Resonance Patterns of the Vocal Folds by Sex and Age during "Quiet" Respiration

The difference of the vocal fold resonance characteristics among normal male adults (17 cases), female adults (19 cases), and children (7 cases) were examined.

In male adults, resonance frequencies of the vocal fold ranged from 91 to 145 Hz (average 128 Hz), and in female adults, 115-167 Hz (average 136 Hz) (Fig.4). Q-values ranged from 2.1 to 5.1 (average 3.4) in males, and from 2.6 to 7.1 (average 4.0) in females. It seemed that the vocal fold resonance frequency and Q-value were higher in females than in males. Figures 5 and 6 show examples of resonance patterns of a male vocal fold and a female vocal fold during quiet respiration.

As to age differences, it would be inappropriate to make any concrete conclusions because the number of children examined was low. However, there seemed to be a trend indicating that higher resonance frequencies and Q-values are observed in children (Fig.7).

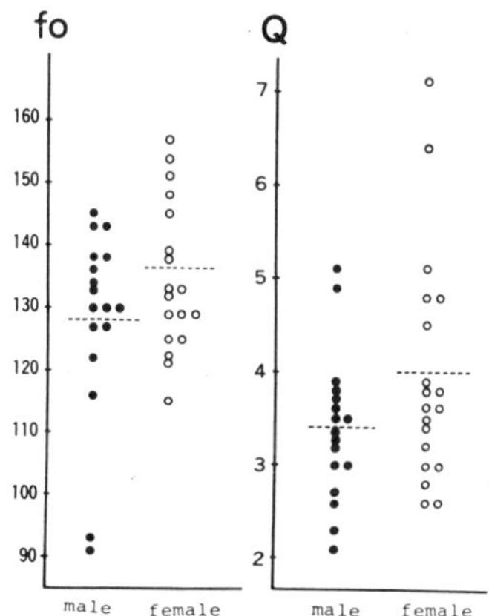

Fig.4. Resonance frequencies f_0 (in Hz) and Q values for a number of different male and female larynges, during "quiet" respiration. Average values are indicated by the dashed line.

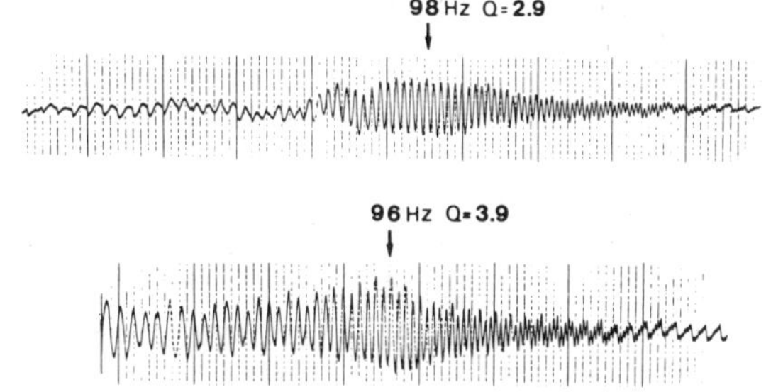

Fig.5. Two examples of resonance patterns for male vocal folds during quiet respiration.

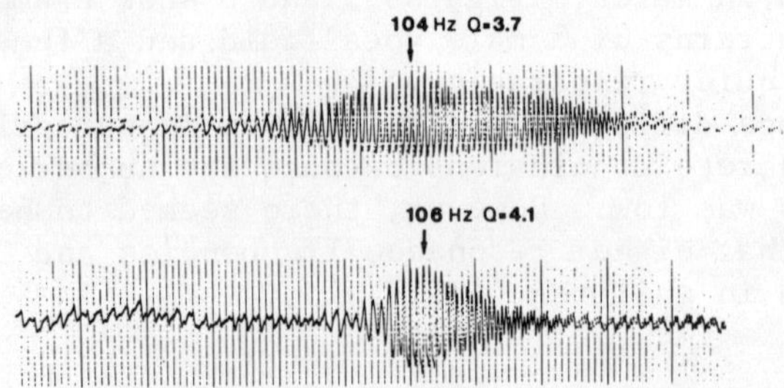

Fig.6. Two examples of resonance patterns for female vocal folds during quiet respiration.

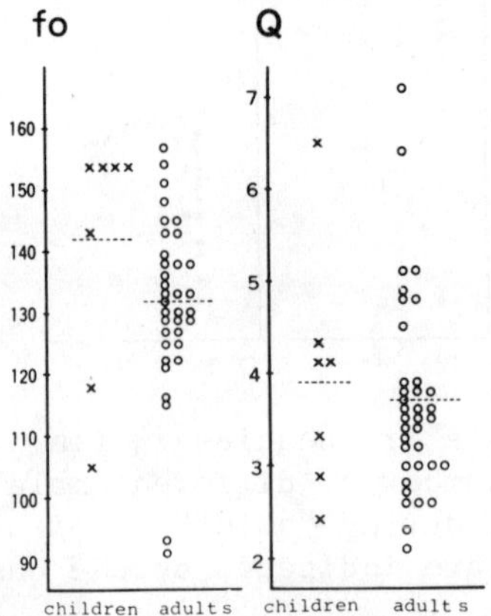

Fig.7. Resonance frequencies f_0 (in Hz) and Q values are compared for children and for adults during "quiet" respiration.

6. Resonance Patterns of the Vocal Fold in the Phonation Neutral Gesture (Without Expiratory Air Flow)

During phonation at various pitches, the biomechanical factors of the vocal folds have to change depending on muscle control. Dynamic properties of the vocal folds during phonation under different conditions are important for analyzing the mechanism of phonation. For this purpose, the resonance characteristics of the vocal folds in phonation neutral positions at several voice pitches were measured. For this measurement, the subject was instructed to prepare voicing in the given pitch. The pitch was ascertained by actual voicing immediately after the measurement. The sweep tone measurement took typically 1.0 to 1.5 seconds.

In Fig.8, the upper half of the figure shows a resonance pattern of the vocal fold, just before phonation, at a low pitch, in this case 100 Hz. A resonance frequency occurred at a point close to the phonation pitch, i.e., 100 Hz. The bottom half of the figure shows a resonance pattern of the vocal fold, just before phonation at 150 Hz. Two distinct resonance frequencies can be observed in this case. The second resonance frequency occurred at a point close to the phonation pitch, i.e. 150 Hz.

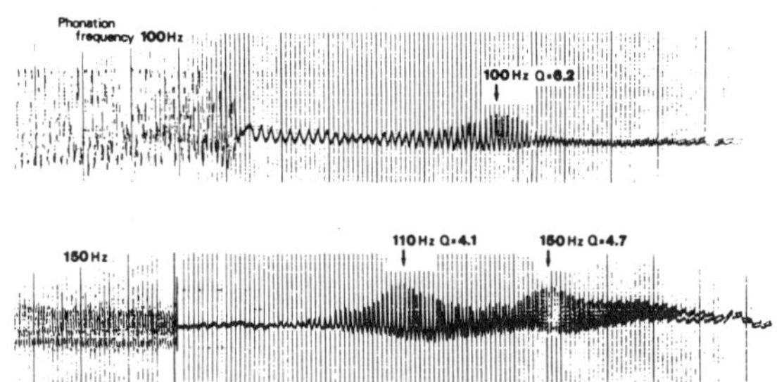

Fig.8. Examples of resonance patterns for male subjects with vocal fold in phonation neutral position just prior to phonating at 100 Hz (upper trace) and at 150 Hz (lower trace).

Two resonances usually occurred in female vocal folds (Fig.9). The lower resonance was observed around 100 Hz, and the second one at over 200 Hz. The second resonance frequency is almost equal to the phonation pitch. It appears that the second resonance is sharper than the first.

VI. REMARKS

During quiet respiration, the vocal fold is relatively relaxed. In this situation, no apparent difference in the resonance characteristics between male and female has been observed. However, once the vocal fold is tensed, such as in "phonation neutral" position, the mechanical properties change significantly, sex being a relevant factor. It has been found that two resonances appear also in an excised larynx (Fig.10), when a longitudinal tension is applied, and that the larger the tension, the higher the second resonance frequency.

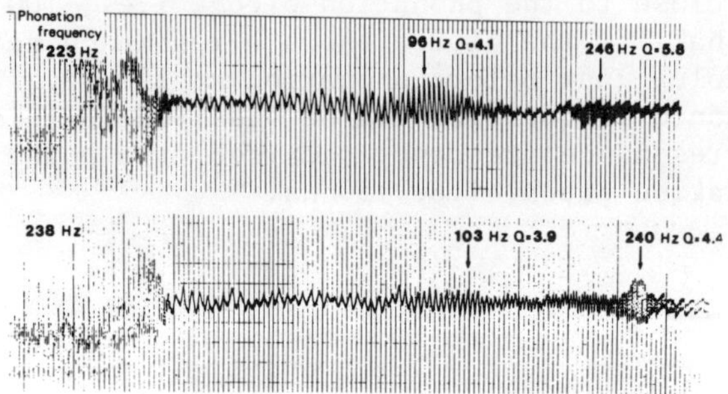

Fig.9. Examples of resonance patterns for female subjects with vocal fold in phonation neutral position just prior to phonating at 223 Hz (upper trace) and at 238 Hz (lower trace).

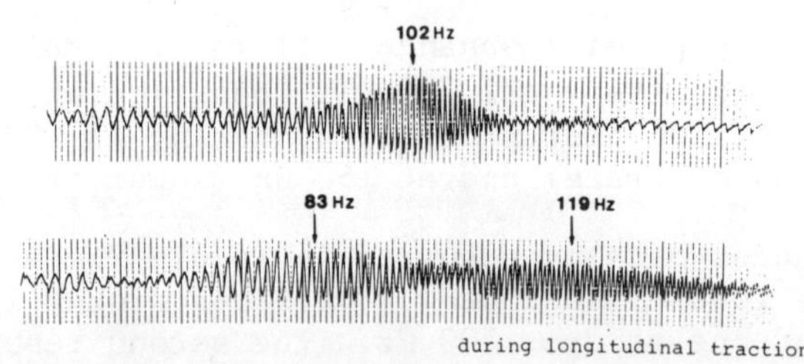

Fig.10. Resonance patterns of vocal fold in excised larynx without longitudinal tension (upper trace) and with longitudinal tension applied (lower trace).

There have been studies dealing with biomechanical properties of the vocal folds, including those of van den Berg, Flanagan, Isshiki, Ishizaka, and Kaneko, as discussed elsewhere in this volume. However, mechanical constants used for these studies were estimated in an excised larynx and not in a living human larynx. This report is the first attempt to evaluate the biomechanical properties of human vocal folds in living humans. The data so far obtained are only preliminary, and more rigorous control of several conditions are necessary in order to derive reliable data (see footnotes).

REFERENCES

Fabre, Ph. (1957) Un procédé électrique percutané d'inscription de l'accolement glottique au cours de la phonation: glottographie de haute frequence. Premiers résultats. Bull. Acad. Nat. Med. (Paris) 121, 66.

Farnsworth, D.W. (1940) High speed motion pictures of the human vocal cords. Bell Telephone Laboratories Record 18, 203.

Ishizaka, K. and Flanagan, J.L. (1972) Synthesis of voiced sounds from a two-mass model of the vocal cords. Bell System Technical Journal 51, 1233.

Kaneko, T., et al. (1974) L'ultrasonoglottographie. Ann. Otolaryng. (Paris) 91, 403.

Kitamura, T., Kaneko, T., and Asano, H. (1964) Ultrasonoglottography. J. Japan Broncho-esophagol. 15, 181.

Sonesson, B. (1960) On the anatomy and vibratory pattern of the human vocal folds. Acta Otolaryng. Suppl. 156, 38.

Timcke, R. (1956) Die Synchron-stroboskopie von menschlichen Stimmlippen bzw. ahnlichen Schallquellen und Messung der Offnungszeit. Ztschr. Laryng. Rhino. Otol. 35, 331.

*1 Dr. Fujimura in the meeting, based on this interpretation of apparent resonance as observed in the echo amplitude, pointed out that the resonance frequency is a robust quantity which can be measured quite accurately regardless of the details of the detection mechanism, which may include antiresonance, nonlinear relations between the amplitude of the induced vibration and the observed echo amplitude, etc. On the other hand, according to him, the apparent Q values are highly susceptible to such unknown factors, and the values cited in this paper can be interpreted at best as qualitative indications.

*2 Dr. Rothenberg suggested that we need to know the resonance characteristics of the vibrator system with realistic loading conditions, particularly in view of the apparent resonance near 100 Hz for all cases. The resonance frequencies of the vibrator cited in the text were measured by the use of a small bone-conduction pick-up (piezoelectric) in contact with the vibrator surface. This caution is certainly important, and further work is needed. One enlightening fact, however, is that for patients with glottal cancer, where the stiffness of the pathologic side is higher than the normal side, the resonance near 100 Hz has been found higher for the abnormal side. This seems to indicate that we are observing biomechanical properties related to the vocal fold proper, rather than artifact related to the measuring system. In this connection, Dr. Titze emphasized the importance of additional monitoring methods that may reveal part of the nature of the induced vibration and possibly properties of different layers and structures of the biomechanical system. Dr. stevens also pointed out that same effect could be induced by acoustic signals applied to the vocal surface via the vocal tract from the mouth. He mentioned that this may excite different vibration modes of the vocal folds.

CHAPTER 25

PHYSICAL PROPERTIES OF THE VOCAL FOLD TISSUE: MEASUREMENTS ON EXCISED LARYNGES

Y. Kakita, M. Hirano, and K. Ohmaru

Department of Otolaryngology, School of Medicine, Kurume University,
Kurume, Japan

1. INTRODUCTION

This paper presents some results of measurements of the viscoelastic properties of the vocal fold tissue. They are useful for discussing the characteristics of the vocal fold vibration, and provide realistic physical constants of the tissues for designing models of the vocal folds.

It has been shown by Hirano (1975, 1977) that the vocal fold tissue is histologically divided into three layers, that is, the epithelium, the lamina propria, and the muscle. We measured the elastic moduli and the viscosity for each layer, with special attention to the lamina propria.

Excised canine larynges were used as the material. The tissue structure of the canine vocal fold is different from that of the human (Hirano, 1975) but the mechanical properties of the histologically similar portions can be assumed to be comparable.

2. ASSUMPTIONS ON THE TISSUE PROPERTIES

This section gives a brief introduction to the theory of elasticity in relation to the basic assumptions about the properties of the vocal fold tissue.

Figure 1 shows a rough sketch of one side of the vocal fold presented in the frame of the cartesian coordinates. The y-axis, which lies in the antero-posterior direction, is called the "longitudinal" axis, while the x- and the z-axes are called the "transverse" axes. In this figure, which shows a small cubic part of a specific layer of the tissue, the planes parallel to the longitudinal axis are indicated by stripes and the perpendicular plane is indicated by dots. In our experiment, the elastic property of each layer of the vocal fold tissue is assumed to be orthotropic and incompressible, following Titze (1976). An orthotropic medium shows different characteristics between the deformation in the planes parallel to the longitudinal axis and the deformation in the plane perpendicular to the longitudinal axis. This latter plane, shown dotted in the figure, is called "the plane of isotropy".

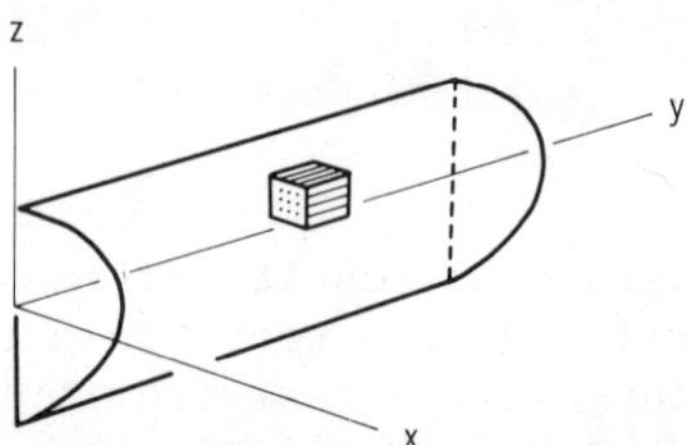

Fig.1. Schematic drawing of the left vocal fold as an orthotropic body. For the small cube embedded in the vocal fold the dotted plane is the plane of isotropy.

Figures 2 and 3 show schematic drawings of various deformations relevant to the elastic properties for an orthotropic body. In Fig.2(a)-(d) several important deformations in the plane of isotropy are shown. The basic notion of isotropy is that there is no distinction with respect to the direction. Therefore, in the plane of isotropy, shown by dots, the tension-compression elastic property in a lateral direction (x direction in Fig.1) shown by (a) is the same as the tension-compression elastic property in a vertical direction (z direction in Fig.1) shown by (c). We generally use Young's modulus E_i to express this kind of elastic property. The subscript <u>i</u> comes from the term "isotropy". There is also a different type of deformation called the "shear" deformation. In this type of deformation, as shown in (b), the forces are exerted along the striped planes and squeeze the dotted plane diagonally. Because of isotropy the elastic property corresponding to the shear deformation (b) is the same as that for the shear deformation (d).

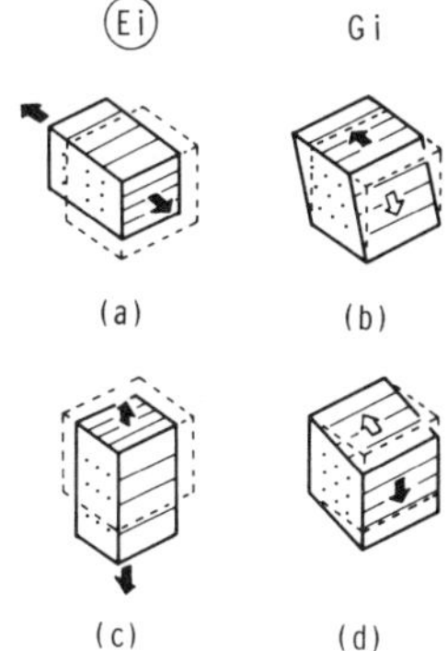

Fig.2. Types of deformation in the plane of isotropy (x-z plane in Fig.1). (a), (c): tensile deformation; (b), (d): shear deformation.

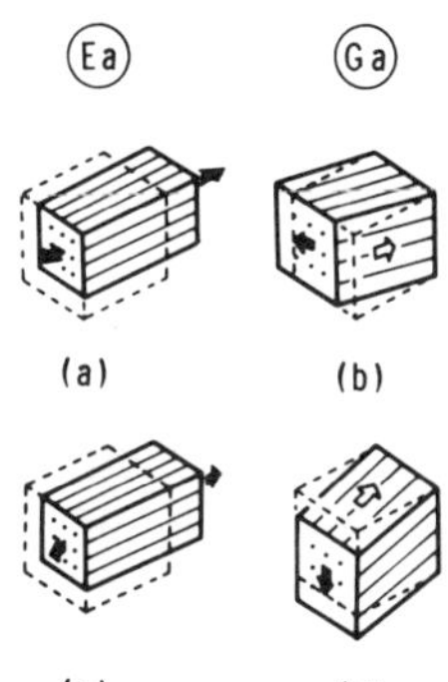

Fig.3. Types of deformations in the two planes parallel to the longitudinal axis. (a), (b): tensile and shear deformations in the plane parallel to the x-y plane; (c), (d): tensile and shear deformations in the plane parallel to the y-z plane.

We use shear modulus G_i to express this kind of elastic property. Furthermore, in an isotropic body, the Young's modulus E_i is related to the shear modulus G_i by a simple functional relation involving the Poisson's ratio ν_i: $E_i = 2(1 + \nu_i)G_i$. Since the Poisson's ratio ν_i is related to the volume change under a deformation, assuming that the medium is incompressible in volume, ν_i takes the value of 0.5. Then G_i can be derived from E_i by calculation based on the functional relation $E_i = 2(1 + 0.5)\ G_i = 3G_i$, for the incompressible medium.

The deformations involving the longitudinal direction are shown in Fig.3. Figures 3(a) and 3(b) show, respectively, the tensile and the shear deformations in the plane parallel to the x-y plane (Fig.1), while Figs.3(c) and 3(d) show, respectively, the tensile and the shear deformations in the plane parallel to the y-z plane (Fig.1).

The two tensile deformations shown in Figs.3(a) and 3(c) are the same, and, because of the assumption of orthotropy, the shear deformations in Fig.3(b) and Fig.3(d) show no difference. However, there is no functional relationship between the Young's modulus E_a and the shear modulus G_a because of the anisotropy with respect to the longitudinal and transverse directions. The subscript a comes from "anisotropy". In this case, too, the Poisson's ratio ν_a is 0.5 if the medium is assumed to be incompressible.

Consequently, three independent elastic moduli E_i, E_a and G_a, circled in Figs.2 and 3, are necessary for specifying the orthotropic, incompressible medium. The same discussion with respect to orthotropy applies to viscosity.

The following sections describe the results of the measurements of E_i, E_a and G_a, with special attention to the lamina propria. The viscosity constants in shear deformation measured simultaneously with G_a will also be presented.

3. YOUNG'S MODULUS

3.1. Material and Method

The larynges were excised from normal adult dogs. The tissue of the vocal fold was trimmed so that only a single layer to be investigated was left between the arytenoid cartilage and the anterior portion of the thyroid cartilage, keeping a portion of these cartilages attached at each end. The layers measured were the epithelium (E in Fig.4), the lamina propria of the mucosa (L in Fig.4) and the muscle (M in Fig.4). The specimen was fixed at the thyroid cartilage and was hung vertically. Various weights were applied to the arytenoid cartilage and the elongation of the vocal fold tissue was measured using a microscope. The deformation occurred along the longitudinal axis, that is, the axis of symmetry for an orthotropic body.

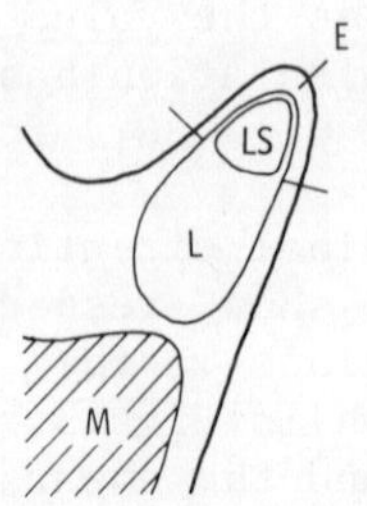

Fig.4. Tissue structure of the canine vocal fold (schematic). The labels indicate epithelium (E), superficial layer of lamina propria (LS), lamina propria (L), and muscle (M).

The Young's modulus, the tensile modulus of elasticity, was calculated from the load-extension relation. The Young's modulus E is represented as

$$E = \frac{\sigma}{\varepsilon} \; [\mathrm{dyne/cm^2}]$$

where

σ = stress (= T/S_0)
ε = strain or unit elongation (=$\Delta L/L_0$)

and

T = tension
S_0= cross-sectional area (normal to the direction of the tension)
ΔL = elongation
L_0= length (at no load).

The experiment was carried out in a room temperature of approximately 25°C.

3.2 Results

The Young's modulus of each layer is shown in Fig.5. The areas labeled E, L and M in Fig.5 show the ranges of the values obtained from more than ten cases.

A histological examination of the specimen used for the measurement of the epithelium revealed that a part of the lamina propria was left attached in all cases. As the epithelium is extremely thin, i.e. 50 - 100 µm, it seems impossible to make a specimen consisting solely of the epithelium. Therefore, the data pertaining to the epithelium in Fig.5 have been corrected on the basis of the ratio between the cross-sectional areas of the lamina propria and the epithelium (Hirano, 1979).

Consequently, the Young's modulus of the epithelium is estimated to be in the order of 10^6 - 10^7, of the lamina propria in the order of 10^5, and of the muscle in the order of 10^4 - 10^5. This result shows that the tensile stiffness becomes smaller in the order of the epithelium (E), the lamina propria (L) and the muscle (M), the regions being separated by roughly one order of magnitude.

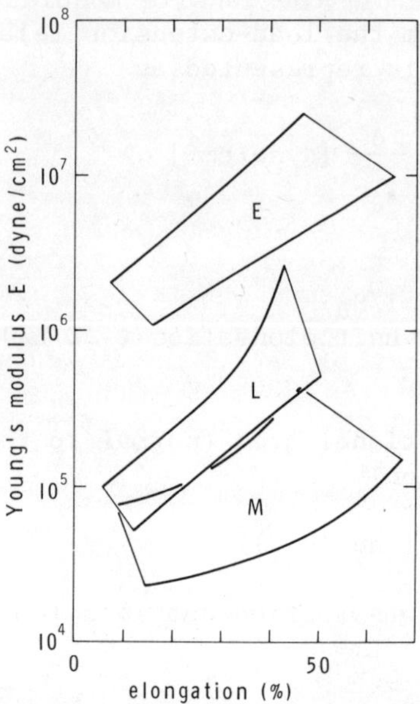

Fig.5. Ranges of values for Young's modulus for each layer of the canine vocal fold as a function of elongation.

4. DIFFERENTIAL YOUNG'S MODULUS

4.1. Material and Method

The material and the method are the same as those described in Section 3.1, except that we used photography for measuring the elongation. This was done in order to shorten the time necessary for measurement, and thus to minimize the change in the tissue specimen.

As shown schematically in Fig.6, the vocal fold tissue has a nonlinear stress-strain relation. During steady state vocal fold vibration, the longitudinal tension (or the length) is considered to be fixed at a certain representative value, and the variation is assumed to be small. What is relevant then is the differential Young's modulus, or the "tangent modulus" at an arbitrary working stress (or strain). The notion of this modulus is shown by a solid tangent in Fig.6, while the Young's modulus obtained in Section 3 is shown by a dashed secant line. This modulus is also called the "secant modulus".

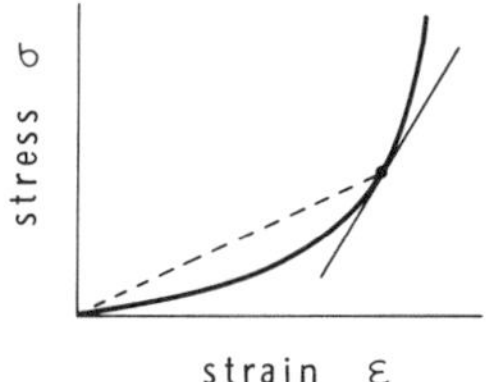

Fig.6. Schematic representation of stress-strain relation showing the differential Young's modulus (tangent line) and secant modulus (dashed line).

The differential Young's modulus is represented as

$$\mathcal{E} = \frac{d\sigma}{d\varepsilon} = \lim_{\Delta L \to 0} \frac{(\Delta T/S)}{(\Delta L/L)} \quad [\text{dyne/cm}^2]$$

where all parameters are measured at a working condition. If the volume of the material V_0 is unchanged, as assumed in this paper, then $V_0 = S_0 L_0 = SL$.

In this experiment, two other measurements were made of the lamina propria. One was of the superficial layer only (LS in Fig.4). This layer, in the canine vocal fold, was reported by Hirano (1975) to be more abundant in the fibrous component, and thus was considered to be stiffer compared with the remaining portion of the lamina propria. The other was the measurement of the modulus made under the tension in a transverse direction - that is, parallel to the plane of isotropy. The modulus for the muscle was not measured since the material was not available. Therefore, the differential modulus for the muscle was obtained by calculation from the data shown in Section 3.

The experiment was carried out in a room temperature of approximately 20°C.

4.2 Results

The range of the values of the differential Young's modulus for each layer is shown in Fig.7. The values of $\mathcal{E}$ become smaller in the order of the epithelium (E), the superficial layer of the lamina propria (LS), the lamina propria as a whole (L), and the muscle (M). They all show the saturation effect with respect to the elongation around the range between 30% and 70%.

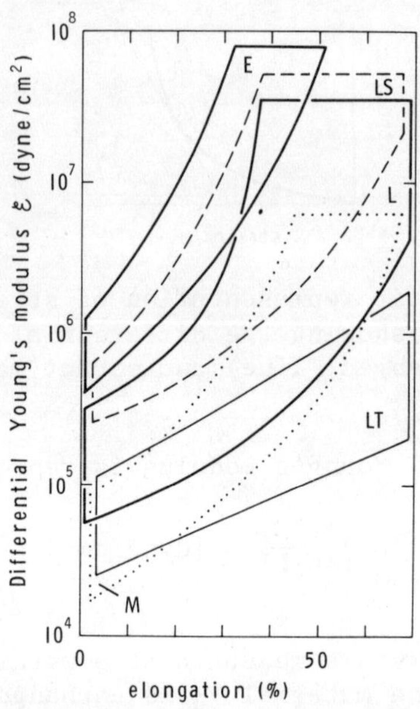

Fig.7. Range of values for differential Young's moduli for various parts of the tissue of the canine vocal fold, as identified in Fig.4. LT represents moduli for lamina propria in a transverse direction.

The moduli for the lamina propria along a transverse direction (LT) show much smaller values compared with those along a longitudinal direction (L). Under a transverse tension the tissue was torn off at around 200% to 300% of its original length without showing any significant saturation effect.

As for the lamina propria, the modulus for L, according to this result, is larger than that for LT by a half order of magnitude in the range of a small elongation, and by one or two orders of magnitude in the range of a large elongation.

5. SHEAR MODULUS AND VISCOSITY

5.1. Material and Method

The shear viscoelastic properties were measured for the

lamina propria and the muscle. The shear modulus and the viscosity were obtained at the same time by the mehtod of free rotational damped oscillation.

It may be appropriate to explain why the shear properties can be measured by a twisting motion. When a twisting force (or torque) is applied to an element as shown in Fig.8(a), the deformation of the small cubic element will be like that shown in Fig.8(b). This deformation is exactly the same as that shown in Fig.3(b), the shear deformation with respect to the longitudinal direction.

The shear modulus of elasticity G is defined as

$$G = \frac{s}{\tau} = \frac{(F/S)}{(\Delta L_1/L_2)} \text{ [dyne/cm}^2\text{]},$$

where

s = shear stress
τ = shear strain
F = force
S = area of the plane in which F is exerted tangentially
ΔL_1= displacement of the plane (indicated in Fig.8 (b))
L_2= length of the part perpendicular to the direction of displacement (indicated in Fig.8(b)).

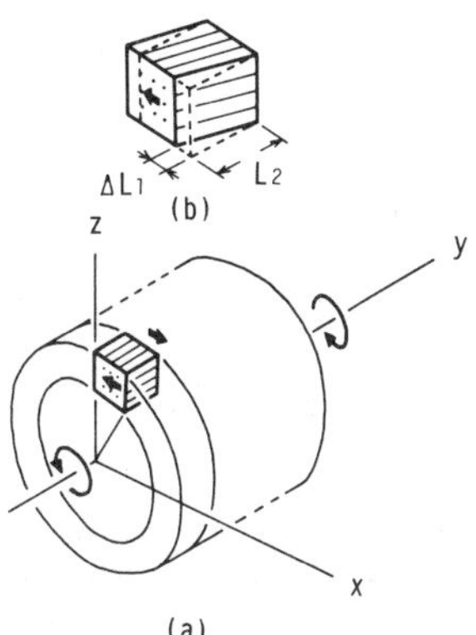

Fig.8. Schematic drawing showing how the shear properties are measured by the twisting deformation. See text.

In the experiment, a specially made disk, having a known moment of inertia and mass, was tightly attached to the cartilagenous part of the specimen. The disk was brought into a twisting motion after a sudden release from the initially twisted position about 10 degrees from the resting position. A change in the rotational angle of the damped oscillation was detected by an optical means using the principle of the optical lever, and recorded on the photographic film by using a continuous recording camera.

Figure 9 shows the procedure for the preparation of the specimen and the condition of the specimen during the experiment. The tissue of the vocal fold was trimmed so that only a single layer to be investigated was left between the arytenoid cartilage and the anterior portion of the thyroid cartilage, keeping a portion of these cartilages attached at each end. (Fig.9(a), (b)). In the specimen shown in Fig.9(b), the portion of the tissue was trimmed so as to maintain a uniform cross-sectional shape as much as possible. The portion of the thyroid cartilage was trimmed in a rectangular shape so that the clamp could hold it firmly. The portion of the arytenoid cartilage was trimmed in a cylindrical shape so that it could fit the hollow shaft of the rotating disk.

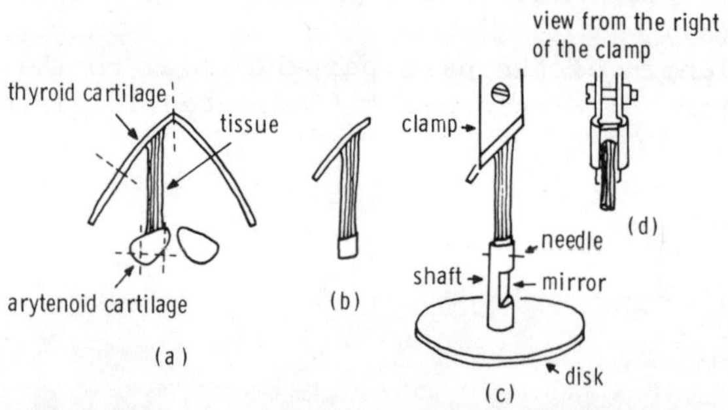

Fig.9. Schematic drawing showing how the specimen is mounted during the measurement of shear viscoelastic properties. See text.

Figure 9(c) indicates how each end of the specimen was fixed by the clamp and to the shaft by a needle. The inclination of the clamp could be adjusted so that the angle between the portion of the thyroid cartilage and the specimen was kept the same as when the specimen was in the larynx. Figure 9(d) shows the view from the right of the clamp in (c) and indicates how the clamp holds the portion of the thyroid cartilage.

The angular frequency ω and the attenuation constant b of the damped oscillation were obtained from measurements on the recorded film. The shear modulus G and the shear viscosity η are calculated by using the following two formulas:

$$G = (\omega^2 + b)\ I/f\ [\text{dyne/cm}^2]$$
$$\eta = 2bI/f\ [\text{P: poise} = \text{dyne}\cdot\text{s/cm}^2]$$

where I = moment of inertia of the disk
f = form factor of the specimen (=J/L)
J = area polar moment of inertia of the specimen (defined as $\int_A r^2 dA$, where radius r and area A are taken perpendicular to the axis of rotation; $J=\pi R^4/32$ for a circular crosssection with a radius R.)
L = length of the specimen.

The frequency of the damped oscillation in this experiment was of the order of 0.1 Hz and the attenuation constant was of the order of 10^{-2}, when a rotational disk with a moment of inertia of the order of 10^2[gr·cm^2] was used. The experiment was carried out at a room temperature of approximately 19°C.

5.2 Results

So far, data have been obtained only for one specimen for each of the lamina propria and the muscle. The values of the shear modulus and the shear viscosity are plotted in Fig.10 with respect to the elongation. A solid circle and a solid square indicate the shear modulus (G), whereas an open circle and an open square indicate the viscosity (η) (right scale). Subscripts M and L indicate the muscle and the lamina propria, respectively. Each data point represents an average of two successive measurements. Points marked a and b indicate moduli under two different longitudinal tensions; the tension for the case b was approximately 40% larger than that for the case a. For reference, the values of the Young's moduli (E_M and E_L, in Fig.10) and the differential Young's moduli (ε_M and ε_L, in Fig.10) for this specimen are also shown.

The values of G_M and G_L show almost the same values of $(2 - 3)\times 10^5$, while η_M is twice or three times as large as η_L, and is of the order of 10^4. G's and η's show a slight increase according to the increase of the longitudinal tension.

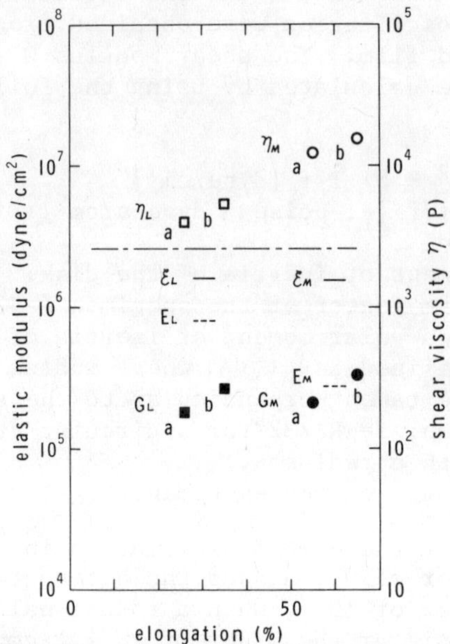

Fig.10. Shear moduli (left scale, solid points) and viscosities (right scale, open points) for the muscle (M) and the lamina propria (L). Two different longitudinal tensions are indicated by points a and b. Values of Young's moduli (E_M and E_L) and of differential Young's moduli (ε_M and ε_L) are shown for reference. See text.

The relation between the shear modulus and the Young's modulus is of interest. Since the shear modulus obtained here is measured under a specific tension, it is the differential Young's modulus that is of relevance. ε_M and ε_L show almost the same values for this region of elongation, and are close to the values in the saturated region in Fig. 7. ε_M is five to eight times as large as G_M, and the same ratio is observed between ε_L and G_L.

6. DISCUSSION

6.1. Elastic Properties of the Vocal Fold Tissue

As described in Section 2, three independent parameters E_a, E_i and G_a specify an orthotropic medium, provided that the medium is incompressible. Among the data so far presented in this paper, the modulus measured under longitudinal tension corresponds to E_a, whereas that measured under transverse tension corresponds to E_i. The shear modulus measured with a rotation around the longitudinal axis corresponds to G_a.

The obtained elastic properties of the vocal fold tissues are summarized in Table 1. There are some estimated data such as G_i and the data for muscle in contraction as well as actually measured data.

Table 1. Elastic moduli relevant to the modeling of the vocal folds

	Epithelium	Lamina propria	Muscle (resting)	Muscle (contracting)
E_i	-	$5\text{x}10^4 - 10^5$	-	-
G_i	-	$(1.5\text{-}3)\text{x}10^4$ *	-	-
E_a	10^7 **	10^6 **	10^6 **	10^7 ***
G_a	-	10^5	10^5	10^6 ***

* Calculated by a functional relation $G_i = E_i/3$ based on the assumption of isotropy in the frontal plane.

** Values shown are read from Fig.7 at around a working length (130% of the length with no load) during the rotational experiment for obtaining values of G_a.

*** Estimated on the basis of what has been described in the literature (Hill, 1970). These values are simply ten times those for a resting muscle.

The values of E_a and E_i shown in Table 1 are the differential Young's moduli taken from the same region of elongation in which the shear moduli were measured.

The order of magnitude of the Young's modulus of the muscle we measured can be said to be that of a resting muscle. In a contracting muscle, according to Hill's experiment (Hill, 1970), the stiffness and the viscosity were observed to be higher in comparison with testing conditions by as much as one order of magnitude.

According to the results shown in Table 1, we can conclude as follows:

(1) For the lamina propria, E_a is larger than E_i by more

than one order of magnitude. This shows that the medium is anisotropic with respect to the tensile deformation between the longitudinal and the transverse directions, and that the tissue is much stiffer in a longitudinal direction than in a transverse direction. A similar relation is observed between G_a and G_i, although the ratio is relatively smaller than that for E_a and E_i.

(2) For the lamina propria and the muscle, E_a is larger than $3G_a$. (For an isotropic, incompressible medium, $E = 3G$, as described in Section 2.)

In what follows we will discuss the directionality of the tissue properties by combining the histological findings with our experimental results with respect to anisotropy. From a histological point of view, the tissue of the lamina propria is composed of (1) collagenous fibers tightly connected longitudinally but loosely connected transversally (Kurita, 1979), (2) elastic fibers running in every direction like a network, and (3) the ground substance having a gelatinous property. The collagenous fibers are reported to have a Young's modulus as high as 10^9, whereas the Young's modulus of the elastic fibers is of the order of 10^6 (Fields and Dunn, 1973). In Fig.7, it is seen that the differential Young's modulus of the lamina propria for longitudinal tension, E_a (L), shows a value with almost the same order of magnitude as that for the transverse tension, E_i(LT), in a small extension region, whereas in a large extension region, E_a (L) is larger than E_i (LT) by more than one order of magnitude. Therefore, the result in Fig.7 suggests that (1) the modulus for L in a small extension region reflects mainly the combined effect of the elastic fibers and the ground substance, and that the collagenous fibers are not under tension, and (2) the modulus in a large extension region reflects mainly the effect of the collagenous fibers. The modulus for LT seems to reflect almost only the combined effect of the elastic fibers and the ground substance, and little effect of the collagenous fibers is present.

The epithelium, from a histological point of view, is composed of tightly connected cells and, therefore, shows the highest value of Young's modulus. Since the arrangement of the epithelial cells does not show any distinct directionality, there is presumably no significant difference between the Young's modulus in the longitudinal direction (E_a) and that in the transverse direction (E_i) (although we did not measure the latter). The muscle is composed of longitudinally oriented fiber bundles, from which we can naturally expect considerable anisotropy.

Histological findings also support the notion that, within the same layer of the tissue, physical properties in the transverse plane show little difference depending on the direction. Thus the assumption of orthotropy seems quite reasonable at least as a first approximation.

6.2. Frequency and Temperature Dependence of the Viscoelastic Properties

The viscous and the elastic properties shown in Section 5.2 were obtained for a very low frequency, i.e., around 0.1 Hz, and at a temperature of 19°C, which is considerably lower than the body temperature. The frequency of interest for us is of the order of 100 Hz and the temperature, about 36°C. High polymers, or more exactly those materials showing "entropy elasticity", have three regions of viscoelastic properties with respect to frequency and temperature, i.e., rubbery, transition, and glassy regions (Ferry, 1960, Chapter 2). In the rubbery region, as in the present case, viscosity is roughly inversely proportional to frequency, while the elastic modulus shows a rather constant value or a slight increase as the frequency increases, whereas both the viscosity and the elastic modulus decrease as the temperature increases, the latter to a lesser extent.

Approximate values of these property changes were estimated from the data in several papers in the literature. For the frequency dependence, we used the shear data of beef muscles measured for a range of 25 - 2500 Hz at 25°C (Fitzgerald, Ackerman, and Fitzgerald, 1957), together with our measurement at 0.1 Hz and 19°C. For the temperature dependence, we used the data for the high polymers (Ferry, 1960, Chapters 2 and 11) whose viscoelastic properties were close to those for muscles.

As a result, at the temperature of 19°C the shear modulus of muscle measured at 100 Hz is estimated to be about 40% larger than its value measured at 0.1 Hz. At a frequency of 100 Hz the shear modulus would decrease by approximately 20% when the temperature increases from 19°C to 36°C. Viscosity at 100 Hz and 19°C is estimated to be slightly less than 1% of its value measured at 0.1 Hz. If the viscosity change is exactly inversely proportional to frequency, the entire rate of decrease should be 0.1% instead of 1% (i.e., 0.1/100 = 0.001 = 0.1%), but the rate of decrease becomes gradually smaller as the frequency increases when the state of the material shifts from the rubbery region to the transition region. At the frequency of 100 Hz, a temperature increase from 19°C to 36°C would result in about 50% decrease in viscosity.

Consequently, based on the data shown in Fig.10 at 0.1 Hz and 19°C, the shear modulus of the muscle at the frequency of 100 Hz and 36°C is estimated to be about 2.5 x 10^5 dyne/cm^2 and the viscosity about 50P. If the same change can be applied for the lamina propria, the shear modulus would be about 2 x 10^5 dyne/cm^2 and the viscosity 25P. At a room temperature of 20°C, Glycerine has a viscosity of about 15P. Therefore, at a frequency of 100 Hz and a temperature of 36°C the viscous property of the lamina propria becomes similar to that of an oily liquid.

The transition frequency, or the relaxation frequency, which is located around the middle of the transition region and is the boundary between the rubbery and the glassy region, has been estimated to be 400 kHz for the shear viscosity of muscle tissue (Dunn, 1962). The fundamental frequency and its harmonics contained in the vocal fold vibration are low compared with the transition frequency. This indicates that the viscoelastic state of the tissue is unmistakably in the rubbery region during vocal fold vibration. Also, as a first approximation, the behavior of the tissue is considered to be almost "purely elastic" instead of "viscoelastic", provided that the tissue is approximated by a Voigt (or Kelvin) model. In other words, the material is less lossy in the rubbery region than in the transition region. The same rule can be applied to the properties of the lamina propria.

For a finer specification of the loss properties, we should mention the "loss tangent". The loss tangent, $\tan\delta$, is defined as $\omega\eta/G$, and is equal to twice the damping ratio. Based on the estimated values of the elastic modulus and the viscosity, $\tan\delta = 0.03$ for 0.1 Hz and $\tan\delta = 0.13$ for 100 Hz at 36°C for the muscle, and about half these values, respectively, for the lamina propria. This result suggests that the tissue vibrating at 100 Hz is about 5 times as lossy as that vibrating at 0.1 Hz. The loss tangent also indicates the energy loss during the vibration per unit time. The above result shows that, at 100 Hz, more than 10% of the vibrating energy in the muscle which is not in contraction and 7% of the vibrating energy in the lamina propria turn into heat.

The tissue hardening of the muscle after death (death rigor or rigor mortis) is worth mentioning here. The result of the shear measurement of the beef muscle shows that there is an increase (hardening) of as much as one order of magnitude for both the shear modulus and the viscosity for the same specimen measured between 5 and 12 hours after death at 25°C (Dunn, 1962). The data on the death rigor of the muscle (Bendall, 1960) suggests that the tissue properties, e.g., extensibility, would be easily reduced by one order of magnitude within several hours. The hardening starts earlier and proceeds faster when the temperature at the experiment is higher, or when the animal is more poorly fed or more exhausted before death. In order to avoid the effect of rigor and to obtain properties close to those for the *in vivo* condition, the experiment should be carried out either in a very short time when the temperature is at in vivo condition or at a sufficiently low temperature to prevent fast change.

6.3. Some Implications on the Behavior of the Vocal Fold Tissue during Vibration

Based on histological findings and speculations, Hirano (1975, 1977) has proposed a functional layer structure of the vocal fold, consisting of the "cover" and the "body", for the purpose of discussing the roles of the vocal fold tissues during vibration. The lamina propria is considered to correspond to the "cover" for the canine vocal folds whereas it is considered to correspond to both the "cover" and the "transition" for the human vocal folds. The epithelium is the surface of the "cover". The vocalis muscle is considered to be the "body". We will discuss the effect of the viscoelastic properties of each layer of the vocal fold tissue with a special attention to the functional distinction of the "cover" and the "body".

The epithelium shows the highest range of values of Young's modulus. However, since the epithelium is very thin (0.1 mm), if this receives no tension, the high elastic modulus will not play its proper role. This suggests that when the epithelium is loosened, it behaves just like a "protective cover sheet" preventing the lamina propria from being blown off, and the transverse force from outside acts almost entirely on the lamina propria. The vibratory modes are thus determined by the properties of the lamina propria combined with the state of the underlying "body". When the epithelium is under an extreme tension, however, the "surface tension" would play a greater role in reacting to the outer force, and consequently the inherent viscoelastic properties of the lamina propria would affect the vibration pattern only to a small extent. The lamina propria would play, rather, the role of a "supporting element".

The lamina propria is the main body of the "cover" when the epithelium is loosened enough. Its elastic property can be changed by a tension from outside, although it can not actively change its viscoelastic properties like the muscle.

As for the muscle, we showed in Fig.10 that its shear modulus and the viscosity have roughly the same order of magnitude as those of the lamina propria. The muscle we measured was assumed to be at a resting state. When the muscle is in contraction, both elasticity and viscosity become greater, and the lamina propria becomes more easily movable than the muscle. If the muscle contraction is extremely strong, the muscle probably shows very little movement during vibration. Thus the muscle, acting as the "body", can change its own viscoelastic properties by means of contraction, whereas the elastic property can also be changed by a longitudinal tension.

As described above, the elastic properties of both the "cover" and the "body" can be changed by a tension from outside, while, in addition, the viscoelastic properties of the "body" can be actively changed only by the muscle contraction. Therefore, by combining various viscoelastic states of the "cover" and the "body", we can obtain a number of substantially different conditions of the vocal fold as a whole, which, in turn, determine the vibratory behavior of the vocal folds.

SUMMARY

The elastic and viscous properties for each layer of the vocal fold tissue of excised canine larynges were measured, and the following results were obtained: (1) The Young's modulus becomes smaller in the order of the epithelium, the lamina propria, and the muscle. (2) The three independent elastic moduli relevant for constructing the vocal fold as an orthotropic medium were obtained for the lamina propria. (3) The shear viscosity values obtained for the lamina propria and the muscle in a low frequency region can be corrected for the purpose of estimating realistic conditions of vocal fold vibration. (4) As a first approximation, the behavior of the lamina propria and the muscle during vibration is considered to be almost "purely elastic", and, as a second approximation, 5 to 10%

of the total energy loss during vibration occurs in these tissues. (5) The assumption of "orthotropy" was shown to be reasonable from a histological point of view. (6) By relating the findings about the tissue properties to the notion of the "cover" and the "body", we may reasonably expect that the viscoelastic properties of the "cover" and the "body" can be independently adjusted to a considerable extent. This would provide a number of substantially different conditions of the vocal folds during vibration.

ACKNOWLEDGMENTS

This investigation was supported in part by a Grant-in Aid for Scientific Research (No. 337040, 557402) from the Japanese Ministry of Education, Science and Culture.

REFERENCES

Bendall, J.R. (1960) Post mortem changes in muscle. In Structure and function of muscle, Vol. 3, G.H. Bourne (ed.), New York: Academic Press, 227-272.

Dunn, F. (1962) Temperature and amplitude dependence of acoustic absorption in tissue. J. Acoust. Soc. Am. 34, 1545-1547.

Ferry, J.D. (1960) Viscoelastic properties of polymers. New York: Wiley.

Fields, S. and Dunn, F. (1973) Correlation of echographic visualizability of tissue with biological composition and physiological state. J. Acoust. Soc. Am. 54, 809-812.

Fitzgerald, E.R., Ackerman, E., and Fitzgerald, J.W. (1957) Preliminary measurements on the viscoelastic properties of animal tissues at audio-frequencies. J. Acoust. Soc. Am. 29, 61-64.

Hill, A.V. (1970) First and last experiments in muscle mechanics. Cambridge: Cambridge University Press.

Hirano, M. (1975) Phonosurgery: Basic and clinical investigations. Otologia (Fukuoka) 21, 239-440.

Hirano, M. (1977) Structure and vibratory behavior of the vocal folds. In Dynamic aspects of speech production, M. Sawashima and F.S. Cooper (eds.), Tokyo: University of Tokyo Press.

Hirano, M. (1979) Structure of the vocal fold in normal and disease states: Anatomical and physical studies. In NIH Conference on the assessment of vocal pathology.

Kurita, S. (1979) Personal communication.

Titze, I. (1976) On the mechanics of vocal fold vibration. J. Acoust. Soc. Am. 60, 1366-1380.

DISCUSSION

Rothenberg: I wonder how much the physiological differences as a function of age or species that have been discussed in the various papers at this conference are due to the reaction of the tissues to the prolonged use they sustain in normal adult humans. It may be interesting to compare, for example, the vocal fold properties of an adult dog that used its voice very little with one that has been in the habit of barking continuously for long periods of time. Would the vocal folds of a person that was profoundly deaf from birth, and vocalized very little, be similar in tissue properties and blood supply to those of a normal-hearing person of the same age?

Hirano: Your point appears to deal with three parameters which cause physiological differences of the vocal fold: age, species, and vocal use. We have no experimental evidence with respect to vocal use, whereas we know about age and species to a certain extent. But I think that the differences caused by vocal use are much less in extent than those based on age or species. Nevertheless, it should be interesting to investigate the effect of vocal use upon the structural and physiological properties of the vocal fold.

Abbs: I have a comment on the concept that human larynx physiology is "optimized" for voice production. We may be too eager, without substantive data, to assume that various nonuniformities and nonlinearities can be viewed as evidence of such processes. There are physiological ranges for muscle force, length, bandwidth, etc., and some of these nonuniformities may in fact represent limiting factors for performance of the larynx. Further, it would appear short-sighted to assume that the peripheral physiology is optimized without parallel optimization of neural system control mechanisms. This latter consideration requires a more global view of laryngeal motor performance (including the nervous system) as a part of our ultimate and best effort.

CHAPTER 26
THE ROLE OF COMPUTATIONAL SIMULATION IN EVALUATION OF PHYSICAL PROPERTIES OF THE VOCAL FOLDS

Ingo R. Titze

Department of Speech Pathology and Audiology,
University of Iowa
Iowa City, Iowa, USA

INTRODUCTION

This conferences has demonstrated that experimentation on laryngeal properties and behavior has become skillful and abundant. Models of the phonatory system have been advanced at several levels, including the anatomical, the neuromuscular, the biomechanical, the aerodynamic, and the acoustic levels. Given these advances, there is a need for coherent and systematic integration of the data to quantify the behavior of the entire complex dynamic system. The problem is one of completeness and internal consistency of observations at many levels.

An experiment involving a manifold of probes at multiple levels is possible, but not necessarily practical. It may be difficult to find subjects for an experiment involving simultaneous recording of EMG, X-ray, stroboscopy, glottography, inverse filtering, subglottal and supraglottal pressure measurement, and high speed cinematography. Even if subjects were available, the limitations in phonatory adjustments resulting from excessive probing might be prohibitive. Furthermore, it is evident that certain measurements, such as the viscoelastic properties of specific layers of vocal fold tissue, can never be made with the entire system intact.

In various descriptions of "the laryngeal system," many of us have tacitly assumed similarly between canines and humans, *in vivo* and *post mortem* conditions, young and old, male and female, and various other individual differences, hoping that somehow we are approximating the description of an "average" larynx.

Questions of considerable interest are, therefore: (1) to what extent can we interpolate or extrapolate data across the boundaries of these specialized experimental conditions? And, (2) what restrictions in the ranges of these measured quantities would we encounter if the measurements had all been performed simultaneously on the same system? We believe a computer model that accepts inputs and predicts responses at many levels of the phonatory process can provide the medium for testing the internal consistencies of the fragments. The task begins with identification of a maximum number of biomechanical measurable quantities, or simply <u>measurables</u>.

DESCRIPTION OF BIOMECHANICAL MEASURABLES

Consider the peripheral phonatory system to be represented by a major system transfer function that accepts muscular tissue stresses as inputs and produces oral acoustic radiated pressure as its principal output, as shown in the block diagram of Fig.1. Let this system transfer function be divided into three blocks that may, somewhat arbitrarily, contain (1) the vocal fold tissue properties, (2) the aerodynamic glottal properties, and (3) the acoustic vocal tract properties. A number of measurable signals are indicated at various levels between the blocks. These signals are expected to provide sufficient clues for determination of parameters within the blocks. Although not specifically indicated, the block describing the acoustic vocal tract properties includes the subglottal system, and the aerodynamic block includes the pulmonary system.

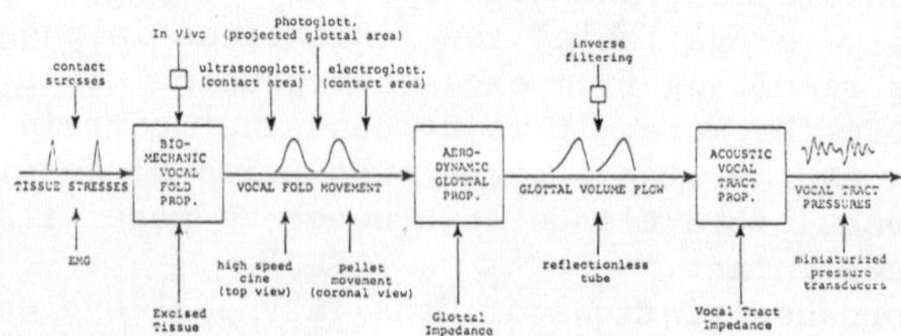

Fig.1. Block diagram showing major system components in phonation. Measurable quantities at various levels are indicated.

Beginning with the input to the first system block, we note that there is an acute need for measurement at the level of muscular stresses. The only established technique from which muscular stresses might be inferred, in theory, appears to be EMG. But the transfer function between recordings of motor unit action potential trains (MUAPT's) and the summated muscle twitches is at least as complex as the entire system described here, making it difficult to derive useful relationships between them. Nevertheless, for isometric contractions that are not heavily dependent upon motor unit recruitment and synchronization, prediction of muscle stress on the basis of average EMG level appears to be within reach.

A more direct approach to the measurement of tissue stress is being investigated by Titze and Scherer (1980) at the University of Iowa. A thin piezoelectric polymer strip is placed between the vocal folds of an excised larynx. A small voltage (in the range of millivolts per pound per square inch) is produced when the piezoelectric material is compressed during vocal fold collision. The voltage can be shown to be proportional to the collision stress. Since collision stress is a natural byproduct in computer simulation of phonatory mechanics, a comparison between measurement and prediction is possible, at least within the restricted domain of phonatory behavior of excised larynxes.

Further data on tissue biomechanics is being gathered at Kurume University, as discussed by Dr. Kakita in Chapter 25 of this book. Shear elasticities and viscosities of various tissue layers constitute the fundamental building blocks for tissue kinetics, allowing stress, strain, velocity, and acceleration of tissue elements to be related to one another via constitutive equations (see Titze's discussion in Chapter 18 of this book).

Direct _in vivo_ measurement of muscle tension in dogs and cats was not reviewed in this conference, but should be mentioned in the overall scheme of identifying potential measurables. We recall earlier contributions by Hirose et al. (1969) and Hast (1966) who stimulated primary laryngeal nerves (recurrent and superior) to induce muscle contraction and recorded the resulting tension with a force transducer. This approach might be revived to obtain length-tension curves for cricothyroid and thyroarytenoid muscles under various levels of contraction. One drawback of this approach, however, is the dissimilarity between natural and artificial nerve stimulation and the resulting muscle twitches.

Indirect in vivo measurement of mechanical properties have been discussed by Kaneko et al. (Chapter 24 of this book). Natural resonances of the tissue can be induced by external vibration of the boundary structures, while the tissue response is measured ultrasonically. This technique leads to measurement of natural resonance frequencies and transient rise and decay times - an indirect indication of effective tissue elasticity and viscosity.

A large quantity of data is available at the kinematic level, i.e., at the level of vocal fold movement. High speed cinematography, as discussed by Dr. Hirano (Chapter 7 of this book), gives details of tissue movement on the superior surface, X-ray stroboscopy with implanted pellets (Dr. Saito and his colleagues, Chapter 8 of this book) provides us with two-dimensional trajectories in the frontal plane, transillumination of the glottis produces the projected glottal area, and electroglottography (not discussed in this conference) or ultrasonoglottography are interpreted to be dynamic representations of vocal fold contact area. It is conceivable that three-dimensional dynamic reconstruction of the kinematics of vocal fold tissue movement is possible from various combinations of measurements of this type.

Moving to the heart of the second block in Fig.1, we once again realize that only a few experiments have been conducted to determine the glottal aerodynamic properties. The pressure-flow profiles and associated glottal resistances reported by van den Berg et al. (1957) need to be extended to less uniform glottal geometries, unsteady flow conditions, and smaller glottal widths. A new study, using scaled-up aerodynamic models, has been initiated by Scherer et al. (1980).

Precise measurement of glottal volume flow has been sought for many years. Inverse filtering of the oral volume flow seems to show the greatest advancement (Rothenberg, 1973), but continual effort to refine the reflectionless tube technique for "direct" measurement of glottal volume flow is being exerted. This measurement is central in the process of relating kinematics to acoustics, since vocal tract excitation is so critically tied to the shape of the glottal pulse.

As a final class of measurables, consider the vocal tract pressures (Fig.1). Miniaturized pressure transducers suspended above and below the vocal folds can provide accurate measurement of excitation and damping, subglottal and supraglottal resonance conditions, and indirect determination of glottal impedance characteristics, as demonstrated by Koike in Chapter 14 of this book.

INTEGRATION OF MEASURABLES BY COMPUTATIONAL SIMULATION

Having identified a group of measurables, we are in a position to discuss the computer simulation strategy (Chapters 17-19 of this book) that links together a large number of these measurements with the common thread of simultaneity and internal consistency. The medium of experimentation is not a human larynx, nor an animal larynx, but rather a set of sequentially executed statements of cause and effect. Heavy usage is made of three established theories of mechanics: (1) the theory of viscoelasticity, (2) fluid flow through constrictions, and (3) acoustic wave propagation in ducts. Each of the major system blocks in Fig.1 contains elements of one of these theories. Simulation begins by assuming, as a first approximation, that human tissue behaves like a viscoelastic polymer, that the glottis behaves like a nozzle, and that the vocal tract behaves like a cylindrical tube of nonuniform cross section. The behavior of these analog systems is well known. What is generally unknown, however, is the degree to which the individual system blocks interact. Fluid flow affects tissue movement and tissue movement affects fluid flow. Pressures in the vocal tract can affect both. Figure 1, therefore, is not to be interpreted as an open-loop system. There are many feedback paths left out for the sake of simplicity. A primary virtue of computer simulation is its relative ease of handling complex interaction between subsystems.

The following parameters are used todescribe the individual system blocks:

Block 1. Vocal Fold Tissue Properties

1. Shear elasticities, Young's moduli, and shear viscosities for each layer in longitudinal and transverse directions.
2. Pre-phonatory geometric factors that specify the boundaries of the tissue.

Block 2. Aerodynamic Glottal Properties

1. Glottal resistance and inertance as a function of glottal aperture, volume flow, air density, air viscosity, etc.

2. Loss coefficients at entry and exit and various other points where flow disturbances and energy loss may occur.

Block 3. Acoustic Vocal Tract Properties

1. Quantized sections of vocal tract area.
2. Resistances and reactances associated with wall, radiation, and air medium properties.

Refinement of these parameters is accomplished by comparing computer simulated measurables with the experimental counterparts at various levels. In the first stage of development, the focus is on excised samples of animal and human tissue. This experimentation provides nominal values for the parameters in Block 1. Parallel with that procedure, static aerodynamic measurements provide basic pressure-flow information for Block 2. The next stage consists of measurements on intact excised larynxes, where tissue movement, contact stress, contact area, and additional intrusive or nonintrusive probes can be combined. In the final stage, extrapolation to the human larynx *in vivo* is attempted on the basis of morphological differences, with nonintrusive measurements (such as inverse filtering and glottography) providing the primary basis for refinement.

SUMMARY

A schematization of major system blocks and signals in the peripheral (biomechanical and acoustic) processes of phonation has been presented. Parameters of viscoelastic, aerodynamic, and acoustic components have been isolated, and strategies for refinement of physical quantities via computational simulation have been outlined. Computational simulation can provide the medium whereby internal consistency and relationships between many observations on the same system can be tested. This approach avoids overloading a human or animal subject with a large number of probes. Furthermore, it can quantify complex interactions between basic system blocks that cannot be investigated if the system is studied in parts.

REFERENCES

Hast, M. (1966) Physiological mechanisms of phonation: Tension of the vocal fold muscle. *Acta Otolaryng*.

(Stockholm) 62, 309-318.

Hirose, H., Ushijima, T., Kobayashi, T. and Sawashima, M. (1969) An experimental study of the contraction properties of the laryngeal muscles in a cat. Ann. Otol. 78, 297-307.

Rothenberg, M. (1973) A new inverse filtering technique for deriving the glottal air flow waveform during voicing. J. Acoust. Soc. Am. 53, 1632-1645.

Scherer, R., Curtis, J., and Titze, I. (1980) Pressure-flow relationships within static models of the larynx. J. Acoust. Soc. Am. 68, Supplement, S101.

Titze, I. and Scherer, R. (1980) Preliminary results on measurement and simulation of vocal fold contact stress, Ninth Symposium: Care of the Professional Voice. The Julliard School, New York.

Van den Berg, J.W., Zantema, J. and Doornenbal, P. (1975) On the air resistance and the Bernoulli effect of the human larynx. J. Acoust. Soc. Am. 29, 626-631.

DISCUSSION

Fujimura: I do believe that modeling work, like the computational simulation Dr. Titze is conducting, is very valuable and in many cases is the only way to relate measurements at different levels by different methods and to integrate the fragmental pieces of information on the same phenomenon into a comprehensive overall picture of the complex mechanism. For some purposes in the study of vocal fold vibration, it may be that Kenzo Ishizaka's two-mass model (Chapter 17) provides a phenomenological descriptive framework. There may be even more functional or partial models that can be used to account for particular phenomena.

As an example of the use of models in interpreting diverse measurements of vocal fold vibration, let us suppose that we can observe, in different experiments, the movements of flesh points on the vocal fold, movement of pellets within the vocal fold of an excised larynx through x-ray techniques, and overall views of vocal fold vibration through high-speed motion pictures. (It is recognized that there may be a deviation from appropriate physiological conditions because of the inertia of the pellets if the pellets have to be relatively large and also because of the unnatural conditions of an excised larynx.) Each of these kinds of observations provides only partial information concerning the three-dimensional movement and the internal movement of the structures. If we could relate the quantities measured by such different methods to each other through appropriate models, we could on the one hand try to reach a comprehensive picture with some confidence, and on the other hand evaluate the validity of a particular model. Once we get such a model then we can use it as an appropriate descriptive framework for processing data and try further to validate it, or improve the model to cover deviant cases - either pathological cases or extreme conditions for pitch control and the like. In some cases control of the larynx for phonemic distinctions in some particular languages may be especially helpful in elucidating some inherent mechanism which may not be easily observed or controlled in other languages. Thus, we may have a battery of tools and methodologies. We now face an opportunity where we can try to synthesize these techniques to arrive at a useful comprehensive picture of the vocal fold physiology and physics.

Titze: There is one area that I would like to have someone help us in deriving some directives. There has been some discussion about the use of animal larynges versus human larynges, and about _in vivo_ observations versus observations on excised larynges. At one time we thought that the dog larynx and the human larynx are fairly close in their physiology. We see now that they may not be quite as close as we would like them to be. Where should we concentrate our efforts primarily? It seems we have a data bank already available of quite a few experiments done on excised dog larynges. Would there be another animal that is perhaps better? Data gathering is time-consuming, and one would like to avoid spending a lot of time working on the wrong system.

Fujimura: I would very much like to see something like Dr. Baer's work with the use of human larynges, excised admittedly. We should try to eliminate at least one dimension of difference from human larynges _in vivo_. I was very impressed when I learned that one of the graduate students in Kurume University has examined 3200 human larynges in dissection. This is a very good environment for working on the larynges. I understand that Dr. Baer had much difficulty in obtaining even canine larynges at MIT.

Baer: How accessible are fresh human larynges for this kind of work in Japan?

Hirano: There is a kind of limitation in terms of the number of fresh larynges. Autopsy accounts for many specimens, but often they are not sufficiently fresh for our purposes.

Strong: There is a potential source of an occasional specimen of superfresh human larynxes and this is persons who are having total laryngectomy and maybe laryngeal frangectomy for extrinsic cancer. We would have to plan ahead and have permission, and this is a sensitive and delicate matter to discuss.

Hirano: That is another possibility, but we have maybe only 10 cases a year, and often they have some anomaly.

Fujimura: I would also like to emphasize the usefulness of computational simulation in, for example, interpreting the torsion data that Yuki Kakita (Chapter 25) has measured under a rather complex boundary condition. The estimation of elastic constants would be much more accurate if we could write a program to simulate that particular situation and interpret the measured quantities in terms of the elastic constants in the realistic ranges of force and frequency and so on.

Rothenberg: I am sure that Dr. Titze has worked long and hard on the computer model that he has up till now. As you proceed with your work, do you perceive that you will move toward a much more complex model, or are you close to achieving the amount of complexity you need?

Titze: The model will not become too much more complex. We built into it enough generality. We can expand, say, the number of elements. I think Dr. Fujimura's point is a good one. What we need along with the large-scale simulation of the entire system is smaller simulations that work on some of the parts of this system. We tend to think that we always have to simulate the whole thing starting from forces all the way to the acoustics.

Unidentified discussant: As a backup, as a reference, you might want a very complex model. Of course one would like to have a simple model to examine the most important features. Maybe a much more complex model wouldn't be necessary if we could make *in vivo* experiments in great detail. However, there are many experiments one might like to do which cannot be done on the living larynx, and that is where the more complex model might be useful.

Fujimura: I think it is very important to have access to a more complex and accurate model as the need occurs. On the other hand, we would like to have simplification and theory that would comprehensively but simply and elegantly describe the essence of the complex phenomena perhaps in different aspects separately depending on the approach we would like to take for the particular purpose in mind. I couldn't agree more when Dr. Stevens mentioned that Dr. Ishizaka's work was very significant in pointing out the essential structural characteristics that were minimally necessary to explain the vocal cord vibration properties, particularly the facility or possibility for the vocal cords to vibrate under realistic conditions. I also have in mind things like his own quantal theory (Chapter 20) which may be oversimplistic for some purposes, and I myself might have some objection in certain aspects. We need some theories which would give us some kind of framework for thinking about the complex mechanism and structure, but it doesn't have to be necessarily complete and cover all the relevant cases and aspects of the problem. We would gain much knowledge by having perhaps oversimplified models as a basic descriptive framework. We can then start from the basic framework and discuss where the complex reality has to be considered in order to estimate deviations from the simple models. Theory has to go with data. I think in this conference we have seen a fruitful coexistence of theory and factual data - very vigorous work producing relevant data, and theoretical discussion for explaining the essence of the mechanisms that underlie the complex phenomena we observe.

Abbs: This conference has focused quite successfully upon biomechanics, aerodynamics, and acoustics of peripheral laryngeal function. However, in some cases perhaps we have taken too restricted a view. That is, it may be important to stress the fact that the peripheral laryngeal mechanism is wholly subordinate to and controlled by the nervous system. Thus, without the brain's elegant regulation and coordination, the muscles, joints, cartilages, and ligaments of the laryngeal apparatus essentially are inanimate and useless tissue. Inclusion of the nervous system capabilities (viz., the brain stem reflexes, the sensorimotor cortex, the cerebellum, etc.) may cast a somewhat different light on some of the issues that have been discussed. For example, it has been suggested several times during this meeting that the biomechanical nonlinearities of the laryngeal system are optimized for performance of phonatory and protective tasks, and/or exploited to enhance that performance. It seems that these interpretations may be an example of the blind men and the proverbial elephant. It is known that many processes of the nervous system also are nonlinear, e.g., sensory receptor responses, lower motoneuron pool recruitment, responses of the sensory cortex to peripheral stimulation, etc. One would expect, then, that if a biological optimization principle were in operation it would include also the nonlinearities of the nervous system as well as those of the laryngeal biomechanics, if, as has been suggested, such optimization is a product of evolution. Likewise, if one adopts the related point of view that nonlinearities are exploited to enhance performance of the laryngeal system, it again is difficult to consider the peripheral biomechanical properties independent from those of the neural control system. Further, if the characteristics of the neural system underlying laryngeal control are part of these optimization/exploitation processes, it may be very difficult to interpret peripheral observations without a better understanding of the underlying motor neurophysiology. For example, discontinuities in vocal performance may reflect either discontinuities in peripheral biomechanics, discontinuities in nervous system processes, or (and most likely), a critical combination of these influences. Likewise, it is possible that what appears to be a system nonlinearity at one level, say the periphery, is compensated for by a mirror nonlinearity at a higher level. Brookhart's experiments with postural responses empirically reflect such mechanisms, viz., several nonlinear components combining to yield a linear system (Brookhart, 1971). The model offered by Houk (1976; 1978) similarly suggests that the nonlinearities in muscle response characteristics are minimized or eliminated by segmental afferent-to-efferent feedback pathways. An example of the potential significance of even a single feedback pathway upon peripheral performance is illustrated in the recent speech aerodynamic modelling work of Müller and Brown (1980).

In general, the implications of these comments are that our models of the peripheral laryngeal physiology must begin to incorporate some additional data that reflect the fact that the "phonatory system" extends beyond ligaments, muscles, and cartilages to include all levels of the sensory and motor nervous system controlling this process. Of course such information is difficult to obtain, and will require some extended work using animal models and parallel studies of laryngeal control in human subjects with selective brain damage. These observations should not be taken as a suggestion that studies of peripheral laryngeal physiology are not extremely valuable; rather, it would appear that interpretations of actual control performance (e.g., vocal registers) are likely to be limited until additional information on the nervous system controller, *per se*, become available.

REFERENCES FOR ABBS DISCUSSION:

Brookhart, J.M. (1971) The technique for investigating central control of posture. In *The Central Control of Movement*, E. Evarts, E. Bizzi, R. Burke, M. DeLong, and W. Thach (eds.), Neurosciences Research Program Bulletin 9, No. 1, pp. 118-127.

Houk, J.C. (1976) An assessment of stretch reflex function. *Prog. Brain Res.* 44, 303-314.

Houk, J.C. (1978) Participation of reflex mechanisms and reaction-time processes in the compensatory adjustments to mechanical disturbances. In *Progress in Clinical Neurophysiology, Vol. 4: Cerebral Motor Control in Man: Long Loop Mechanisms*, J.E. Desmedt (ed.), Basel: Karger, 193-215.

Müller, E.M. and Brown, W.S., Jr. (1980) Variations in the supraglottal air pressure waveform and their articulatory interpretation. In *Speech and Language*, Vol. 4, N. Lass (ed.), New York: Academic Press.

CHAPTER 27
CONCLUDING REMARKS

I. Kirikae

Department of Otolaryngology,
Jichi Medical School,
Tochigi-ken, Japan

First of all, I want to offer congratulations on the success of the Conference on Vocal Fold Physiology, in which very active and fruitful discussions have been carried on from different aspects of modern research for the last four days. Thanks to the efforts of Dr. Hirano, Dr. Gould and Dr. Fujimura, who planned the conference, we have been able to learn a great deal about the recent concepts on vocal fold physiology, and also to obtain foresight on the future problems in this field of science as summarized by Dr. Hirano and Dr. Fujimura.

It seems quite natural, I must say, that the conference was held here at Kurume where important contributions have been made to laryngeal physiology, the results of which were recognized by presentation of the Gould Award to Dr. Hiroto and his successor, Dr. Hirano.

I also want to take this opportunity to acknowledge the support under the Voice Foundation of New York and a Grant-in-Aid for Scientific Research, given by the Ministry of Education of the Japanese Government.

I. HISTORICAL REVIEW OF LARYNGEAL PHYSIOLOGY

I would like to review some of the historical work in laryngeal physiology with respect to the modern concepts presented at this conference. Personally, I have always been interested in laryngeal physiology ever since I started stroboscopic research on vocal fold vibration some 40 years ago under the guidance of Dr. Satta and, therefore, it is my real pleasure and honor to have this opportunity to attempt this historical review.

Early in 1840, Johannes Müller described the vocal fold as showing full-thickness vibration in the chest register, but vibration of only the medial margin in the head register or falsetto. Twenty years later in 1862, Markel already stated that the difference between the chest and head registers originated from a kind of counteraction between the internal thyroarytenoid and the cricothyroid muscles. At that time, Manuel Garcia, who invented the laryngeal mirror, also described the difference in vibration mode between the chest and head registers based on his laryngeal observations.

In 1863, Helmholtz discussed the nature of vocal fold vibration in his famous book "Die Lehre von den Tonempfindungen", under the title of "Klänge der Zungenpfeifen". He interpreted the vocal fold as a membraneous plate or "membranöse Zunge", the thickness of which was considered to be adjustable. In other words, the human vocal organ was "Membranöse durchschlagende Pfeife" according to his concept (Fig.1).

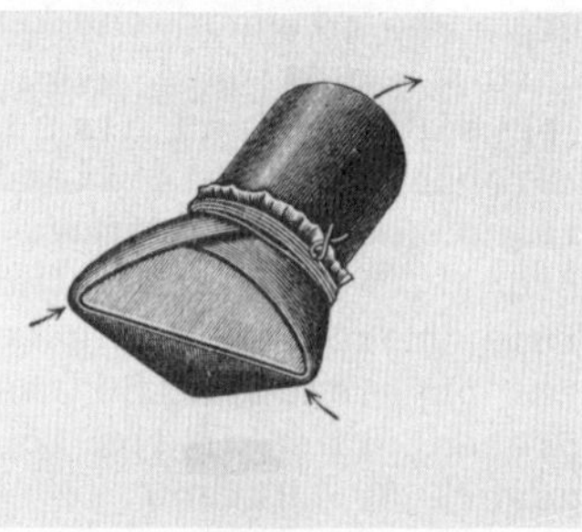

Fig.1. Artificial larynx ("membranöse Zungenpfeife") (Helmholtz).

In 1898, the famous physiologist Ewald advocated the concept of "Polsterpfeife" or "cushion-pipe" (Fig.2), which was comparable to the principle of "Gegenschlagpfeifen" or "counterbeating pipe" claimed by Nagel in 1909 (Fig.3). Most of you may be familiar with these old theories and concepts.

At about the same time, Oertel (1895) and Musehold (1913) introduced the technique of stroboscopy of laryngeal research and made very precise observations on the vibratory pattern of the vocal fold. In particular, observations made by Musehold are really surprising.

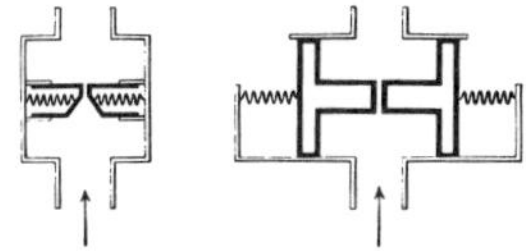

Fig.2. Schematic pictures of cushion pipe ("Polsterpfeife") (Ewald).

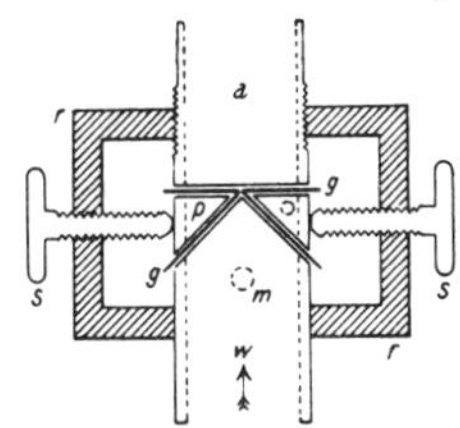

Fig.3. Counter beating pipe ("Gegenschlag-pfeife") (Nagel).

Musehold took very clear pictures of the vocal folds in different vibratory phases under indirect laryngeal mirror using magnesium flash light and under the stroboscope. Figures 4 and 5 are photographs selected from his publication. Figure 4 shows that the surfaces of the vocal cords look like cushions as if the upper and lower lips of the mouth are closely pressed to each other. In Fig.5 the glottis is not so tightly closed and the glottis line is visible a little deeper.

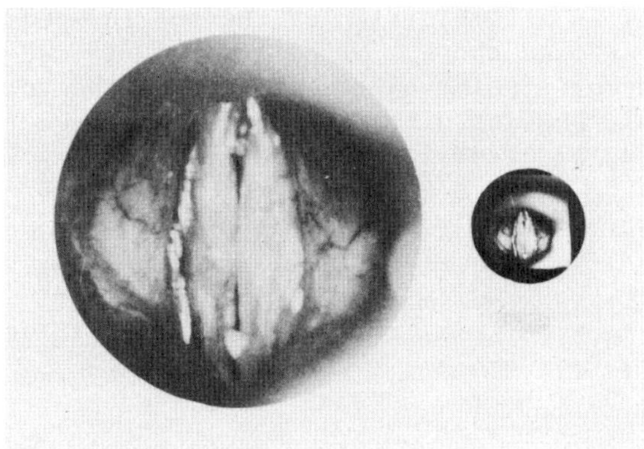

Fig.4. Stroboscopic photography of the larynx (Musehold). Taken at the chest register C^1; closed phase of the glottis.

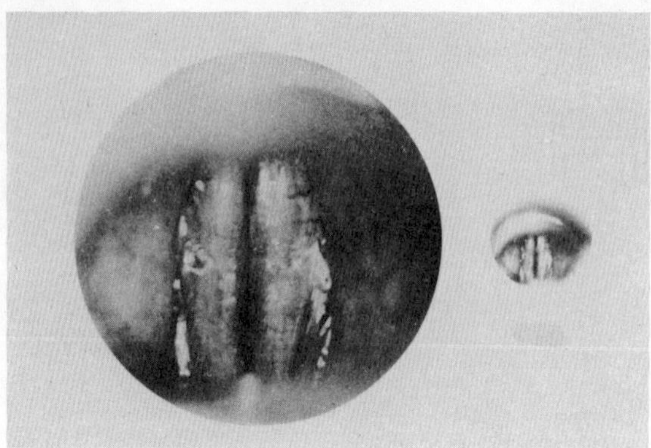

Fig.5. Flash light photography (Musehold). Taken at the same tone as in Fig.4.

Oertel observed the wavelike movement travelling laterally on the surface of the vocal fold and described it as "Knotenlinie" or nodal line, which was not recognized by Musehold.

According to the concept of Musehold or Nagel, the vocal folds are neither purely "durchschlagende Zungenpfeife" or up and down beating reed pipe having vertical mobility, nor purely "gegenschlagende Pfeife" or counter beating pipe showing exclusively lateral movements. Instead, they assumed that the vocal fold moved on the trajectory of a flat arch or "flache Bogen" having an upward convex shape shown as dotted arrows B and C in Fig.6. In other words, the trajectory is a combination of the two independent components mentioned above. Nagel further claimed that the trajectory of a point on the surface of the vocal fold was elliptical, showing different courses between the lateral and medial excursions in one vibratory cycle.

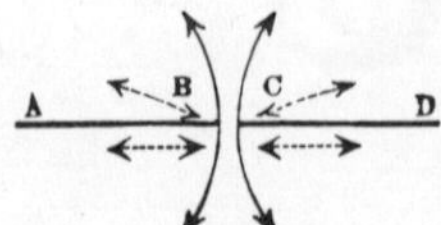

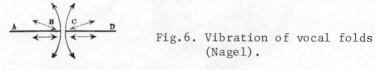

Fig.6. Vibration of vocal folds (Nagel).

II. RECENT PROGRESS IN LARYNGEAL PHYSIOLOGY

When we refer to the results presented at this conference, we do realize that we are really in a new, different age from those old days.

a. Ultra-High-speed Movie Technique

Observations of the vocal fold movement by means of ultra-high-speed movie techniques have clarified the detailed nature of the vibratory mode, and Dr. Hiroto established his mucoviscoelastic aerodynamic theory based on the results of observations using these techniques. Dr. Hirano further developed the body-cover theory, which has been repeatedly discussed during the conference. I am certain that the introduction of the concept of differentiation between the cover and body of the vocal fold sheds a new light in the field of laryngeal physiology and contributes very much to progress on the theoretical aspects of vocal fold vibration.

b. X-ray Stroboscopy

Another great success has been made by the introduction of X-ray stroboscopy, by which the elliptical trajectory of the vocal fold vibration has been ascertained in the frontal section. By this technique, even the vibratory mode of the deeper part of the vocal fold has been investigated.

c. Muscle Physiology of the Larynx

With respect to muscle physiology of the larynx, some of the basic concepts claimed by old scholars on the counteractions between the vocalis and cricothyroid are proved to still hold true. However, recent improvements in recording and processing techniques of electromyography have revealed a number of interesting findings in both speech and singing. Regulation of pitch, intensity and register of voice, and the contribution of external laryngeal muscles have been precisely investigated. Detailed EMG analysis of laryngeal articulatory adjustment in various conditions of speech production is an example of recent progress in laryngeal physiology which could not be imagined in the old days.

d. Physical Properties of the Larynx

Besides the physiological studies mentioned so far, studies on the physical properties of the vocal fold tissues are quite important. In this conference, the results of measurements on real tissues as well as theoretical discussions related to these problems have been presented. Interestingly, Helmholtz (1863) briefly discussed the elasticity of the vocal fold in reference to the frequency of vibration in his publication.

It seems to me that Ewald (1898) also took into consideration the concept of elasticity in some sense in his theory of "Gegenschlagpfeife" or counterbeat pipe, since he drew spirals lateral to the vocal fold tissues as shown in Fig.2. In the pipe a on the left, only the cushions themselves are elastic; in the pipe b, cushions are connected to the walls with elastic springs. The left pipe can be blown only from the inferior direction but the right pipe can be blown from both superior and inferior sides.

It is hard to understand the exact concept of "elasticity" of these old scholars, but they would certainly be surprised if they were able to learn the results of such recent findings as those presented in this conference.

e. Aerodynamic Aspect of Vocal Fold Vibration

Aerodynamic aspects of vocal fold vibration are also very important to an understanding of vibration mechanisms. Tonndorf (1925) once reported on his study of stream-line formation or "Stromlinienbildung" during phonation, applying the aerodynamic theory at that time to the mechanics of vocal fold vibration, and it attracted the attention of investigators in this field. Figure 7 from Tonndorf's article shows that at the narrow lumen between the two walls parallel descending stream lines suddently gather densely, and the velocity of the stream increases. Thus the pressure at the narrow lumen decreases and both lateral walls are attracted toward the direction of the arrows. Nowadays, various methods for aerodynamic investigation have been developed for both clinical and fundamental studies, and evaluation of vocal efficiency has become possible. Also, application of techniques using miniature strain gauges has made it possible to register the supra- and subglottal pressure variations and to estimate the coupling phenomena between the two parts of the vocal tract.

f. Simulation Studies

Detailed analyses of the mechanism of vocal fold vibration have been attempted by simulation studies using computer-assisted models. These studies are considered to be an important part of the recent approaches to the problem, and provide a detailed theoretical component to modern research in vocal fold physiology, in parallel with other experimental studies.

Fig.7. Experiment of streamline formation (Tonndorf).

g. Multidisciplinary Approach in the Research

I have pointed out several different topics discussed in the conference, but needless to say all of these topics relate closely to each other in determining the nature and characteristics of vocal fold vibration. In this sense, each of the physical, acoustical, biomechanical and neurophysiological research approaches, and the multidisciplinary combination of these different approaches, has opened new directions in research that is exploring the real nature of the vocal fold function.

h. Interpretation of Old Theories

It can be said that vocal fold vibration is purely a physical phenomenon as long as the physical properties of the vibrating mass and aerodynamic components are once determined by physiological parameters in a given condition. There was an apparent controversy between the "Membran Theorie", that means "resonance theory", and "Polsterpfeifen Theorie" or "cushion pipe theory" in the past in interpreting the mechanism of vocal fold vibration. Referring to the nature of frequency of vibration, resonance theory seems to be correct, but morphological aspects with respect to the vibratory mode seem to support "Polsterpfeifen Theorie".

In other words, looking at the two apparently different theories of "membranöse Zungen Theorie" and "Polsterpfeifen Theorie" in the present perspective, it can be said that the two theories were simply different in their viewpoints from which exactly the same phenomenon was observed.

In those days when I started my study of vocal fold vibration, there was another discussion on the nature of the interrelationship between the vocal tract and the larynx in vowel production in terms of controversy between the so-called resonance theory and puff theory. In this case, too, I think that two theories were simply different in their viewpoints from which exactly the same phenomenon was observed.

III. SUMMARY

In summarizing, I would like to repeat that this conference has made a significant contribution to the progress in this field of science, particularly by bridging between the substantial physiological data and the theoretical framework. I hope that continuing efforts will be made for exploiting the nature of vocal fold vibration along the research lines presented in this conference, and I further hope that future research will be aimed at understanding the mechanism of the central nervous system in voice and speech production.

REFERENCES

Ewald, J.R. (1898) Die Physiologie des Kehlkopfes und der Luftröhre Stimmbildung. In _Handbuch der Laryngologie und Rhinologie_ Vol. 1, P. Heymann (ed.), Vienna: Hölder, p. 165.

Helmholtz, Hermann von (1863) _Die Lehre von den Tonempfindungen_ Braunschweig: F. Vieweg und Sohn, Ausg. 1.

Merkel, C.L. (1866) _Physiologie der menschlichen Sprache_ Leipzig.

Musehold, Albert (1913) _Allgemeine Akustik und Mechanik des Menschlichen Stimmorgans_ Berlin: J. Springer.

Müller, Johannes (1840) _Handbuch der Physiologie des Menschen_ Vol. 2, Coblenz: J. Hölscher, p. 180.

Nagel, Wilibald A. (1909) Physiologie der Stimmwerkzeuge. In _Handbuch der Physiologie des Menschen_ W.A. Nagel (ed.), Braunschweig: F. Vieweg und Sohn, pp. 691-792.

Tonndorf, W. (1925) Die Mechanik bei den Stimmlippenschwingungen und beim Schnarchen. _Zeitschr. f. Hals-, Nasen-, und Ohrenheilkunde_ 12, 241-245.